Neal N Bogaer

September, 2007

What others are saying about *Fixing American Healthcare . . .*

"Dr. Fogoros accomplishes the near-impossible—he makes an equitable and effective healthcare system seem achievable. This is a must-read for all Americans who want to be part of the solution. Best, his advice for patient empowerment will help people today, even with the healthcare system we have right now."

—KATE GROSSMAN, MD
Medical Director
www.About.com

"A great and important book. Fogoros's impassioned and logical arguments will touch a chord in any person who cares about patients. Absolutely required reading in medical school and for every physician."

—KEN ELLENBOGEN, MD
Professor of Medicine
Virginia Commonwealth University

"Fogoros ushers America's healthcare system out into the light and asks *What are we pretending not to know?* . . . and then proceeds to answer that question."

—JAY WARREN
President and CEO
Cameron Health, Inc.

"Dr. Fogoros has hit the nail on the head with a bold, insightful critique of the U.S. healthcare system and a plan for radical reform that just might work. *Fixing American Healthcare* is a much-needed antidote to the fruitless incrementalism that dominates contemporary debate."

—DAVID E. WILLIAMS
www.HealthBusinessBlog.com

"Must reading for all people involved in health care.
"Reading *Fixing American Healthcare* is like reading an Ayn Rand novel, a murder mystery (how the doctor–patient relationship has

been killed), a philosophical treatise, an investigative report, and an exposé of Wonkonians' and Gekkonians' agendas. Richard Fogoros reasserts the primacy of the doctor–patient relationship by proposing a balanced solution to the healthcare crisis that addresses the needs of society, physicians, patients, business, and government. Quite an accomplishment."

—Lynn D. Carlisle, DDS
www.SpiritOfCaring.com

"Dr. Fogoros has finally explained how patients, who should benefit the most, are instead getting the shortest end of the American health care stick. It's proof positive that our health care system is not about health or care; it's about sickness and money.

—Trisha Torrey
www.EveryPatientsAdvocate.com

"Dr. Fogoros provides rare insight into the truth about American healthcare. Even as a physician for twenty years, I never realized the depth to which government agencies and profit-motivated HMOs alike have usurped and corrupted the doctor–patient relationship, industry incentives, and even medical research. But rather than taking the easy way out and pretending the Canadian or British systems would work in the U.S., he provides a rational blueprint for a system that is compatible with American ideals, while restoring doctor–patient trust and fiscal stability. His book offers an entirely fresh look at the American healthcare system that every physician and patient must read."

—Ron Berger, MD, PhD
Professor of Medicine
and Biomedical Engineering
Johns Hopkins School of Medicine

"A great read. A spicy mixture of witty commentary, white-hot criticism, and battlefield wisdom."

—Joseph M. Smith, MD, PhD
Vice President
Microelectronic Technologies
Cordis Corporation

Other books by the author

Electrophysiologic Testing

Antiarrhythmic Drugs: A Practical Guide

Fixing American Healthcare

Fixing American Healthcare

Wonkonians, Gekkonians,
and the Grand Unification Theory
of Healthcare

Richard N. Fogoros, MD

PUBLISH OR PERISH DBS • PITTSBURGH

Fixing American Healthcare: Wonkonians, Gekkonians, and the Grand Unification Theory of Healthcare

Richard N. Fogoros, MD

Publish or Perish DBS
P.O. Box 13251
Pittsburgh, Pennsylvania 15243
www.publishorperishdbs.com

Reach the author by e-mail at DrRich@GUTHealthcare.com

First edition

LCCN: 2007932504

Manufactured in the United States of America

11   10   09   08   07   5   4   3   2   1

Disclaimer: Nothing in this book should be construed as specific or personal medical advice.

Design and composition: www.dmargulis.com

Publisher's Cataloging-In-Publication Data
(Prepared by The Donohue Group, Inc.)

Fogoros, Richard N.
   Fixing American healthcare : wonkonians, gekkonians, and the grand unification theory of healthcare / Richard N. Fogoros. — 1st ed.

   p. : ill., charts ; cm.

   Includes bibliographical references and index.
   ISBN: 978-0-9796979-0-6

1. Health care reform—United States.   2. Medical care—United States.
3. Medical policy—United States.   I. Title.

RA395.A3 F64 2007
362.1/0973   2007932504

To my children and yours.

"Like other risk bearing organizations, HMOs take steps to control costs. These measures are commonly complemented by specific financial incentives to physicians, rewarding them for decreasing utilization of health-care services, and penalizing them for excessive treatment. Hence, an HMO physician's financial interest lies in providing less care, not more. Herdrich argues that Carle's incentive scheme of annually paying physician owners the profit resulting from their own decisions rationing care distinguishes its plan from HMOs generally, so that reviewing Carle's decision under a fiduciary standard would not open the door to claims against other HMOs. However, inducement to ration care is the very point of any HMO scheme, and rationing necessarily raises some risks while reducing others. ... Congress, which has promoted the formation of HMOs for 27 years, may choose to restrict its approval to certain preferred forms, but the Judiciary would be acting contrary to congressional policy if it were to entertain an ERISA fiduciary claim portending wholesale attacks on existing HMOs solely because of their structure."

—Justice David Souter, writing for a unanimous U.S. Supreme Court, in PEGRAM ET AL. V. HERDRICH (98-1949), 530 U.S. 211 (2000)

Contents

Foreword

DRRICH HAS BEEN MY colleague for the better part of a decade, both of us serving as health guides at the About.com network of websites. DrRich's site focuses on heart disease, while I cover thyroid disease. We share a dedication and resolve to help educate and empower our readers with health information. We also share the passionate belief that when consumers understand their health concerns, they are far better able to take an active, productive role in their medical care.

All this is to say that DrRich and I are clearly on the same page—with one important difference: Richard N. Fogoros is an MD, and a talented and greatly respected one at that, with all the medical education and qualifications that come with those credentials. And I am not a doctor. I'm a thyroid patient.

I fall in that category DrRich fondly calls patients behaving badly. By this he means patients who ask questions, explore options, and do not naively assume that doctors—or any of the key players in the healthcare industry—have our best interests and health truly at heart.

I'm a particularly troublesome patient behaving badly, because, after being diagnosed with a thyroid condition in 1995, I not only took an active role in my own healthcare but also evolved into a patient advocate. In that role, I openly encourage other patients to take a similarly empowered role on their own behalf. To add insult to injury, I also provide tools—writing articles, books, and websites, and conducting outreach campaigns—to help patients become more effective advocates for their own healthcare.

And I do this even though there are no initials after my name—no medical degree or medical education (in the medical world, a degree in international business doesn't count).

"They" say that my lack of formal medical education makes it inappropriate—even *dangerous*—for me to provide health information to anyone. "They" say that the only safe and appropriate place to get medical information is from a doctor. And who are "they?" They are the healthcare industry, as it exists today, including most doctors, the HMOs, the insurance companies, the hospitals, the biomedical companies, the drug manufacturers—all of them. They are the gatekeepers in our healthcare system and those who profit most from it.

They don't want me, or any patient advocate, involved, because we make their lives more difficult.

- We provide information to patients and yet have no allegiance to any drug company, HMO, medical society, or insurer.
- We encourage patients to ask questions, to explore options, to pursue alternatives—activities that are not conducive to a gatekeeper's bottom line.
- We make patients aware that when it comes to discussing diagnosis and treatment options, the gatekeepers are leaving out quite a bit of crucial information, and deliberately at that. It's knowledge that can have a profound effect on the course of diagnosis and treatment.

The allegiance of a true patient advocate is to patients, so there is no incentive for us to leave anything out. Our greatest usefulness is in pointing out what *Is* being left out; in telling patients the part the gatekeepers don't want patients to know. If a patient advocate is effective, a patient walks away from an article, book, or encounter armed with accurate information, questions for practitioners, knowledge about options, and the savvy to recognize when gatekeepers are providing self-serving, incomplete, or even downright dangerous information.

Perhaps most important, a patient walks away with the confidence needed to *act* on this newfound knowledge and understanding. It's just that confidence that DrRich has inspired in so many patients and will inspire in a new generation of patients who discover him by reading *Fixing American Healthcare.* DrRich is a unique breed of patient advocate, one who is able to understand healthcare from the perspective of both practitioner and patient. This dual role makes him an even more potent force for change.

It's one thing for the gatekeepers to argue that patients should be seen and not heard, and that those of us without medical credentials have no right to enter the debate (I don't agree, of course, but medicine is notorious for revering credentials). But it's impossible for them to dismiss DrRich. Here's a medical expert who has *all* the right credentials. He trained and practiced in some of the best schools, including Duke, Ohio State, the University of Pittsburgh, and Stanford. He became internationally known in his chosen field of cardiac electrophysiology. And he was a professor of medicine. The medical establishment simply cannot ignore DrRich.

Not only does he have the credentials; he has the ideas. What DrRich has done in *Fixing American Healthcare* is nothing short of amazing. He has analyzed healthcare in America and developed a comprehensive system to explain it: he calls it the Grand Unification Theory of Healthcare. The Grand Unification Theory of Healthcare explains how it all works now and, better yet, how it *could* work if key improvements were made. And DrRich's theory and recommendations take into account the nature of Americans, and capitalize on our best qualities to recommend a unique yet practical plan to improve our healthcare system.

I can't emphasize this enough. It's quite radical: DrRich actually lays out a plan. *Fixing American Healthcare* takes a hard look at America and America's health system, and offers a uniquely *American* solution, a roadmap, really, for transforming our ailing healthcare system into a more robust and equitable system that can work because it fits our national character.

Perhaps the most unexpected part of DrRich's plan is how much it relies on patients. Usually, when you think of "healthcare reform," it's mostly about politicians, HMOs, insurers, regulators, and doctors, and all the things they will have to do—or stop doing—to fix the system. Have no doubt: DrRich has outlined plenty of tasks for the healthcare players. But he has also mapped out how the patient community can serve to catalyze a solution to the healthcare problem in America.

Patients as catalysts? Yes! Sure, it's radical—but fundamentally sensible. In *Fixing American Healthcare*, DrRich explains that transforming the healthcare system requires each of us to become a patient behaving badly.

DrRich first introduces us to the important idea of what he calls covert rationing, the often invisible mechanisms by which our present healthcare system denies us access to information, experts, procedures, and treatments we may need. Once we're enlightened about how covert rationing works and the dangers it poses, *Fixing American Healthcare* explains how we can take steps that will protect our loved ones—and ourselves—from falling victim to it.

We need to be informed not only about our particular diseases and health risks but also about the history, process, and current operation of the healthcare system. *Fixing American Healthcare* helps us understand where we've come from so we can see how to move forward. *Fixing American Healthcare* makes clear why it's crucial to know about all the options available to us—within our healthcare system and in partnership with our doctors—so we can get the care we need.

At the same time, *Fixing American Healthcare* outlines why we need the focused tools and systems in place to help us become better informed and more empowered and to help us make better decisions.

Thanks to DrRich, we now have *Fixing American Healthcare*, a roadmap for change in America's healthcare system. We have the power to transform America's healthcare system for the better—but the first step is to study the map DrRich has provided us, know where we're going, and get started on the journey.

Behave badly—and live well!

MARY J. SHOMON

www.thyroid-info.com

www.thyroid.about.com

Kensington, Maryland

July 2007

Acknowledgments

I WOULD LIKE TO THANK the many readers of my websites, as well as my colleagues, who have encouraged me over the years to put these ideas into a book. I send my love and appreciation to my family, who once again indulged the temporary inattentiveness that always accompanies my efforts on a project like this one. And I would especially like to thank my editor, Dick Margulis, whose astounding breadth of knowledge on diverse subjects (including healthcare, economics, religion, algebra, ethics, politics, the history of Western civilization, and pop culture from at least the 1950s), kept me honest in what I was saying; whose knowledge of good writing helped me say it much more clearly than I otherwise could have managed; and whose sense of humor kept my spirits up despite the quarts of red pixels he expended (each drop of which might otherwise have been as painful as if it had been my own blood). Betty Dobson proofread the pages, and Bobbi Swanson produced the detailed index.

Fixing American Healthcare

Introduction

IN PHYSICS, THE GRAND unification theory (GUT) brings together three fundamental forces of nature into one overarching whole, and thus goes a long way toward explaining the Way Things Are. Physicists assure us that once they figure out how to fold in the one remaining fundamental force—the force of gravity—their GUT will at last become the theory of everything; or, in deference to St. Paul, Muhammad, Buddha, and several others, it will become *another* theory of everything.

The grand unification theory of healthcare (GUTH), the subject of this book, is far less ambitious than the one being gnawed over by physicists. While their GUT ultimately aims to explain everything that has ever happened or ever will happen in the universe, the GUTH merely purports to explain everything about the American healthcare system.

That seems quite ambitious enough.

What do I mean by "everything?"

If you are an American who has been paying attention to the general state of the republic, you know that our healthcare system is plagued by serious problems. You may believe that it is broken beyond simple repair, that it is already too late for incremental reforms of the sort that politicians commonly talk about, and that instead it requires a complete restructuring, that we need to blow it up and start over. But whether the present state of American healthcare elicits in you a revolutionary fervor or just moderate consternation, if I were to ask you what is wrong with it, your answer would likely depend on who you are or what your role is with respect to the healthcare system.

If you are a patient you might complain of avaricious HMOs, distracted doctors, or the difficulty of getting decent health insurance. If you're a doctor you'll carp about demanding and litigious patients or managed care organizations and government agencies that swamp you with paperwork and won't let you practice good medicine. If you happen to be a managed care executive or a Medicare official, you will fume over doctors who use too much expensive technology on too many grasping patients—patients who (you'll mutter) refuse to make lifestyle choices to prevent their expensive illnesses in the first place. If you run a biomedical company, you'll bemoan the regulators who live only to prevent you from introducing your life-saving inventions to the marketplace. And if you're one of those regulators, you'll complain about a fickle public whose whining results in your being constantly hauled before congressional subcommittees, today for rushing unsafe products to market before they are fully tested, tomorrow for delaying the approval of critical medical products for the sake of your self-serving bureaucracy.

Like blind men feeling an elephant, we see the problems troubling the healthcare system as being narrow, well defined, tractable—and personal. We see solutions with a false sense of clarity: to fix healthcare we should institute universal health insurance or pass tort reform or let market forces reign or loosen FDA regulations or tighten FDA regulations. And we have a hard time understanding why the politicians and policymakers refuse to institute whichever simple fix we've set our hearts on.

So what about those politicians and policymakers, those charged by an angry public with figuring out what's wrong with the healthcare system and then doing something to fix it? Those few who try to understand the healthcare system from a more global and less circumscribed viewpoint often become paralyzed by the chaos they find there. Examined as a whole, the American healthcare system is dysfunctional, operating under policies, traditions, priorities, and behaviors that are counterintuitive, counterproductive, and seemingly inexplicable. Smart politicians realize that tweaking policies in the midst of this bedlam—that is, instituting the simple solutions that many of their constituents call for—will make things worse. And they'll be blamed. Their logical recourse is to take no real action at all but instead to utter platitudes, point the finger at those in the opposing party whose job it really is to fix things (or whose obstructionism is preventing *them* from fixing things), and pray that the final healthcare implosion won't occur until they are safely out of office, when it will have become somebody else's problem. Given the chaotic nature of our healthcare system, this hot potato approach is understandable.

Another way of dealing with the current chaos would be to start over, completely restructuring the American healthcare system. Many Western nations have instituted fundamental reforms that render their healthcare systems more organized and equitable (while arguably less technologically advanced and innovative) than ours. None of these systems is perfect—everyone understands that—but they are widely supported by their citizenries. Why can't our leaders take one of these systems—the Canadian model is the most commonly proposed—make a few tweaks, and adopt it as our own?

The answer is that politicians, individuals whose livelihoods depend on understanding their constituencies, think Americans won't stand for such a solution, at least not once they grasp the implications. For while reforming the healthcare system in the name of fairness and efficiency is something all Americans can support in concept, countries that have moved toward this goal have done so in ways that are incompatible with American expectations. Your typical American political leader will break out in a cold sweat contemplating the prospect of requiring voters with coronary artery disease to join an eighteen-month queue for bypass surgery. Just consider what happened the last time one of our leaders was brave enough to try restructuring our healthcare system. The Clintons' attempt to remake American healthcare in 1993–94 became a political debacle that led to a stunning Republican takeover of Congress (a result that persisted for twelve years, until the Republicans managed their own debacle). The result of the Clintons' effort is a stark reminder to any present-day officeholder with similar inclinations.

What is it about the American character that makes an acceptable solution to our growing healthcare crisis so difficult to imagine? The least charitable explanation is that we Americans have become as selfish, greedy, and unreasonable as spoiled children; and as a result we refuse to compromise on our expectations. We want healthcare reform, but it had better guarantee access to the best doctors, the best hospitals, and (above all) the best technology money can buy, whenever and wherever we need it (ignore for now whether such an expectation has ever been realized for more than a few Americans).

More charitably, and I believe more correctly, the American attitude toward proposed healthcare reforms reflects the principle upon which our society is based, that is, the principle of the essential primacy of the individual. We individuals are, our founding document assures us, endowed by our Creator with certain unalienable rights, and among these are life, liberty and the pursuit of happiness—but especially life. So how dare any politician ask us to get in line and *wait* for a medical therapy, a therapy that is in fact available and is being applied routinely to thousands of patients every day, and that, if applied, promises to restore health—especially knowing many of us won't make it to the front of that line (which is the point of having a line in the first place)?

Any fundamental reform of American healthcare ultimately relies on rationing. The proposed rationing schemes are disguised as "efficiency measures" or "quality checks" or "guarantees of fairness" or some other euphemism. But as soon as we start looking at the details of the proposed plan (or as soon as we examine the realities of the recommended "model" healthcare systems in place around the world), the rationing becomes obvious. And it is hard to reconcile the notion of rationing healthcare—that is, of rationing life, of delegating to the government or some other centralized agency the power to rank the worth of individuals, so as to determine who gets what—with the foundational American ideal of autonomy and the ultimate worth of each and every individual.

From this point of view, Americans' resistance to global healthcare reform runs deeper than mere selfishness. At some fundamental level, we perceive the kinds of global reforms that have commonly been proposed as a threat to what it means to be an American; and, as our politicians seem to realize, we are likely to greet such proposals (and their proponents) with a bristling resistance nearly matching that of our nation's founders against British rule.

If we're going to fix American healthcare before the current system leads us, as many economists promise it will, to a fiscal crisis big enough to threaten societal disintegration, it would be useful to visualize a new kind of healthcare system that is financially stable, that is equitable, efficient, and effective, but that does not undermine the founding principles of our culture—or even better, one that actually reinforces those principles.

The grand unification theory of healthcare is a conceptual model that describes the universe of possible healthcare systems. By mapping any proposed or existent healthcare system in this model, we can fully describe its essential characteristics and behaviors. The GUTH also allows us to predict how a given healthcare system will respond when we subject it to a proposed reform. Perhaps most important, the GUTH allows us to design a healthcare system from the ground up to display the characteristics and behaviors we want it to. Specifically:

- *The GUTH fully explains the current state of the American healthcare system, why it behaves the way it does, how it got this way, and where it's headed.* It elucidates the bizarre behavior of our healthcare system in all its disarray and irrationality. After we analyze the American healthcare system in light of the GUTH, behaviors that are initially incomprehensible should become explicable and even predictable.

- *The GUTH guides individuals in their interactions with the healthcare system.* Whether you're a patient, doctor, or healthcare entrepreneur, the GUTH predicts how the healthcare system behaves when you interact with it. It suggests ways in which you might manipulate the healthcare system to your own personal benefit, to do your health-related job or run your health-related business more effectively or, more importantly, to improve your odds of surviving when you get sick.

- *The GUTH points to an American solution to the healthcare crisis.* The GUTH, because it encompasses all conceivable healthcare systems, allows us to imagine a global fix for the healthcare system that is uniquely American. That is, it can point us toward a healthcare system that not only meets the "fairness, efficiency, and effectiveness" criterion that every Western nation strives for, but that also honors basic American ideals.

How this book is organized

Part I of this book jumps right into the GUTH; it provides a quick overview of the model I am proposing and all its implications. After

reading Part I, you can judge for yourself whether the GUTH lives up
to these admittedly extravagant claims and thus whether it is worth
your further exploration.

Part II applies the GUTH to an analysis of our current, chaotic
American healthcare system, revealing how and why it came to be the
way it is; how its illogical and counterproductive behaviors are actually
consistent with and necessary to the underlying operating principles
assigned to it by society (that is, by us); and where its current trajectory
promises to deposit all of us one day.

Finally, Part III uses the GUTH to find a uniquely American solution to the healthcare crisis. Applying the GUTH to six general principles that define an ideal American healthcare system, we will discover
how we might build such a thing in a civil fashion, without blood flowing in the streets and without criminalizing what is good about our
current healthcare system. We will see how the GUTH offers immediate help to anyone who today must—through voluntary career choices
or through ill luck—interact with the American healthcare system.
And we will see how individuals who understand the GUTH and then
act accordingly, in their own self-interest and without any notion of
perpetrating healthcare reform, can become the catalyst for achieving
that ultimate American healthcare system, a system that is equitable,
efficient, and effective.

Part I

The Grand Unification Theory of Healthcare

An Overview

1

A Model of the Healthcare Universe

IN MY CONSULTING BUSINESS, I have often had to explain the inner workings of the American healthcare system to engineers. Engineers usually like systems. Systems—scientifically sound, mathematically logical, internally consistent, well-designed systems—are the stuff of the engineering profession. But the healthcare system was not designed by engineers.

In fact, the healthcare "system" wasn't designed by anybody. It evolved. And over many decades, it became an accretion of disjointed, inconsistent, centralized policy decisions, mixed with scattered and often bizarre local customs. Its behavior varies tremendously over time and space, and is modulated by inconstant human desires, prejudices, illogic, and wishful thinking. The healthcare system is more suitable for study by sociologists than by engineers.

So it gets confusing for them.

Over the years I have devised conceptual models that explain various aspects of the healthcare system. But I quickly learned that engineers aren't going to sit still, much less pay me, for a two-day seminar on the manifold faces of the healthcare system. Instead, I needed an intuitively obvious, easy-to-remember framework for describing everything you might want to know about the healthcare system, something I could lay out for them in a fifteen-minute presentation (or outline in a five-minute hallway conversation) and on which I could hang more detailed explanations as they became relevant to the work at hand.

Given that my goal was to make this intelligible to engineers, I wanted to show that framework on a simple graph. Relying on my own experiences as a doctor, patient, and entrepreneur; on the thoughts and writings of those smarter than I; and on a love for the intuitively attractive, I eventually arrived at the scheme shown in Figure 1.

Graphing healthcare

We can represent the healthcare universe with a simple, two-dimensional graphic model. This model takes into account

+ Who makes healthcare decisions (the horizontal axis in Figure 1)
+ Whether those decisions are of high or low quality (the vertical axis)

Within the universe defined by this model, we can fully characterize the behaviors of any healthcare system we could plausibly devise.

In Figure 1, on the horizontal axis, we ask if healthcare decisions are made by the individuals most directly affected by them (the patients

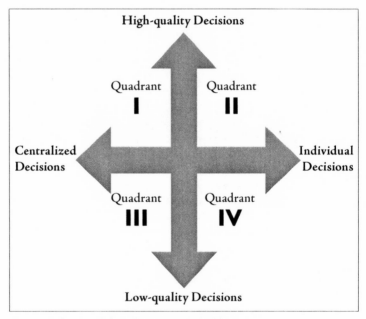

Figure 1. A framework for talking about the healthcare universe.

and their doctors) or, instead, if they are under the control of some centralized authority (such as the federal government or giant insurance carriers). On the vertical axis we ask if the decisions are of high quality, based on good, solid, scientific evidence or if they are of low quality, made on some other basis, such as political considerations, intuition, superstition, or emotion.

These two axes (individual versus centralized decision-makers, and high-quality versus low-quality decisions) divide the healthcare universe into four quadrants. Each of these four quadrants carries with it a set of inherent properties that largely determine the behavior of any healthcare system operating within that quadrant. This four-quadrant model of the healthcare universe, along with four corollaries that we will derive from it, constitute the grand unification theory of healthcare (GUTH).

In later chapters we will see how the GUTH explains the chaotic and illogical characteristics of the current American healthcare system, predicts the way that healthcare system will respond when we interact with it (whether "we" are individuals, institutions, or enterprises), and helps us to optimize those interactions to our own benefit. More important, we will see how this model points the way toward a new kind of healthcare system that is, at last, equitable, efficient, and innovative.

But in this chapter I will just give a general overview of the GUTH and attempt to demonstrate its potential. To this end, I will show that

- Until recently, the American healthcare system operated in Quadrant IV of the healthcare universe.
- Operating in Quadrant IV was always an unstable and time-limited proposition; there was never any possibility that we could stay there.
- The momentum of change has moved us into Quadrant III.
- The defining characteristics of Quadrant III explain the strange behavior of today's healthcare system.
- By understanding where we are on this healthcare landscape and how we got here, we can see how to advance to a more favorable position (Quadrant I or Quadrant II).

The GUTH: Where we are today

The traditional, Quadrant IV healthcare system

Beginning around World War II and until the early 1990s, the American healthcare system resided in Quadrant IV of the healthcare universe. Medical decisions were made, for the most part,

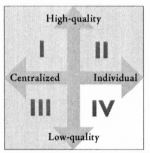

by individual doctors and their patients, based on what was perceived to be best for the patient (or sometimes, we must admit, for the doctor). But healthcare decisions were not driven by high-quality, data-guided reasoning. The decisions were generally of low quality. A system of low-quality decisions made by individual doctors and their patients planted us squarely in Quadrant IV.

Medical decisions were generally of low quality during the Quadrant IV era for several reasons:

+ Until recent years most medical decisions were not based on rigorous clinical science, a fairly recent invention. That is, the information that doctors used to make medical choices tended to come from personal experience, anecdotal case reports, or the opinions of medical gurus instead of from large, controlled, randomized clinical trials.

+ Doctors have traditionally had the ethical and professional imperative to place the needs of the patient first. But at least in the era before managed care, the more stuff doctors did, the more they got paid. So they tended to do more than was necessary. This tendency was enhanced by the general dearth of evidence. Without hard evidence doctors relied on a synthesis of soft data from many sources of their own choosing; it was easy for them to shade their decisions, often subconsciously and more or less in good faith, in the direction of doing the things they got paid for.

+ Overt, old-fashioned, in-your-face medical paternalism (which persists to this day to some extent) was the rule during much of the Quadrant IV era. According to this paternalistic viewpoint, patients are supposed to rely on the opinion of the experts, that is, their doctors, in sorting through the complex nuances of medical decisions. Patients aren't at all capable of understanding this sort of thing themselves, the reasoning goes; after all, this is why their doctors spent all those years in training.

As a result of these three factors, healthcare decisions during the Quadrant IV era were of relatively low quality.

Using World War II as a starting point is somewhat arbitrary, but two events occurred around that time that initiated a new era in American healthcare. The first was rapid innovation in medical care because of advances made during battlefield surgery, and because of insights gained from the effort to produce penicillin in large quantities. The second event, and for us the more important one, was the spread of group health insurance, which American companies began offering to their workers during the war in partial compensation for the wage freeze that was in effect.

Health insurance proved to be so popular that after the war (encouraged by the federal government through tax incentives), it quickly became a nearly universal benefit for American workers. Then, in 1965, the federal government created Medicare and Medicaid, providing health insurance to millions more (and suddenly making the government itself the biggest third-party payer). This rapid adoption of a third-party payment system for healthcare changed everything.

Thanks to this new third-party funding mechanism, we in the U.S. evolved a mentality that remains unique when it comes to healthcare. We expect and insist on nothing but the best healthcare available, whenever we want or need it, and the Tooth Fairy picks up the tab. Such a system, where the individuals making the purchasing decisions are spending someone else's money, made Quadrant IV healthcare financially unstable and doomed it to failure.*

The Tooth Fairy financing system yielded many benefits. It was this system, fiscally unstable as it was, that triggered fifty years of industry-driven advances in healthcare (if you build it and it works, someone will pay for it). Countries with saner financing systems contributed relatively few medical innovations during that period. The Tooth Fairy has been the lifeblood of the American pharmaceutical and biotech industries and the patients they serve. And for a few decades it seemed as if we had enough money in the system (if we didn't look too closely) to finance the insanity.

* Such a reimbursement system, by encouraging profligate spending, inherently produces low-quality decisions and thus always resides in Quadrant IV.

The Tooth Fairy has been pushed beyond her limits. Providing every kind of useful healthcare to anyone who needs it is a fiscal black hole, the cost to payers is outstripping revenues, and insurance premiums and Medicare costs are growing at many times the rate of overall inflation. The government and insurance carriers are becoming more aggressive in their efforts to curb spending.

A system where individuals can choose whatever healthcare they want and someone else picks up the tab is not sustainable. It might have worked when medical science didn't have much to offer sick people, when doctors were still lancing boils and getting paid in chickens and couldn't spend much money delivering healthcare no matter how hard they tried—a situation that existed not so many decades ago. But the medical advances financed by the Tooth Fairy system have produced an environment in which this system can no longer exist. We had to exit Quadrant IV. And the direction of movement as we did so was resolutely to the left, toward centralized decision-making.

Moving leftward

Two powerful forces are moving us leftward within the healthcare universe.

+ Individual patients (and their doctors) do not take the needs of society into account when they decide how much of society's money to spend on their own healthcare. Thus, society has a strong incentive to take those spending decisions out of the hands of individuals and place them in the hands of some central authority.
+ We have a growing conviction that healthcare is an entitlement for all Americans. This conviction itself is at least partly a result of latter-day Quadrant IV healthcare, where exploding healthcare costs (fueled by exploding expectations) have outstripped the ability of individuals to pay for their own care.

This notion of entitlement has taken root. Witness, for example, the 2003 Medicare drug law, which is the largest new federal entitlement program in forty years and which, tellingly, was sponsored by Republicans. During the acrimonious Congressional debates over this plan, neither major party disagreed with the idea that the government should be providing such a benefit; instead, the major disagreement at the time was over how much money to spend in providing it (a huge amount versus a humongous amount). Whatever you may think about the merits of this new program, the manner of its adoption illustrates how deep is our sense of entitlement to healthcare. This sense is not unique to the U.S. It is even stronger in most other Western nations and has been fully incorporated into most other healthcare systems in the developed world.

Declaring healthcare to be an entitlement forces the centralization of healthcare, as any large entitlement requires the redistribution of wealth, which is possible only with a powerful central authority. If there were no such authority (but, of course, there is), a healthcare entitlement would necessitate creating one.

So: both the need to curb the profligacy of individuals and the entitlement mentality have driven the American healthcare system leftward in the healthcare landscape, toward the centralization of medical decision-making. Such centralization enjoys, if not popular support, at least popular resignation. Centralizing healthcare is inherently appealing to bureaucrats and those of the left-of-center political persuasions. It is increasingly acceptable to growing millions of citizens from across the political spectrum who are frustrated and disgusted by a healthcare system that is progressively exclusive, chaotic, and hostile, and who see centralized control as the least bad of the potential solutions. While there are political forces standing against such centralization, they are fighting a rear-guard action. And as a result, our healthcare system has moved leftward.

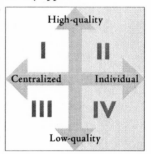

Given this strong move to the left within our healthcare landscape, it is now time to introduce the **First Corollary** of the GUTH:

Left = Rationing

When any healthcare system is operating in either of the two left-hand quadrants of the healthcare universe, whether Quadrant I or Quadrant III, it is necessarily operating under a system of rationing.

Let me be clear on what I mean by healthcare rationing, because the rationing of healthcare is a central theme in this book, and it is important to establish exactly what I am talking about. I am not talking about something bland or benign, such as the allocation of scarce healthcare resources, or the fair distribution of available benefits, or goods, or commodities. Such definitions are (intentionally, I think) misleadingly soothing. There is nothing pretty about rationing healthcare. Rationing is bad, and if we're doing it we should at least be willing to acknowledge exactly what we are doing. So here's the definition I like: *To ration healthcare is to withhold medical services from individuals who would probably benefit from them because we have decided not to buy those services for everybody who needs them.*

I like this definition because it is straightforward. Also, it puts the onus on us (since we're the ones deciding not to buy the services) instead of on those nasty "scarce resources" themselves. That makes it harder for us to dance around the real issue, which is: If we're going to ration healthcare, then we ought to do it in the least harmful way possible.

Why is the First Corollary true? Why is it that any healthcare system operating on the left half of healthcare landscape must necessarily employ rationing? It is because centralized decision-making means that some central authority is controlling a pool of money, created by society, from which healthcare costs are to be paid.* Because there will always be limits to how much money can be placed into such a pool, while there will never be limits on what can potentially be spent on healthcare, whenever the healthcare system is operating in one of the two left quadrants, rationing is occurring. (Because the First Corollary is so central to the GUTH, we will explore its proof in much more depth in Chapter 2.)

* There may actually be several pools of money, some controlled by government agencies and others by insurance carriers or managed care organizations—but the principle remains the same.

Why Quadrant III looks inevitable

Just as there are powerful forces pushing the healthcare system leftward, toward centralized decision-making and thus toward rationing, so is there an equally powerful force pushing it downward, into Quadrant III, and away from Quadrant I.

That force is the culture of no limits. That and the entitlement mentality are the two main cultural imperatives shaping the American healthcare system today. Unlike the entitlement mentality, which is nearly universal in Western countries, the culture of no limits is uniquely American.

The Culture of No Limits

In America we have and will continue to have the best healthcare in the world, the best doctors, the best hospitals, and the best technology. Since one cannot place a price on human life, everything that can be done for a sick person must be done, as long as there is some small hope of a beneficial outcome. Finally, every disease is potentially curable, and as a matter of policy we will strive to learn how to cure every disease, death itself being merely a manifestation of insufficient technology. In summary, where healthcare is concerned there are and can be no limits.

So, at the same time we find ourselves up against inherent spending limitations that require rationing, we find that there can be no limits.

These two fundamental tenets—the entitlement mentality and the culture of no limits—are incompatible with one another. And our need to simultaneously hold onto these two incompatible but necessary imperatives is strongly driving our healthcare system toward Quadrant III, toward a system of centralized, low-quality healthcare decisions. Quadrant III is the only place on the healthcare landscape where we can create a centralized entitlement program operating under the fiction that no rationing is necessary.

To see why this is so, consider what it would mean to ration healthcare in a manner that produces high-quality medical decisions, that is, what it would mean to operate our healthcare system in Quadrant I. High-quality rationing would require that the rationing be fair and equitable to the extent possible and therefore would require the full and open participation of society in devising the rules for rationing. But we can't do that, because it would be rationing. And our culture of no limits strictly forbids rationing.

The only remaining option, since we must ration but cannot admit it, is to operate in Quadrant III. Quadrant III allows for low-quality healthcare decisions, and so offers a haven from which to entertain our two mutually exclusive cultural imperatives. We can ration while declaring there are no limits. We can deny that any rationing is occurring at all. We can ration deceptively. We can ration covertly.

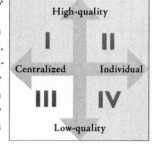

Thus, we reach the **Second Corollary** of the GUTH:

Covert rationing requires Quadrant III.

That is, covert rationing *requires* low-quality decisions and therefore will always result in Quadrant III healthcare.

This analysis reveals that the deceptions being promulgated by our Quadrant III healthcare system are not being foisted on an unsuspecting public by evil bureaucrats. Instead, the public willingly subjects itself to these obvious deceptions; otherwise people would have to face the fact that either entitlements are impossible or rationing is unavoidable. And either of these options would require some tough choices that we are not prepared to make.

Life in Quadrant III

The Second Corollary shows that covert rationing is the hallmark of Quadrant III healthcare. This goes a long way toward explaining the chaos, confusion, and inefficiency that plague today's healthcare system. I will give the mechanisms and consequences of Quadrant III healthcare a full treatment in Part II of this book. Here I just want to

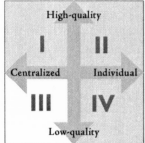

offer a short survey of life in Quadrant III, just enough to provide a flavor of how destructive such healthcare can be to individuals and to society.

The central authorities we have deputized to control healthcare costs have a lot to gain by accepting this responsibility (for governmental bureaucracies, incredible power; for insurance executives, incredible profits). But they have to work hard for that gain, because it is going to be difficult, if not impossible, to control healthcare costs under even the best of circumstances.

And the central authorities are not working under the best of circumstances. Their only option is to institute some form of rationing. But they cannot ration openly. They cannot accomplish the necessary rationing by decree or even by open negotiation, nor can they be hamfisted in enforcing the rationing. Instead, a subtle, covert, plausibly deniable kind of rationing is necessary. This constraint leaves them with only one good choice: They need to coerce the doctors into doing the rationing for them. So covert rationing must occur at the bedside, during the physician–patient encounter.

The central authorities have many methods for coercing the behavior of physicians, because they have empowered themselves to determine the individual physician's viability as a practitioner. The central authorities have at their disposal an arsenal of subtle weapons, and an occasional nuke, to assure that doctors relegate the needs of their patients to a secondary position and instead take pains to keep their true customers—the central authorities—satisfied. The medical profession has mostly caved in to this pressure, albeit under duress.

A direct result of covert rationing is the systematic destruction of the classic doctor–patient relationship—the relationship under which doctors are supposed to act from a position of trust, solely as their patients' advocates, and to place the needs of their individual patients above all other considerations. We cannot have both covert rationing and an intact doctor–patient relationship at the same time. Thus, the Third Corollary:

Covert rationing destroys the doctor–patient relationship.

The loss of the traditional doctor–patient relationship has profound implications.

> One day, down on your luck and in need of some quick cash, you decide to rob a convenience store. You rush in brandishing a .38, and order the clerk to hand over all the cash. He turns out to be a wise guy; you panic and shoot him. You quickly clean out the cash register and head for the door—where you run smack into two burly police officers who happen to be entering the store right then for some of that good hot coffee. You are quickly and none too gently disarmed and arrested. So there you are—caught red-handed, money in one hand, gun in the other, the blood of the clerk on your shirt, and for good measure the whole episode has been recorded by a hidden video camera.

Now, here's the question: What rights are you entitled to?

Despite the fact that anybody can see how guilty you are, you have many rights. You have the right to a fair trial. You have the right to be considered innocent until a jury of your peers declares you guilty. And you have the right to appeal the verdict (assuming, of course, that you are not going to like it).

But above all else, you have the right to counsel, an advocate, an individual who is obligated to defend you and to protect your interests.

As a physician, I envy the ability of lawyers to embrace their advocacy role. Lawyers retain this luxury because society recognizes that the legal system is a morass of rules and regulations that ordinary citizens cannot hope to navigate on their own. We acknowledge the right of any citizen caught up in the legal system to have a lawyer who holds that citizen's interests above all others (within the constraints of the law). Even those accused of heinous crimes are entitled to legal representation; even if the evidence against them seems overwhelming, their lawyers are expected to jealously guard their rights. Some of us may object to the rights that accrue to (in our eyes) an obviously guilty party. But most of us understand the wisdom of such a system. And we shudder to think of the abuses that would occur if these protections were removed.

Sick people are no more capable of navigating the complex healthcare system than are accused felons the complex legal system; and they are no less in peril if they run afoul of that system. A patient's need of an advocate, a professional whose job it is to protect the patient's interests against the conflicting aims of the system, is no less vital than that of the felon. When you are sick, you should be entitled to at least the same protections as when you rob a convenience store. And the doctor–patient relationship is supposed to ensure those protections.

Over the ages the doctor–patient relationship has been defined through rules of ethics and rules of law as a relationship founded in trust. When a patient seeks a physician's help and the physician agrees to give that help, a special covenant is made. The patient agrees to take the physician into her confidence, to reveal to him even the most secret and intimate information related to her health. The physician, in turn, agrees to honor that trust, and to become the patient's advocate in all matters related to her health, placing her interests above all others— including his own personal or financial concerns.

The doctor–patient relationship was never pure in actual practice, even in the good old days. During those Quadrant IV good old days, doctors all too often shaded their recommendations according to how well they would be reimbursed. Nonetheless, a strong relationship of trust is what patients have expected, what most doctors have striven for, and what everyone else (the medical ethicists, professional societies, and those who write and enforce the laws of the land) have traditionally agreed—and even demanded—should be the standard. It represents the fundamental expectation of how doctors and patients are supposed to behave toward one another.

The loss of this doctor–patient relationship has obvious consequences for patients. Patients, when they are sick and thus least able to fend for themselves, are left without a true, dedicated advocate as they try to navigate the hostile halls of the healthcare system. Most doctors still try their hardest to do what's best for their patients, but they can only do so within the constraints of maintaining their ability to practice medicine; and such constraints often are not trivial. Loss of the traditional doctor–patient compact leaves patients marginalized and floundering at the time they are most vulnerable.

Less obvious are the consequences of a damaged doctor–patient relationship to the profession of medicine. Abandoning that relationship means that physicians have committed the original sin. They have abdicated their traditional, ethical, and legal roles as patient advocates; they have broken a pact. They have compromised themselves as professionals and find themselves standing naked before their enemies—the very enemies who forced this abdication.

Finally, we arrive at the **Fourth Corollary:**

Covert rationing corrupts everything it touches.

Part II of this book elaborates on the Fourth Corollary. There I show how covert rationing has corrupted the principles of managed care, the regulatory environment of the healthcare system, the conduct and analysis of medical research, the ethical issues surrounding end-of-life care, and even the founding principles of American society.

A less obvious manifestation of the Fourth Corollary is that covert rationing abhors simplicity and straightforwardness. Byzantine policies, self-contradictory directives, tangled incentives, and endlessly shifting regulations help keep the flow of money and resources in the healthcare system a mystery. The resulting confusion is essential for creating many of the subtle incentives necessary to produce covert rationing. This is why the efforts periodically initiated to simplify and streamline healthcare, sometimes introduced with great fanfare, get stuck in the bureaucratic molasses, just one more layer of glom in a vast conglomeration of regulations. All this systematic confusion is inefficient and wasteful and negates most if not all of the savings produced by rationing in the first place.

Herein lies the great irony of Quadrant III healthcare, the final joke: In Quadrant III, the need to keep the rationing covert is the primary objective, even more important than actually reducing costs. As I'll show in later chapters, improvements in practices, processes, or technologies that, if implemented, would reduce the cost of healthcare often, through the transparencies they create, threaten the bureaucracies that keep rationing covert—and therefore they are stifled or suppressed.

This phenomenon makes life difficult for everybody. Companies whose products are aimed at making healthcare more efficient or cost effective have failed by assuming that the healthcare system will embrace their efforts, that is, will pay for these benefits. If, in addition to saving money, their products also threaten the infrastructure of covert rationing, they will be disappointed with the results.

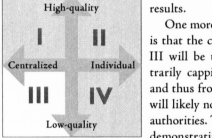

One more consequence of Quadrant III healthcare is that the central authorities operating in Quadrant III will be unable to restrain themselves from arbitrarily capping the profits of biomedical companies, and thus from stifling medical innovation. This result will likely not be particularly upsetting to the central authorities. They will portray the lack of innovation as demonstrating how corrupt these biomedical companies are, and they will promulgate even more regulations to further centralize control.

To summarize, our current healthcare system is so wonderfully and intractably dysfunctional precisely because it operates in Quadrant III. We're not dealing with a sound healthcare system that has a few aberrancies we can identify and fix. Instead, we're dealing with a healthcare system that traffics in covert rationing, a system in which complexity, inequity, and inefficiency are foundational operating principles.

The GUTH: What will tomorrow bring?

Must we stay in Quadrant III?

I am convinced that healthcare in Quadrant III is undesirable. But we're in Quadrant III for a powerful reason—our only other option is to give up either our notion that healthcare is an essential entitlement or our conviction that there can be no limits on healthcare. Until we're willing to abandon one of these mutually exclusive societal imperatives, we had better get used to what we've got—and get ready for more of it.

After spending some more time with the perfidies of Quadrant III healthcare, we in the American public may get to the point where almost anything would sound better—even abandoning one or both of our deeply held tenets. But it won't matter unless we are able to move to a place on the healthcare landscape where a well-functioning healthcare system is feasible. We've already tried two of the four quadrants within the healthcare universe; we have found Quadrant IV healthcare unsustainable and Quadrant III healthcare intolerable. What assurance do we have that the remaining two quadrants will be any better? Before trying to figure out whether we should embark on a likely painful effort to leave Quadrant III, let's briefly examine Quadrant I and Quadrant II, the only other places we can go.

Healthcare in Quadrant I

In Quadrant I, decisions are still made centrally. This implies (most likely) government control of the healthcare system.* Control of healthcare decisions would remain centralized, so rationing would be necessary (from the First Corollary). The rationing decisions that are made in Quadrant I, however, are of high quality; that is, they are based on good scientific and economic information appropriately and equitably applied, using processes that are open to, vetted by, and monitored by the public.

* A variant could also be postulated such as a privatized authority based on the health insurance model, but with a strong federal regulatory presence.

Rationing healthcare openly and transparently, while necessary for high quality rationing choices, is a daunting prospect, and it is hard to think of circumstances that would render American society willing to engage in such a thing. In today's environment, under a no limits

imperative, no bureaucrat or politician in their right mind would publicly entertain the notion of open rationing.

Even if we Americans were to agree in principle to openly ration
healthcare, the policymakers would then have to guide us through a
difficult process. Consider a few of the more obvious problems:

+ They'd have tell us that we really can't have all the healthcare
  we want or need; that indeed, there will be times when curable
  illnesses will go uncured and preventable deaths will not be prevented, not because of inherently limited resources (as, say, with
  heart transplantation) but because, well, they've got to draw the
  line somewhere, and sometimes we're just going to fall below the
  line.

+ They'd have to come up with a system for deciding which of us
  will get treatment and which others will not. Will they base
  these rationing decisions on the diseases we have, on our age, on
  some measure of our worth to society, or on whether our illness
  resulted from chosen behaviors such as smoking, overeating, or
  leading a sedentary life?

+ They'd have to determine how much money to put in the pool,
  how to collect it, and who pays it.

+ They'd have to explain either to those of us who are poor why the
  rich can buy life-saving therapy outside the system when we can't
  have it or to those of us who are rich why we can't buy uncovered,
  but available, life-saving therapy with our own money.

+ They'd have to sell the whole program to at least a majority of
  us.

It is easy to see why policymakers are not keen to tell us that rationing is necessary: Should we ever buy into that idea, their lives will
instantly become hell.

Any way you cut it, Quadrant I healthcare seems unlikely. But if
it were somehow to happen, there would be many advantages over
Quadrant III healthcare. Because the rationing would be open instead
of covert, there would no longer be a reason to separate the interests
of doctors from the interests of their patients, and the doctor–patient
relationship could be restored. Doctors, working within a universal
and well-defined set of rules, could advocate actively and aggressively
for the needs of their individual patients within those rules. (More routinely than doctors can get away with today, their role might become

more like that of attorneys, who aggressively work within the confines of the law to offer every advantage to their clients.) Patients would still be subject to rationing, just as they are today—but the rationing would be open for all to see, and it would be far more equitable. Everybody's access to the benefits of healthcare would be constrained by the same set of rules. The elimination of covert rationing would remove the impetus to corrupt the science of medicine and would encourage instead of stifle genuine reforms aimed at streamlining healthcare and maximizing efficiency.

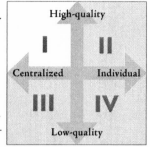

Shifting to a Quadrant I healthcare system would substantially slow the pace of medical innovation. Most medical advances do not reduce the cost of care— instead, they increase the overall cost. Incentives for advancing medical technologies whose measurable benefits are far outweighed by their costs would be stifled in Quadrant I. On the other hand, Quadrant I would offer entrepreneurs a more stable and predictable environment for doing business with the healthcare system than does Quadrant III. As long as their products and technologies decrease overall health costs, they could be sure of finding a pathway into the healthcare marketplace (not the case today). This predictability would focus the talents of biomedical entrepreneurs.

Quadrant I healthcare is compatible with and actually encourages a civil, long-lasting, stable society. Implementing a successful Quadrant I healthcare system would be a challenge, likely the greatest non-wartime challenge America has ever faced; but the current alternative— Quadrant III healthcare—promises to become a disaster.

A system of open rationing can be imagined that is preferable on all levels to a system of covert rationing. We aren't choosing here between open rationing and no rationing at all; we're choosing between two different forms of rationing. Quadrant I healthcare has the potential of becoming a decided improvement over the Quadrant III healthcare we have today.

Healthcare in Quadrant II

In Quadrant II, medical decisions are made where they should be made—on the ground, by individual doctors and patients. What differentiates this from Quadrant IV (that is, the Tooth Fairy system) is that in Quadrant II patients will be paying for these decisions themselves, out of their own pockets. They will be willing to do so either because the healthcare they are purchasing is so compelling they are delighted to shell out the money or, more likely, because they are being systematically incented to pay for a large chunk of their own healthcare through some tax program. And because the individuals receiving the medical services will be paying for them, healthcare economics will begin to look like other, more typical economic spheres, and the quality of purchasing decisions will tend to increase.*

* I realize that the sophisticated and costly healthcare we now have is far too expensive for individuals to purchase themselves, and a self-pay healthcare system—no matter what the tax incentives—is impossible. My purpose is not to suggest that a pure Quadrant II healthcare system is a real option for us but merely to consider some of the theoretical benefits that would accrue from such a system. Later we'll look at how some of these benefits might be realized despite the fiscal realities.

The quality of medical decisions made in Quadrant II will rely on solid, well-designed clinical science, just as it would for decisions made under open rationing in Quadrant I. But as patients will be paying for their own care, the quality of their decisions must be more broadly defined; that is, "quality" is less dependent on what's good for society, less reliant on randomized data for therapies whose benefits are intuitively obvious to the purchaser, and more dependent on what the patient perceives as being good. Just as a person buying a car might gain more satisfaction from buying a Lincoln Town Car than a Ford Focus, so a person buying a healthcare product might gain more satisfaction from, say, a feature-laden medical device than a bare-bones device. And not only would that more expensive purchase be perfectly okay, from an economic standpoint it might be something to encourage—just as we encourage people to upgrade when they buy their next car. (On the other hand, if it were seen as the government's responsibility to provide transportation to everybody, under the theory that in today's mobile society a car is every bit as important to wellbeing as healthcare, then we would all—except for legislators—drive Yugos.)

Whereas it becomes possible to restore the doctor–patient relationship under a Quadrant I system of open rationing, Quadrant II makes restoration of this relationship automatic. This is because in Quadrant II, doctors aren't paid by a central authority anymore—they are paid by their patients. Patients become once again their doctors' primary customers, the ones who determine their doctors' professional viability, and the ones their doctors will need to answer to above all others.

Quadrant II healthcare would revolutionize the business model for healthcare entrepreneurs. For the first time it is the patients, those whose money is being spent, who ultimately would make purchasing decisions (with the assistance and advice of their doctors, now in their employ). This means that companies for the first time would begin developing medical products that appeal directly to patients and give those patients what they need and value. Quadrant II healthcare thus would stimulate a new kind of medical innovation—it would stimulate the invention of products and services aimed at helping patients determine their own medical destiny. Medical innovation would explode, and in an entirely new direction.

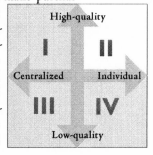

So at least in theory, Quadrant II healthcare seems more desirable than Quadrant III healthcare.

A synthesis of upper-quadrant healthcare

What Quadrant I and Quadrant II healthcare have in common is that in both upper quadrants healthcare decisions are of high quality; that is, these decisions satisfy the needs of, and create value for, the respective purchasers. Because the purchasers are not identical (in Quadrant I the purchaser is society; in Quadrant II the purchaser is the individual patient), the healthcare decisions that are made in these two quadrants may not be the same. But in both quadrants those decisions will be made by the entity that is spending the money, with knowledge of the medical options, their respective costs, and the potential risks and benefits of each one.

Given that either upper quadrant would create an environment for high quality and high value healthcare decisions, each of them has a strong potential of being less destructive to society and less dangerous to individuals than the system we have today. But neither of these upper-quadrant models is ideal. And it is hard to imagine how either could be feasible.

However, a synthesis of Quadrant I and Quadrant II healthcare—an "upper-quadrant" healthcare system—may be possible. Such a synthesis, if designed with some care, could provide the advantages inherent to each of the upper quadrants while minimizing the disadvantages. Part III of this book describes such a system in detail. For now I will just say that the GUTH not only explains the vagaries of today's healthcare system but it also suggests at least one achievable model for a future healthcare system that is equitable and efficient. With at least some small hope that such a thing is possible, then, it is reasonable to begin thinking about how we might escape Quadrant III.

How can we escape Quadrant III?

Denying the inevitability of healthcare rationing ultimately pushes us into Quadrant III. That is, it is mass self-deception that makes covert rationing necessary. The same self-deception makes covert rationing possible. For, not seeing all the widespread rationing behavior—which is quite apparent all around us—requires a willful failure to see it. Covert rationing utterly depends on this willful self-deception.

This observation has important implications. When motivated individuals concerned with their own wellbeing acknowledge that they are navigating a healthcare system founded on covert rationing, the healthcare system can no longer practice covert rationing against them.

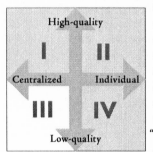

Covert rationing requires that patients remain passive and compliant, trusting that their doctors, the insurers, and the federal authorities—but especially their doctors—have their individual welfare at heart, will do right by them, and will tell them whatever they need to know. Patients are strongly encouraged by society to trust their doctors and their health plans, and traditionally they have willingly done so. Indeed, when such "ideal" patients notice activities and behaviors that seem contrary to their best interests, they usually attribute those events to aberrations, mistakes, inadvertent inefficiencies, or just someone having a bad day. They might sue someone for malpractice, but it never occurs to them that these events are systematic and even intended.

On the other hand, for those who are appropriately suspicious during each and every encounter with the healthcare system and who entertain the possibility that a chief goal of their doctors, the insurers, and the federal authorities may not be so much to improve their individual health but to avoid spending too much money on them, covert rationing becomes much more difficult to pull off. If a critical mass of citizens were to take this attitude, each one acting in enlightened self-interest, then covert rationing as a national modus operandi would become impossible. If enough individual citizens were to see the light, the healthcare system could no longer operate in Quadrant III.

What about the doctors?

The situation with doctors is different. It will be much harder for doctors, acting on their own, to stop covert rationing. Doctors lost their standing to do so when they abandoned the doctor–patient relationship. Many doctors are distraught at having been forced into this compromised position. Their inability to do what's best for their patients, rather than loss of income, is what is creating so much widespread frustration and dissatisfaction among American physicians. And many are looking for ways to remedy the situation. But by acquiescing to covert rationing (even though the pressure to do so has been irresistible), doctors have destroyed the ethical underpinnings of their profession, in turn diminishing any moral authority they might have had to call a stop to Quadrant III behaviors. Doctors have declared that their interests no longer line up with those of their patients.*

Doctors can redeem themselves and their profession only by entering into a new covenant with patients, and reestablishing a new doctor–patient relationship. They cannot do this alone. They first need a new kind of patient, one who can enter such a relationship not as a supplicant or an inferior, but as an equal—or even senior—partner.

* We will see in later chapters that this change in the ethical precepts of the medical profession has now been rendered official by several respected medical organizations. Doctors have formal authorization, by a new code of ethics, to ration healthcare at the bedside.

So it comes down to the patients. They are the entities within the healthcare system who have the moral authority and the ability to demand a halt to covert rationing. Patients have to recognize that covert rationing exists, that it presents a clear, present, and *personal* danger—a danger that directly threatens them and their loved ones—and further that it is within their power to stop it in their own personal encounters with the healthcare system. All they have to do to reduce their personal danger is to be alert for rationing behavior, to know what it looks like, and to call its name when they see it.

Knowledge is power

Intelligent patients who understand that covert rationing is occurring and that they can no longer rely on their doctors or their insurers to do what is right for them know that they need appropriate knowledge to protect themselves from the dangers of hidden rationing. Covert rationing depends on patients trusting their doctors to be the main, and preferably only, source of healthcare advice. If their doctor doesn't tell them about it, the paradigm goes, it doesn't exist (which is why controlling physician behavior is essential to a healthcare system based on covert rationing). Knowledgeable patients wreck covert rationing.

Becoming sufficiently knowledgeable is difficult. Patients are trying, though. American adults are going to the Internet by the tens of millions to find out what their doctors are supposed to be telling them and doing for them. This quest for knowledge is difficult, because so much contradictory, incomprehensible, and just plain wrong information abounds. Even reliable sources cannot tell them whether the information applies specifically to them.

Can patients become sufficiently empowered to block covert rationing? Yes, they can. Looking at the healthcare system historically, it seems likely that many of them will. For we are in the midst of a revolution in information technology that is radically changing every economic sphere it touches. This revolution is just beginning to affect the healthcare system.

A hallmark of the information revolution is that it puts the end user in direct contact with the source of products and services, thus eliminating or marginalizing the middlemen (those who traditionally served as high priests of data, guarding the information that was too sacred or too complex for the small minds of the masses and doling it out, piecemeal, in exchange for appropriate consideration). Examples of formerly powerful, now displaced middlemen include the medieval Church (violently opposed to laymen having direct access to the word of God), stock brokers, music publishers, travel agents, real estate agents, and educators.

Healthcare has been relatively impervious to the information revolution. Here, the high priests of data mongering include doctors, managed care organizations, and the government. All three groups see the information revolution coming but seem confident they'll be able to manage it. They are anxious to have the data themselves but intend to keep it locked up and out of sight (they all agree that medical information is far, far too complex for mere patients to grasp, and so it is clearly in the patients' best interest for the experts to husband that data for them). * They'll interpret the data and parse it out to the patients on a need-to-know basis, thank you. And before it's distrib-uted, it can be spun to support covert rationing.

The middlemen here are fighting history. They're also fighting the growing demands of patients, who sense they've been marginalized by the healthcare system (though they don't yet realize how systemati-cally they have been marginalized), and who—based on their experience in other economic spheres—don't understand why they can't have the information they need to guide their own healthcare. The elderly patients that doctors see today may not yet have this attitude, but many aging boomers do. In ten years the demand by patients for empowering information will be much greater than it is today.

* For example, the privacy provisions of the Health Insurance Portability and Accountability Act (HIPAA), ostensibly aimed at protecting patients' medical records from prying eyes, have made it harder for patients (or their advocates) to gain access to their own medical records.

This analysis shows what seems like a pretty good way to make some big bucks in healthcare while simultaneously saving lives: Figure out how to empower patients. Any enterprise that can supply patients with clear, correct, relevant, personal, and specific knowledge that enables them to protect themselves and their loved ones within our hostile healthcare system will endear itself to those patients. Furthermore, anyone supplying such knowledge will be feeding a growing need for more. People's desire for the information to manage their own health-care and the means to act on that information will become more than just a desire—it will become an expectation. A massive business opportunity awaits.

Three points bear repeating:

+ Individuals who recognize that the healthcare system operates under a model of covert rationing can immediately take steps to prevent themselves and their loved ones from being victims of that rationing. It is hard to covertly ration against enlightened patients.
+ Once a critical mass of the population becomes so enlightened, Quadrant III healthcare will no longer be feasible.
+ Given the history so far of the information revolution and given the information-seeking behavior of a growing proportion of American patients, the enlightenment that will render Quadrant III healthcare impossible seems likely if not inevitable.

Thus does the GUTH finally lead us to a place that a while ago may have seemed almost incomprehensible. It leads us to a place of optimism or, at least, relative optimism. There may be a path out of Quadrant III, and it is a path we're likely to find ourselves taking. It's a path that does not require legislation, political action committees, tax incentives (or disincentives), a majority vote of the entire population, or bloodshed. It merely requires that a critical mass of Americans begin acting in their own enlightened self-interest and that a cohort of doctors and entrepreneurs finds ways of enabling them to do so.

What will healthcare be like after Quadrant III?

When a sufficient proportion of our population ends the self-deception, recognizes covert rationing for what it is, and thus makes Quadrant III healthcare no longer feasible, what happens then?

The only way to gracefully exit Quadrant III is to abandon—or compromise on—one or both of our mutually exclusive societal imperatives. And a moment's reflection shows that it is the no limits imperative on which we have to loosen our grip.

It will be the widening recognition of covert rationing (that is, the overt recognition of limits) that, I'm postulating, finally breaks the back of Quadrant III healthcare. We at last will have to admit that society can't afford, contrary to everything we're being told today, to buy for all Americans all the healthcare they could ever want or need. There are limits to the amount of healthcare society can provide.

For another thing, while the no limits imperative can be viewed as an exaggerated form of the primacy of individual interests (and therefore as a deeply held attitude), its counterpart, the entitlement imperative, has become more nearly a law of physics—or at least of economics. No matter how you try to arrange it, few Americans can actually afford to buy for themselves and their families all the available healthcare they might ever want or need. But even these fortunate individuals cannot afford to establish their own private healthcare systems. They will have to rely on whatever healthcare infrastructure exists for society as a whole, an infrastructure that must be financed though a system that includes a strong component of centralization. Every American citizen will have a role in supporting that centralized financing mechanism and therefore will be entitled to a fair share of whatever healthcare benefits end up being parceled out.

As we exit Quadrant III, then, abandoning or at least compromising on the no limits imperative but maintaining the entitlement imperative, we will move toward Quadrant I, toward a system based on open rationing.

But how can open rationing be accomplished in the United States? There are several ways this could happen.

+ We could attempt the kind of process I described earlier of designing a system of "pure" open rationing, a process that appears forbiddingly painful.

+ We could devise (as many recommend) a Canadian-style rationing system. This kind of system looks less painful because the rationing, while quite open and visible, is never mentioned publicly, allowing for those Canadian citizens who are on the credulous side (and virtually all Americans who profess envy toward their system) to imagine that there really isn't that much rationing going on after all. The Canadian system of open rationing can be thought of as covert rationing light (we can visualize it as straddling the border between Quadrant III and Quadrant I), and it is developing many of the problems we are seeing today in the U.S.* Even with its increasingly apparent shortcomings, though, a Canadian-style system of healthcare rationing would be more equitable than the system we have today, just as many proponents of healthcare reform often tell us.†

+ We could allow the GUTH to suggest a way of openly rationing healthcare that is uniquely American, one that salvages something important from the no limits paradigm, morphing it into a few limits paradigm and incorporating it into an overall healthcare system that is designed to honor individual autonomy. Such a system, which could be visualized as straddling

* A 2002 report from the Fraser Institute concluded that, compared to many other industrialized nations, the Canadian healthcare system "produces inferior access to physicians and technology, produces longer waiting times, is less successful in preventing deaths from preventable causes, and costs more than any other system that has comparable objectives." See http://www.fraserin-stitute.ca/admin/books/chapterfiles/Executive%20Summary-pages1-6.pdf#1.

† Canadians (and other peoples more civilized than we are) can afford to be smug about their rational healthcare systems at least partly because the irrational American healthcare system exists. Their rich can come here for care, thus decompressing what otherwise might be a powerful force for change. Foreign companies can invent and build products, knowing that a market exists for selling those products at a profit—it exists here. Finally, American ingenuity percolates to all other nations over time (and our products are available in those nations at famously discounted prices), so there is indeed continued medical progress in other nations—it's just that the progress is subsidized by American taxpayers. It is partly the existence of our irrational healthcare system that makes the more civilized healthcare systems of other nations acceptable to their citizens. If our great engine of healthcare progress should finally fail, healthcare would change radically not only here but all over the world.

Quadrant I and Quadrant II, would attempt to combine the best features of upper-quadrant healthcare while avoiding the worst. In Part III of this book I will outline in some detail a system in which routine maintenance healthcare is based on an individual, self-pay model; with an umbrella of publicly funded coverage for non-routine healthcare under a system of open rationing; with a safety net to cover even the routine expenses for people in the lower economic brackets; and with additional provisions to stimulate continued market-driven medical innovations.

But we have some ground to cover before we get to such a fix for the entire healthcare system. In fact, before we go any further, we need to explore in more depth the most fundamental and inescapable conclusion that falls out of the GUTH, namely that unless we are going to revert to a completely self-paid model for healthcare—a fiscal impossibility—we have no choice but to ration. So in the next chapter I will expand on the First Corollary, and show why rationing healthcare is not an option; only the manner in which we ration is an option.

First Corollary

> *Left = Rationing*

Second Corollary

> *Covert rationing requires Quadrant III.*

Third Corollary

> *Covert rationing destroys the doctor–patient relationship.*

Fourth Corollary

> *Covert rationing corrupts everything it touches.*

2

Why There's No Alternative to Rationing

IN CHAPTER 1, I CLAIMED, as a First Corollary to the GUTH, that if we are operating in either of the two left quadrants of the healthcare landscape, we are rationing healthcare. I justified the First Corollary with the observation that centralized decision-making will always be accompanied by a centralized funding mechanism whose size, while possibly very large, will still always be limited, whereas the potential healthcare expenditures for the population are effectively limitless. Hence, there is no alternative but to ration healthcare.

I find this justification of the First Corollary to be convincing. But I realize that, because rationing healthcare is such a horrific idea to contemplate, some otherwise reasonable people might not be convinced yet. So in this chapter I will further develop the notion that, any way you cut it, unless we're going to operate in Quadrant II, where people are buying all of their own healthcare with their own funds, we've got no choice but to ration.

We can begin by agreeing, I think, that rationing healthcare is bad, and we should avoid it unless we have no alternative; if we ration, it should be as a last resort. Then the central issue is whether sufficient financial resources are available so we can avoid rationing. In considering this issue, we should ask the most difficult question first—is there a limit to what we should be willing to spend on healthcare?*

You can't put a price on human life

This noble sentiment—that human life is priceless— is often invoked to justify heroic efforts to save lives

* Note that this is a different question from: Is there a limit to the amount of healthcare Americans should expect to receive when they need it? We have a culture of no limits when it comes to receiving healthcare but not when it comes to paying for it. Here we're discussing paying for it.

(though hardly ever by those who are paying for those efforts). You most often hear statements about the pricelessness of life outside the context of healthcare—for instance, by rescuers engaged in a massive effort to save a pretty college student who has managed to get herself wedged in

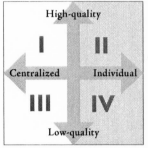

a crevasse in Alaska, during her summer vacation. The notion that life is priceless is an understandable and endearing trait, and most of us find ourselves agreeing with it, especially after watching the victim's distraught parents on TV for a few days. There are two major problems with this sentiment, however.

First, in the context of healthcare financing, it is a showstopper. If all human life were priceless, then we could not justify any limitations on the financing of healthcare. And we could not complain if, for example, we had to tax ourselves at a ninety percent level in order to buy every bit of life-extending healthcare for every person. Indeed, if human life were priceless it would be completely unethical for any of us to own any item beyond adequate food, clothing, and shelter until every person in America (or, for that matter, in the world) had access to adequate healthcare. So the next time you hear somebody saying human life is priceless, ask them about their plasma TV.

Second, this notion is demonstrably untrue. We tacitly place a price on human life, the lives of ourselves as well as others, every day: It is theoretically possible to build an airplane with enough safety features to assure that its passengers would survive most crashes. The reason such airplanes do not exist is not greedy airline executives. It is that crack market researchers have informed those executives that not enough of us in the flying public are willing to pay $2.5 million to fly to Cleveland. Similarly, not all U.S. citizens own, nor do we insist on buying for all our fellow citizens, those expensive cars that perform best in crash tests.

More to the point, Medicare has already set a de facto limit on how much money it is reasonable to spend to extend a life. In general, the government will pay for a therapy if the average cost of that therapy is less than $50,000 per life-year saved. (To save a life-year is to extend one person's life by one year.) This figure was decided empirically, in the 1970s, when Medicare was compelled by Congress to pay for kidney dialysis. Dialysis is a life-extending therapy that happened, at the time, to cost approximately $50,000 per year per individual. This $50,000 limit is not official, but it is broadly understood by the bio-medical industry as the target figure that needs to be reached if you want the government payers to purchase your product.

So, whether we like it or not, we as individuals and we as a society make decisions every day that tacitly place a price on human life. This means that invoking the pricelessness of human life to stifle a discussion on rationing healthcare is groundless.

But just because what we can spend to save an individual's life is limited, it does not necessarily follow that there must also be a limit on healthcare spending for our entire society. Should there be such a limit, and how high should that limit be?

How much should we spend on healthcare?

During the great healthcare debate of the first Clinton administration, it was generally held as abhorrent that healthcare was consuming thir-teen percent of the gross domestic product (GDP). While there was disagreement at the time as to whether or not the entire healthcare system should be managed by the government, I don't remember much public disagreement on whether the total amount of spending was too high. Clearly, said the consensus, it was.

On the other hand, many of my physician colleagues in those days, as not-quite-disinterested observers whose incomes depended on society's willingness to spend lots of money on healthcare, were say-ing: Who says thirteen percent is too high? If not healthcare, what should we spend the money on? Caribbean cruises? Sports cars? Why not spend twenty or twenty-five percent or even more of the GDP on healthcare?

I cannot blame my doctor friends for asking a question as reason-able-sounding as this one. The correct answer, however, is not the one they expected. For there is indeed a fundamental limit on how much society should spend on healthcare. We were exceeding that limit in 1994, and we're certainly exceeding it now.

That limit is defined by a straightforward economic principle: When we are buying consumable products that we are consuming ourselves—products like Caribbean cruises, sports cars, ice cream, and health-care—we should spend no more than we are able to pay ourselves.

We are spending more on our healthcare than individuals are able
to pay, and we have been for quite some time. In 2002, for instance, we
spent an average of $5,440 per year on healthcare for every person in
the United States. This is far more than most Americans could com-
fortably pay by themselves, without the benefit of employer-supplied,
taxpayer-subsidized health insurance.

More importantly, this amount is greater than we are able (or at
least willing) to pay on a collective basis. Instead of paying for our
healthcare as we go, we're adding much of the cost to the national debt.
The expense accrues to the debt two ways. A big chunk of American
healthcare is provided directly through government programs like
Medicare and Medicaid. But even private healthcare is supported by
the government through tax deductions for insurance premiums; so
even for those of us with private health insurance, much of the cost of
our healthcare gets added to the national debt. Thus have we arranged
to pass on a huge and growing financial burden to our children, grandchildren, and generations yet unborn, in violation of the principle that
those who consume products or services ought to pay for them.

So is this just a fairness argument?

It is unfair to ask future generations to bear the debt we accumulate
when we consume healthcare for our own benefit. But, you may be saying, so what? Lots of things are unfair, and who said life was supposed
to be fair, anyway?

Whether one has sympathy for the stoicism or disdain for the cal-
lousness inherent in such sentiments, the ethics of how we finance
healthcare is important. However, its importance does not lie in our
concern over people's feelings if they should be treated unfairly, nor in
our worry that people who are dealt with unjustly might become angry
or jealous or disgruntled enough to hurt others, nor in our conviction
that any unfair application of society's resources is immoral. Instead,
its importance lies in the fact that the type and magnitude of unfairness we're dealing with here goes well beyond the routine, unpleasant
injustices we deal with every day.

Mundane, everyday unfairness—the kind about which an American
stoic might advise, "Just suck it up!"—abounds in our Quadrant III

healthcare system. Here's one example: Millions of struggling, low- to middle-income Americans, who themselves have no health insurance, find that precious dollars are deducted from their paychecks to pay the Medicare expenses of well-to-do retirees. Unfair? Sure. A travesty of justice? Of course. Should we fix it? Certainly. (And we probably would, too, if making it almost impossible for millions of Americans to get health insurance weren't such an effective form of covert rationing.) But that's just one of the routine injustices we see every day.

The injustice we're talking about here, where the massive and continually growing bill for our own healthcare is being passed on, via the national debt, to future generations, is of a different species. It's bad enough that we're creating an economic yoke for today's children that rivals the one our own forebears faced during the Great Depression (and in doing so, slapping away the small hand that reaches up for ours); but the burden we're handing them is more than just a big debt. We're handing them the seeds of societal disintegration.

Those seeds are sown when we choose to violate the economic principle which dictates that people need to pay for their own consumable products. There's a reason this is a principle and not just a nice-to-have: Following this principle is necessary to keep our economy, and our society, stable.

Our society takes pains to keep individuals from violating this economic principle, specifically by enforcing strict limits on how much debt a person can accumulate. People are allowed to borrow large amounts of money, as long as they promise to repay it and their credit rating is high enough. Individual borrowing is vital to the growth and stability of our economy. But if anyone fails to pay back what they owe according to a predetermined schedule, society takes steps to interrupt further borrowing and tries to force them to repay. If they get in too deep, society ushers them into bankruptcy, where they can slowly make themselves whole again. But society does not allow individuals to accumulate more and more debt indefinitely.

Any society that expects to thrive will do the same, that is, will not permit individuals to accumulate more debt than they can repay in a timely fashion. The reason is that people die. If people were routinely permitted to compile large amounts of debt until the day they die, finally leaving all that debt to be borne by people who haven't died yet, the economic system would collapse. That's why we insist that when individuals buy things, they pay for them before they die or make arrangements for their estate to cover their debts. In this way, there is a natural ceiling on how much a person can spend for consumable products during their lifetime.

The same economic principle—purchasing no more than one can pay for—holds for society as well as individuals. Society must pay, eventually, for everything it buys through its agent, the government.

But for society the timeframe for repayment is very different than for individuals, because society lives "forever." The accumulation of debt, even large amounts of debt, is less alarming, because society will always be there to pay it back.

Indeed, the ability to carry a large debt for long periods is important to the normal functioning of any complex society. The ability to accumulate national debt allows us to maintain a buffer for economic stability, enables us to smooth out boom–bust cycles, and renders our economy less volatile, more predictable, and more amenable to steady growth. The ability to carry very-long-term (that is, multi-generational) debt enables the government to borrow the money it needs to do the long-term things that benefit multiple generations of humans— things like improving the nation's physical infrastructure, maintaining national defense, advancing medical research, and engaging in other forms of non-commodity spending that will allow our country to progress, to grow stronger, and to steadily improve the lives of successive generations of its citizens.

The right kind of national debt, then, is a chief enabler of economic growth and prosperity. It is an investment in the nation's future. When we ask future generations of Americans to share the financial burden of a new hydroelectric plant, for example, we do so knowing they'll also get to share the benefits. In this case, they partake not only of electricity but also of the economic growth and prosperity that will be stimulated by the new power plant. Future citizens will reap its benefits, so it is fair and proper to ask them to bear part of the debt that made those benefits possible.

On the other hand, things begin to go awry when we burden society with the wrong kind of debt, the kind that represents an open-ended promise to purchase products and services that are consumed by individuals, such as healthcare. There are two reasons this kind of debt creates a problem.

First, this kind of debt tends not to be an investment for the future. It does not benefit future generations like a power plant would. Instead, it primarily benefits the individuals who are the direct recipients of the consumable services, leaving no direct benefits but an ever increasing debt burden to those who will be paying the bills decades later.

Second, while there is a natural ceiling on how much a person can spend for products and services they consume during their lifetime, once the responsibility for these consumable services shifts to society, there is no longer an obligation for individuals to settle their accounts before they die. Society will "always" be there, so the debt can be borne (and accumulated) over multiple generations. The natural ceiling on an individual's consumption of products and services disappears, and there is no longer an inherent limit to how much can be spent.

Without these inherent limits, the provision of such services to individuals quickly comes to be regarded as an entitlement. And with entitlements, the checks and balances that apply to other parts of the federal budget are no longer effective. If somebody wants the government to pay for a new hydroelectric plant, they've got to lobby for it and compete for funding with somebody else who wants a new airport. Maybe they'll get the plant, or maybe the other guy will get the airport, or if things are flush maybe both will get what they want. But whatever the results (and however economically sound those results may turn out to be) there's a complex process they've got to go through—perhaps including sophisticated economic analyses, the lobbying of legislators, or even blackmail and bribery—before a funding decision is made. And while we often complain about out-of-control congressional spending, it remains true that before any public works project gets federal approval, it has to be at least nominally justified within the federal budget.

Entitlements such as healthcare do not work that way. If Uncle Doug needs quadruple bypass surgery, he's simply entitled to it. As long as he can get his doctor to admit that he needs it, he gets it. Healthcare spending decisions are made by individual doctors and individual patients, 1.5 million times a day, and these spending decisions are added to the long-term, multi-generational debt burden. There are no checks to this kind of expenditure.

When a society faces an accelerating debt burden that is completely open-ended and not subject to normal checks and balances, that society is dealing with what I'll call a disproportionate economic variable (DEV). DEVs are dangerous. Unless brought under control they push an economy toward collapse.

Until a few decades ago, healthcare in America acted like any well-behaved economic sector. The size and growth of spending on healthcare was directly related to the size and growth of the GDP—that is, it was a proportionate economic variable. Specifically, until the 1950s the cost of healthcare was a fairly steady 4 percent of the GDP. This began to change during the early 1950s (at about the time the Tooth Fairy variety of Quadrant IV healthcare was becoming established), so that by 1960, the cost of healthcare was growing much more rapidly than the overall economy. Healthcare spending accounted for 5.3 percent of the GDP in 1960, 7.3 percent in 1970, 10.2 percent in 1980, 13 percent in 1993, and 14.9 percent in 2002. Over a relatively short period the demand for healthcare took on a life of its own, with an apparently endless capacity for growth that is disproportionate to the growth of the overall economy.

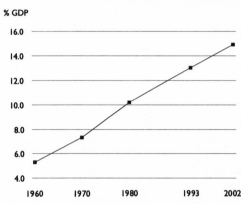

There are few examples of DEVs in real-life economics, because they are inherently unstable and destructive. The only common example occurs during wartime, when the demand for military spending grows far out of proportion to the overall economy. Wartime spending is a tolerable DEV, because wars are temporary. The expenditures for conducting war can usually be borne as debt, and are gradually paid back by society after the war ends. It is a debt that is accepted as the price of long-term societal existence. It is another form of investing in the future.

One reason warfare is temporary is that in a prolonged war a nation can spend itself into oblivion. The demise of the Soviet Union was directly related to the ever-increasing military spending that we forced on it by our ever-increasing military spending during the Cold War. The defunct Soviet Union is the poster child of DEVs.

Whereas warfare is temporary, our growing demand for healthcare is not. The demand for healthcare spending is bottomless; there are no apparent limits. Healthcare expenditures are behaving as a relentless, voracious, DEV, one for which there is no end in sight.*

The GUTH tells us there are two ways to get control of the DEV that healthcare has become. One way is to have everybody pay for their own healthcare, out of their own pockets (that is, move to Quadrant II healthcare). Because individuals cannot engage in unlimited deficit spending as the government can, the growth in healthcare spending in Quadrant II would slow dramatically and eventually would find its natural ceiling. We can't do that, however, because healthcare is an entitlement, and individuals cannot be expected (or even permitted, according to some) to pay for it themselves. The second way is to ration healthcare openly (as in Quadrant I healthcare), which would give us the opportunity to select the proportion of the GDP we think ought to be spent on healthcare, and hold expenditures, through rationing, to that level. But we can't do that, either, because it would be rationing.

* This is why the argument that society's healthcare spending pays for itself is false. Our spending on healthcare indeed employs millions and grows the economy, and if healthcare spending could be limited to some reasonable proportion of the GDP, the resulting economic growth would be a positive thing. But it is not limited. It is a DEV. Despite robust economic growth, our spending on healthcare consumes an ever larger proportion of the GDP. Unless this changes there is no foreseeable prospect but disaster.

So we've backed ourselves into a corner. We've taken a sphere of commerce that economic principles dictate ought to be paid for by individuals—given that it delivers products and services consumed by individuals—and we've convinced ourselves that the government ought to pay for it. Yet we still claim the right to make all the spending decisions ourselves. In other words, we've embraced the entitlement mentality and the no limits mentality at the same time, and it has driven us into Quadrant III, where we can support our fantasy of unlimited-but-free healthcare. And in creating this fantasy, we've created a fiscal time bomb, one that is scheduled to go off in our children's or, at best, in our grandchildren's lifetimes and whose massiveness will gravely threaten societal cohesion.

> DEV disproportionate economic variable
> GDP gross domestic product
> GUTH grand unification theory of healthcare

We need to admit that there is a limit to what we can afford to spend on healthcare, even if we liberally define that limit as something less than would eventually cause our society to disintegrate. So far we are failing to meet even that modest limitation.

Conceding that there are limits to what we should spend on healthcare does not necessarily lead to the conclusion that we must ration.

Before coming to that conclusion, we should leave no stone unturned. Therefore, let us examine the reasons healthcare is so expensive. If we understand the costs, perhaps we can avoid rationing by figuring out how to bring those costs down.

Why is the cost of healthcare so high?

In the debate on healthcare that took place during the first Clinton administration, Mrs. Clinton had a straightforward explanation for the uncontrolled growth in healthcare spending. To paraphrase loosely: There are too many greedy doctors using too much expensive technology.

The problem in trying to refute this synthesis, at least for those of us physicians who do not like being characterized as avaricious and for the biomedical engineers who do not like their remarkable inventions being characterized primarily as expensive, is that there is a lot of truth to it.

However, most healthcare economists agree that there are at least four factors driving up the cost of healthcare. These are:

+ Waste
+ Fraud
+ Increasingly expensive medical technology
+ A rapidly aging population

The first three correspond to the Clintons' explanation of the problem. The difficulty with their explanation (aside from its being insulting to some of us) is that it downplays the most pressing cause for the rising cost of healthcare. And with good reason. It is easy, even advisable, to criticize doctors for being wasteful, greedy, and felonious. It's even okay to criticize technology as long as you don't get too specific about it. But it's not nice, or politically wise, to criticize people for getting older.

Let us examine these four factors to see if we can characterize what each of them contributes to the rising cost of healthcare.

Waste

In Chapter 1 I suggested that waste and inefficiency are built in to the healthcare system as an essential feature of covert rationing. We'll return to that kind of waste and inefficiency shortly, but that's not the kind that the government or the big health insurance companies (the entities managing the covert rationing) are talking about when they decry the waste in healthcare. They're talking about the kind perpetrated by doctors and patients when they make decisions on which healthcare services to employ—which indeed gives us a lot to work with.

Eliminating this sort of inefficiency was the major justification given for pushing the American public into managed care in the 1990s. Thanks to policies established by managed care organizations, the American healthcare system over the past decade has made great strides toward eliminating wasteful doctor–patient decisions; and those efficiencies are generally credited with the sudden but temporary reduction in healthcare inflation we enjoyed for a few years in the late 1990s.

Unfortunately for managed care organizations, it looks as if this variety of efficiency—the kind that culminated with disastrous attempts to enforce so-called drive-through childbirth and mastectomies—has been taken as far as it can go. The public has informed managed care organizations they've had about as much of this kind of efficiency as they are willing to tolerate; to further improve efficiencies, managed care will have to look elsewhere.

Other varieties of waste and inefficiency are often mentioned as targets for improvement. Whenever they are justifying the takeover of yet another hospital or of a smaller managed care organization, for instance, healthcare conglomerates often bring up the need to eliminate inefficient duplication of services, sloppy record keeping, wasteful policies and procedures, expensive human resource practices, and outdated data management systems. As smaller managed care organizations consolidate into a handful of giant companies, such efficiencies of size and scale are realized.

The need to improve efficiency is often brought up by those who advocate for government control of healthcare. Just think, we are urged, of the incredible efficiencies that would flow from a single-payer healthcare system!

Clearly then, many of the pleas we hear for eliminating waste and inefficiency in the healthcare system boil down to arguments for centralizing the control of healthcare.

If the centralization we are being urged toward were to end up as the Quadrant I variety—that is, if open healthcare rationing were to be the result—then concerted efforts to curb waste and inefficiency would occur. Eliminating waste would be a moral and societal imperative under an acknowledged system of open rationing, where every wasted dollar would directly equate to withholding medical care from someone.

Unfortunately, the kind of centralization we're actually adopting is the Quadrant III variety, so the rationing is covert. And under covert rationing, efforts at efficiency, streamlining, and transparency most often fail. While the need to gain efficiency is used as an argument for centralization, the kind of centralization we're getting actually defeats efficiency.

Doesn't *anybody* understand the healthcare system?

In April of 2000, just as venture capitalists were feeling that first queasiness over all the billions they'd invested with Internet visionaries who were going to Transform Life As We Know It (by, among other things, selling dog food over the Web), I found myself in New York City, attending a conference called Internet Healthcare 2000. As was still typical for any Internet-themed gathering of would-be entrepreneurs, the atmosphere surrounding Internet Healthcare 2000 was wildly upbeat. The attendees all knew a little something not only about the Internet but also about healthcare, and, recognizing the interconnectedness promised by the one and the chaos projected by the other, they imagined many exciting and lucrative synergies.

In the most anxiously awaited session of the conference, Charlie Rose did a live interview of Jim Clark. Clark was a bona fide hero of the early Internet era, and to this day remains the only person to ever have started three separate billion-dollar Internet companies. So nobody snickered when Rose introduced him as one of the smartest men on the planet and perhaps healthcare's greatest visionary. Fresh off his first two Internet triumphs (Silicon Graphics and Netscape), Clark was now using his formidable talents to create his third and most important venture, the crowning achievement of his business career, and the company that was going to lead an Internet-driven revolution that would save the failing American healthcare system—WebMD.

The crowd listened, rapt, as Charlie Rose drew from Clark the story of WebMD and how he had come to create it. Casting about for a new challenge after he had sold (and just in time, too) his earlier Internet ventures, Clark was drawn to the healthcare system. Here was a huge and riotously disorganized economic sphere that was wasting much of the 14 percent of the GDP it consumed; what's more, the reason for much of the waste, as anyone could see, was inefficient data handling. And the Internet—of which Clark was, however humbly, a recognized guru—was the ultimate data-handling entity in the universe. Here was an opportunity made in heaven.

Clark conceived of WebMD as the central clearing station for all health-related data. WebMD would become a platform for seamlessly connecting the major players in the healthcare system—doctors, patients, third-party payers and others—to improve communication, streamline transactions, reduce medical errors, and otherwise squeeze much of the costly inefficiency out of the healthcare system, while simultaneously capturing for its shareholders untold millions in modest transaction fees. With this vision in mind, Clark had been working his magic for several years, building the complex infrastructure such a venture would require, through investments, strategic acquisitions and alliances, all of which he detailed and explained. Now, Clark concluded, the last pieces had been put in place, and WebMD was finally ready for business.

Wild applause ensued. And deservedly so, as Clark had given a brilliant exposition on the vision, planning, and execution behind WebMD, providing a virtual how-to for all the future Internet healthcare magnates in his audience, many of whom obviously now felt inspired to go forth and do likewise.

But then Charlie Rose had the temerity to ask, "How's business going so far?"

Clark deflated just a little. Well, he admitted, business was ramping up a bit more slowly than he had planned. Indeed, unexpected resistance was being encountered, and from virtually all parties, to the seamless interconnectedness promised by WebMD. Doctors claimed they were "just too busy to learn about new things." (Aside from being a source of frustration to high-tech healthcare entrepreneurs like Clark, such an assertion should worry anyone who suspects they might some day end up as a patient.) Some doctors, Clark added almost plaintively, actually admit they really don't *want* better communication with their patients.

But even more disturbing and even less explicable was the reaction of third-party payers to the cost-slashing opportunities offered by WebMD. Clark noted that it cost the typical health plan $7.00 to process an average medical claim. By using WebMD, health plans could process the same claim for $0.70, saving ninety percent of transaction costs, and in a tiny fraction of the time. Considering the scores of millions of transactions they typically process each year, health plans could save stunning amounts of money and time by using WebMD. This air-tight business proposition was how Clark had raised all the money to build WebMD in the first place.

But health plans were nearly unanimous in turning their backs on these enormous savings. In fact, an increasingly exasperated Clark went on, they were almost hostile to the notion of using WebMD to process their claims.

Noticing that the audience was quickly becoming subdued, Clark moved immediately to reassure. Look, he said, whatever the subtle cultural reasons health plans may have for not entrusting their transaction processing to a Web company, whatever the vagaries within the healthcare system that are keeping them from taking an action that is clearly in their own best interests, one thing remains true. Health plans are businesses, and like any other business they are obligated to operate in such a way as to increase shareholder value. And, given the tremendous savings they will realize by partnering with WebMD, savings that their shareholders will surely demand once they understand the opportunity, well, sooner or later the apparently dense if not frankly Luddite health plan directors will simply have to start behaving logically—or be replaced. Indeed, Clark said, he was so confident in the solidness of WebMD's business model that, just a couple of weeks earlier, he and a partner had pledged to contribute an additional 200 million dollars of their own money to the enterprise.

Relieved at this reassurance that their dreams remained alive, his audience again broke into applause—though perhaps somewhat more reservedly than before. Clark was able to leave the stage more or less in triumph.

Within a few months, WebMD's market value had plummeted, Clark had been jettisoned from the company (never having made good on his 200 million dollar pledge), and most of the conference attendees had slunk back to their day jobs. To this day the processing of healthcare claims remains painfully primitive, slow, and expensive.

What happened? Nobody can deny that Clark is a smart guy. He clearly understands the Internet and he understands business, probably as well as anybody. His track record confirms that. Furthermore, his idea for making money with WebMD had little in common with Internet schemes that crashed and burned (such as those selling groceries, pet supplies, or other bulky-and-thus-expensive-to-ship commodities over the Web). It had far more in common with the successful Internet enterprises, the ones that made difficult or unpleasant chores (such as banking or shopping for insurance) convenient and inexpensive. So Clark's idea—taking the cumbersome, time-consuming, paper-laden processing of healthcare claims and making it rapid, easy, electronic, and cheap—made plenty of sense. It's just that it didn't work. Whether he was healthcare's greatest visionary or not, obviously something was flawed about Clark's vision for WebMD.

What was flawed was Clark's understanding of how health plans actually make their money. He just didn't understand his customers' business model. This is a mistake that healthcare entrepreneurs make all too often. When your customer is in the business of covertly rationing healthcare, then what they say their business is—the stuff they write down in their mission statements and vision statements and quarterly reports—is just smoke. How can they say what their business really is when it's covert rationing? If they told everybody, then it wouldn't be covert.

Health plans aren't interested in opportunities to save huge amounts by streamlining medical claims. If they had been interested in doing so they wouldn't have waited for WebMD; they would have done it themselves a long time ago. Does their indifference toward improving the efficiency of claims processing mean that health plans behave differ-ently from all other businesses? No, it does not. Just as Clark insisted, like any business a health plan will strive to increase shareholder value. Instead, what it means is that they actually increase shareholder value to a greater extent by making claims processing less efficient, not more efficient.

To see why this is so, consider what health plans actually do. They collect insurance premiums from their enrollees and then pay money out when somebody has provided an approved medical service to one of those enrollees. Do they make money by processing these claims efficiently? No, they do not. If they must pay out a claim at all, they can only make a profit by delaying the payment of the claim as long as possible and keeping that money invested in corporate or government bonds in the meantime. In fact, the inefficient processes that allow them to do this are often the chief source of profit for health plans.

The only thing better than delaying the payment of legitimate claims is to not pay the claims at all. This is because health plans get to keep, forever, whatever premiums they don't have to spend caring for the sick. This is their payoff for covertly rationing healthcare (an other-wise thankless job that somebody has to do). Health plans have learned that complex claims processing procedures can reduce the number of claims they have to pay. By creating ever-changing, lengthy, and com-plicated claim forms that are time-consuming, loaded with ambigui-ties, and frustrating enough to make the filing of income taxes seem simple by comparison, and by imposing arbitrary deadlines beyond which, unless a form is submitted perfectly in each and every detail, no payment is required, health plans not infrequently get away with not paying legitimate claims.

This dysfunctional payment system has induced some doctors to forego submitting claims at all for low-paying medical services, because the administrative cost of chasing reimbursement outweighs whatever paltry revenue they might eventually collect. It's just a small step for the doctor to stop providing that low-revenue service altogether. Why should they provide a service they can't get paid for? Once again, inef-ficiency furthers the cause of covert rationing.

Institutionalized complexity can hold many advantages for health plans. It delays the payment of claims that need to be paid. Sometimes it altogether frustrates legitimate claims. And best of all, if the claims process is particularly odious, doctors may choose not to provide certain medical services in the first place.

Now, into this scene of managed care nirvana imagine the arrival of Mr. Jim Clark, with some cockamamie Internet scheme he says will make claims processing quick and efficient and that will save everyone a bundle on transaction processing. What an absurd proposition! It's not easy or cheap for health plans to keep claims processing as slow, cumbersome and inefficient as they've been able to make them. It takes significant effort, especially in the era of information technology. Expensive transaction processing is a cost of doing business, a part of the business model. What is this Clark guy thinking?

The bottom line on waste is that, yes, waste and inefficiency are significant contributors to the high cost of healthcare. But they are necessary to a system that relies on covert rationing. And most of the solutions that politicians propose to eliminate the waste—namely, more centralization of the Quadrant III variety—are likely to make things worse.

Fraud

Nobody knows how much fraud exists in the healthcare system. Any amount of fraud is inexcusable, and the federal government has identified the rooting out of fraud as a potentially fruitful means of cutting the cost of healthcare. To this end the Health Insurance Portability and Accountability Act (HIPAA) of 1996 introduced powerful anti-fraud provisions, and the government has launched a major campaign to root out fraud.

To the extent that true fraud is rooted out, this federal government activity is good. But the heavy-handed means used in this effort are having a chilling effect on every healthcare provider. The mandate to eliminate fraud presents a powerful and devious mechanism for coercing doctors to behave in certain ways and thus for covertly rationing healthcare. I will address this topic in detail in Chapter 5.

But the politically popular notion that fraud is behind the rising cost of healthcare and that therefore sufficient fraud must exist such that rooting it out will offset the rising cost of healthcare is not credible. It is certainly not taken seriously by healthcare economists. Even if every third doctor were a clone of John Gotti, there wouldn't be enough fraud to account for the accelerating costs we're seeing in healthcare.

Increasingly expensive medical technology

The increasing use of technology in medicine is driving up the cost of healthcare. Unfortunately for payers, both patients and physicians see technology as offering substantial value in medical care.

Thanks to managed care, the use of high-cost technology in medicine is not quite the free-for-all it was a few years ago. Hospitals and practitioners, faced with reduced reimbursement, have begun controlling high-cost interventions (and, for that matter, low-cost interventions), in order to stay in business.

The problem is, most of this high-tech stuff works as advertised. High-cost medical technologies provide at least some benefit, even if that benefit is marginal. If the technology exists to help patients, both physicians and their patients want to use it. If the technology does not exist, people lobby Congress and hold telethons to pay someone to invent it.

But technology is expensive. Consider what it will do to our healthcare budget when we succeed in developing a practical, safe, fully implantable artificial heart. Such a device will probably cost $100,000 apiece, give or take a few tens of thousands, and upwards of a half million Americans each year will become potential candidates for it. This one new (highly sought after, fervently desired) technology alone would break the bank.

Reconsidering our use of technology will take a major adjustment in attitude. Advanced medical technology is included in the no limits model, and Americans expect to receive whatever medical benefits the biotech industry has to offer. Americans also expect continuing advances in technology to cure every medical disorder we can think of, including death itself.

To rein in the cost of healthcare by addressing the high cost of technology, we have to reevaluate our insistence on more technology (a proposition that currently seems out of the question) or we have to stifle innovation through covert rationing. So far, the latter approach is what we've chosen. In Chapter 6, I will describe how this is beginning to happen.

A rapidly aging population

This is where the real money is. Old people use a lot of healthcare resources, because the aging process even in the best of circumstances is accompanied by health problems. The median age in the United States has been gradually increasing for decades, both because of demographics and because, thanks in part to all that technology, people are living longer. The increased costs incurred by our aging population dwarf the costs attributable to waste and fraud in the healthcare system. While economists can argue about whether the aging population or medical technology accounts for more of the increase in medical spending, the fact remains that technology won't cost much if there aren't a lot of patients who need it. As the elderly will probably always need more healthcare technology than the young, an aging population acts as a multiplier of the cost of that technology.

We will soon have a lot more old people than we have ever had before. The baby boom generation, of which I am a proud member, is seventy-six million strong, fifty percent larger than the previous generation. As we boomers start to retire, American society will be transformed, and the magnitude of the transformation will be wondrous to behold. By 2020, when you walk the streets of an American city you won't know if you're in Tampa or Denver, because the proportion of old people across the entire United States will be the same as it is in Florida today. By that time one in five Americans will be over sixty-five. And the number of old-old individuals, thoseeighty-five and older, is skyrocketing. By 2040, there may be as many old-old as preschoolers.

Demographics will have a profound impact on our healthcare spending. Taking into account both the absolute number of old people who will be alive and the fact that so many of them will be in the super-consuming old-old category, by the year 2030 the cost of healthcare has been projected to be as high as $12,000 per capita (in 1994 dollars).* This figure, which doesn't take into account the massive new Medicare drug entitlement, is even more alarming when you consider that Medicare is already going bankrupt—at a time when we're spending about $6,000 per capita, when the number of retired elderly is still relatively small, and when most of the boomer generation is still in its productive, taxpaying years.

Social Security actuarial data shows that paying for Medicare and other federal healthcare programs in the year 2040 will require nearly

* If Martians were to come to Earth and study the U.S. federal budget, they would immediately see (given their entirely objective, completely apolitical, incinerate-entire-cultures-now-and-ask-questions-later natures) that the main job of the now-defunct US government had not been defense, regulating interstate commerce, social welfare, law enforcement, administration of justice, research, the arts, or any combination of these. Instead, they would see that the main job of the federal government—judging from the amounts it spent on Medicare, Medicaid, Social Security, federal pensions, and veterans' benefits—had been to take money away from the young and give it to the old.

fifty percent of the nation's taxable payroll. If you add Social Security payroll taxes to the mix, then more than two-thirds of every working person's paycheck will go toward covering federal entitlements for the elderly.*

I don't think so. It won't happen. The only question is how it won't happen. In some manner federal entitlements to the elderly, especially the healthcare entitlements that account for a major portion of our looming fiscal burden, will be significantly reduced. They can be reduced through violent revolution or through some more civilized process, but one way or another they will be reduced.

* While there is always some degree of speculation in these sorts of calculations, in this case the speculation is minimal. After all, everybody who has been promised these entitlements for the next fifty years is alive today. You can count them.

How can we reduce the cost of healthcare?

We have surveyed the causes for the high cost of our healthcare. Now let's look for a method to bring those costs down in our attempt to avoid rationing.

There are only two ways to reduce healthcare costs. We can *reduce wasted expenditures* (that is, reduce fraud and inefficiencies in the system), and we can *reduce useful expenditures* (that is, ration care).

The public discussion on healthcare spending in the United States to date has rested on the assertion that waste accounts for the high cost of healthcare—waste in the form of administrative overhead and suboptimal utilization of resources or outright malfeasance. This argument, which allows us to imagine that we can control healthcare costs by eliminating those unneeded expenditures, is the only politically feasible one that can be made today (because, if this argument were not true, our only remaining alternative would be to ration healthcare). Therefore, nearly all the methods that have been proposed for dealing with the high cost of healthcare are based on the assumption that all we need to do is remove inefficiencies in the system. (It is worth noting here that such an argument is what politicians offer for public consumption. Experts in the field of healthcare economics, in their scholarly writings, accept the need for rationing.)

Nobody denies that there are plenty of inefficiencies in the healthcare system. And nobody disagrees with the notion that we should make every effort to eliminate unneeded expenditures. The problem with relying on a reduction in inefficiencies as the primary means of controlling the rising cost of healthcare, however, is that it won't work.

David Eddy, in his 1996 book, *Clinical Decision Making*, examines the feasibility of reducing inefficiencies as a means of controlling the cost of healthcare. Suppose, he postulates, that in 1970 a severe austerity program had been initiated within the healthcare system that accomplished all the following things:

+ Cut all administrative costs by fifty percent
+ Cut the costs of all prescription and nonprescription drugs, plus the costs of all other consumable medical goods, by fifty percent
+ Cut physician services by twenty percent
+ Eliminated all government public health programs
+ Eliminated all construction of healthcare facilities
+ Eliminated all medical research.

Further, assume that these cuts had been maintained, at the same levels, for the next twenty-one years.

One would expect such a drastic program of cuts to significantly reduce national healthcare expenditures. And in fact, it would. The following table compares actual U.S. healthcare expenditures for that twenty-one-year period to the expenditures that would have occurred under Eddy's austerity program (values are reported in billions of dollars):*

* Eddy DM. *Clinical Decision Making,1996*: Jones and Bartlett Publishers, Sudbury MA;1996. www.jbpub.com. Reprinted with permission.

	Actual spending	Eddy's austerity spending
1970	74.4	59.2
1980	250.1	206.4
1989	604.3	499.5
1991	751.8	623.6

Notice that this austerity program saves a lot of money right away. In 1970, the first year of the cuts, $59.2 billion would have been spent, compared to the actual expenditures of $74.4 billion. The savings persist over time. In 1991, $623.6 billion would have been spent under the austerity program compared to $751.8 billion in actual spending.

But the amazing outcomes of this exercise are twofold. First is the astounding increase in expenditures over the twenty-one-year period, even had the austerity program been instituted. And second, the

amount of money spent in 1989 is roughly the same as the amount that
would have been spent under the austerity program only two years
later, in 1991. In other words, all that we would gain after twenty-one
years of an austerity program even as improbable and severe as this one
would be a little time; in this example, a little less than two years.

Why? It is because the rate of increase in healthcare expenditures
is largely unrelated to anything that was cut under Eddy's austerity
program. So when the cuts were made, society got a one-time savings,
but then healthcare costs continued rising at the same rate as before—
they just started from a lower baseline. The rate of growth—the chief
determinant of economic instability—did not change. So the only
thing that would have been saved with this effort is time, and not all
that much of it.

Eddy is highly regarded as an expert in healthcare policy and
healthcare economics, but we can nonetheless quibble with his analysis.
Who's to say that his math was correct, or that his underlying assump-
tions were reasonable? His exercise boils down to simple conjecture.
We don't really know what would have happened if such an austerity
program had been followed.

But in many ways we do know. In western countries like Canada
and Great Britain, countries that have tightly controlled, strictly bud-
geted, single-payer healthcare systems with overt rationing measures
in full view, while overall healthcare spending is significantly lower
than in the U.S., the rate of growth in healthcare spending is similar
to the double-digit rate we're seeing here. The economic crisis we are
experiencing is shared, and recognized, by most developed countries
around the world, despite tightly managed healthcare systems in many
of those countries.

This same phenomenon—a one-time savings from drastic reform
efforts—has been seen in the U.S. The wholesale move to managed
care and the subsequent reforms that managed care organizations put
into place in the mid-1990s brought the annual rate of growth in healthcare to below five percent for a few years. However, the growth rate
rapidly returned to its former double-digit pace. So, as Eddy's analysis
predicted, administrative reforms of the sort that managed care can
institute may significantly reduce the cost of healthcare, but that does
not change the underlying rate of growth. Therefore, the basic assumption made by virtually every party in the healthcare debate (that is, that

centralizing control and thereby reducing inefficiencies is all that is needed), is wrong. Inefficiencies certainly account for a substantial proportion of healthcare costs, but they cannot possibly account for the underlying double-digit rate of growth. And this unrelenting growth rate is the real problem. If we are to gain control of healthcare costs, somehow we must deal with this rate of growth.

What is responsible for this unrelenting growth in the cost of healthcare? If it's not waste and inefficiency, the only possible answer is that it's due to an increasing volume of actual, useful healthcare consumed per capita. And this, as we have seen, is due both to advancing technology (which is potentially controllable but, practically speaking, only with rationing), and to an ever-aging population (which is not controllable at all, save by uncivilized methods).

To cut into that growth rate, we have to find ways to reduce not just waste and inefficiency but also the volume of healthcare services being delivered per capita—even though many of those healthcare services are apparently useful. In other words, to reduce the rate of increase in healthcare spending, we have to ration care.

And as we have seen, we must reduce the growth in healthcare spending. The economic pressures that will occur in the next few decades will dwarf any pressure we are experiencing today. We need to gain control of these costs not just for our own near-term economic health, and not just to be fair to our children and grandchildren. Controlling healthcare costs is what we must do in order to avoid societal chaos. And because rationing is the only way to gain that control, rationing is what we must do. It is an economic imperative. It will happen (and is happening) whether we accept its necessity or not.

As we haven't accepted its necessity, our only option so far has been to ration covertly.

Rationing in Quadrant III

In Part I, I have tried to accomplish two things. First, I have introduced the GUTH, describing the theory itself in broad outline and identifying the characteristics of each of the four quadrants defined by this model of the healthcare universe. Second, I have attempted to demonstrate the validity of perhaps the most important conclusion that can be drawn from the GUTH—that as long as we insist on (or are forced into) turning over the financing of our healthcare system to central authorities, rationing is unavoidable.

Our uniquely American attitude toward healthcare—our conviction that limits on healthcare are unacceptable—has dictated that this rationing must be covert. Accordingly, over the past few decades we have drifted inexorably into Quadrant III, where covert rationing is king.

In Part II we will take a more detailed look at convert rationing—why we're doing it, how it is being accomplished, and what it is doing to us as individuals and as a society. We will see how covert rationing explains all those maddening, seemingly counterintuitive behaviors we observe in our encounters with the healthcare system. We will see how covert rationing systematically destroys the doctor–patient relationship, leaving patients exposed and marginalized and doctors impotent and frustrated, and how it corrupts everything it touches.

By the end of Part II we will have laid the groundwork for the third and final part of this book, in which we will explore how individuals can begin to protect themselves from the perfidies of Quadrant III healthcare; and finally how, by thus acting in their own self-interest, they can catalyze a reformation in our healthcare system, transforming it into one that straddles the upper two quadrants—a healthcare system that is fair, efficient, and effective, and that preserves individual autonomy.

Part II

The Corrosive Nature
of Covert Rationing

3

An Introduction to Covert Rationing

ANYONE CAN UNDERSTAND WHY our society, faced with the necessity of rationing healthcare, might opt to do it covertly. Trying to visualize how we might conduct open rationing is enough to give us nightmares. Just imagine: There, on C-SPAN, in some Congressional hearing room, the American Heart Association is squaring off against the American Cancer Society in the battle for dollars. Later, tune in to watch a group of women with breast cancer testify as to why they should get funding priority over those children with leukemia sitting at the next table.

As we will see in a later chapter, open healthcare rationing doesn't have to be that bad. Nonetheless, open rationing is something we Americans are not willing to contemplate. And this leaves us no alternative but to ration covertly.

In this section of the book, we embark on a survey of covert healthcare rationing as it operates in the U.S. I am confident that when we are finished, any lingering doubts we might have about the Fourth Corollary—that covert rationing corrupts everything it touches—will have been abolished. We begin, in this chapter, with a brief overview of covert rationing, including an introduction to the main players in the battle over how covert rationing is to be conducted in the U.S. and who gets to control it.

Is covert rationing a vast conspiracy?

It might seem impossible to conduct widespread rationing in a huge industry like healthcare, which consumes nearly fifteen percent of the

GDP and directly affects all of us, and to do it in secret. Wouldn't the rationing of such a visible commodity be apparent to everybody?

Actually, it is quite apparent if you look for it. But we've more or less agreed not to look. Covert rationing is not a conspiracy being foisted on millions of innocent Americans by a vast and evil cabal. Much of the rationing activity is only poorly hidden, and its covert nature relies on a willful failure to recognize it for what it is. Most of the individuals who are actually conducting the rationing—the doctors, the hospital administrators, the managed care and insurance executives, the scientists, the policymakers and regulators—subscribe to the same no limits mentality as everyone else. Most probably find the notion of rationing healthcare repugnant and would take offense at being accused of carrying it out.

The covert rationing of healthcare is a textbook case of *subconscious collusion*. Subconscious collusion is a defense mechanism invoked by any social order faced with a condition that is both unavoidable and unacceptable. It is an unspoken, often subliminal decision to coexist with the unacceptable condition but not to notice it, acknowledge it, or confront it. Consider the wife who subliminally decides not to notice that her husband is having a string of extramarital affairs. And consider the German populace during World War II, apparently failing to notice the Holocaust. Subconscious collusion is a common survival technique that allows a social order to persist, for a time, when some fundamental tenet of that order has been severely compromised. The problem with subconscious collusion is that it allows the root problem to grow unchecked—and by definition unnoticed—until the social order being protected by this defense mechanism implodes.

In the case of healthcare rationing, subconscious collusion operates like this: First, the economic forces that require rationing and the social forces that forbid rationing line up to foster a certain attitude, a certain way of looking at things. Then, within every entity in the healthcare system, those who embrace such an attitude become ascendant, not by conspiracy or plot, but by natural market forces.

That certain correct attitude, the new "right stuff," is the ability to suggest ways of limiting healthcare services, while spinning those suggestions as being consistent with the culture of no limits. This kind of thinking allows organizations to direct the rationing of healthcare while advancing the notion that rationing is unnecessary.

There is surprisingly little hypocrisy under this scenario. While some of the individuals directing the rationing behavior understand exactly what they are doing, most continue to subscribe to the myth of no limits. Most believe (or want to believe) that their actions are not reducing useful services, that, instead, they are reducing waste and improving the efficiency of the system. Those who do understand the true nature of their actions shield themselves from having to communicate that knowledge. They become the quiet, private CEOs or directors whose spokespersons and PR specialists (individuals who are entirely sincere about what they are telling the public) do their speaking for them.

So there is no conspiracy. The covert rationing of healthcare is conducted by a myriad of organizations, acting independently and responding to economic and social imperatives. The key for organizations that want to flourish within our Quadrant III healthcare system, then, is to identify leaders who can respond both to the need to ration healthcare and to the need to rationalize such behavior in terms acceptable to the rest of us. Those individuals, men and women of vision, are the Most Valuable Players in Quadrant III healthcare.

The visions advanced by such individuals—visions that enable covert rationing to go forward freely and often profitably—fall into two schools of thought that we will examine in coming chapters. A brief introduction will suffice for now.

The two schools of covert rationing

School of thought number 1—the Wonkonians

Governmental regulators, politicians, public health officials, political liberals, and policy mavens (wonks, in other words) espouse the Wonkonian school of thought.

Wonkonians believe that the root cause of the problems in our healthcare system lies in human weakness (specifically in too many greedy doctors using too much expensive technology). The fix for these problems therefore rests in setting policy and promulgating regulations to hold that greed in check. Philosophically, Wonkonians believe in original sin, in the essential evil of man—if you give a fellow too much freedom, he'll probably do something bad.

That the traditional (Tooth Fairy) Quadrant IV healthcare system institutionalized the natural human greed of physicians supports the Wonkonians' argument. Under that Quadrant IV system, the more technology doctors use, and the more procedures they perform, the more money they make. This system fosters profligacy, waste, and the overuse of expensive resources.

According to the Wonkonian school, the greed inherent in our healthcare system is confirmed by the fact that millions of Americans are shut out of the system (or at least shut out of health insurance). Where is the cry of outrage from our "compassionate" physicians over the high number of uninsured? The greed is further reflected by a lack of quality in our present healthcare system—consider the high infant mortality rate and lagging life-expectancy in the U.S. as compared with rates in other developed countries. Again, where is the professional outrage? Clearly there is a fundamental problem with our healthcare system, a problem that stems from the misguided incentives and maladjusted motivations of healthcare practitioners and other profiteers.

Politicians and policymakers gravitate toward this school of thought because its basic premise is that the problem with healthcare results from misguided incentives coupled with human greed. This premise places the solution in the hands of policymakers, who can do the job with stricter regulations and more enforcement muscle.

School of thought number 2—the Gekkonians

The insurance industry, healthcare executives, many physicians, and most proponents of a free-enterprise economy, including most political conservatives espouse the Gekkonian school of thought, named for Gordon Gekko, the character in the movie *Wall Street*, who argued that greed is good.*

* Gekko was the point man for a leveraged buyout of a family-owned manufacturing company. He expressed his famous formulation at a meeting with the employees he was firing, as a rationale for why they should be happy about losing the jobs they'd held their entire working lives.

The Gekkonian premise is that the open marketplace offers the best solution to society's problems. Gekkonians believe in the essential goodness of man— give a fellow his freedom, and just watch the good things flow.

Gekkonians assert that the healthcare crisis stems directly from the fact that, while doctors may be good at practicing medicine (or may not), they're not businesspeople. And healthcare is a business, like any other economic enterprise.

Leave it up to the doctors, and they'll forever practice medicine the way they did in 1910—hundreds of thousands of independent guildsmen, each running their own shop, duplicating expensive services, multiplying inefficiencies, and shutting out the competition. No wonder the healthcare system is such an inefficient, wasteful mess. Instead, the healthcare industry should be just like any other market, and not some sacred, protected economic sphere.

Let those who know how to run a business run the business of healthcare, and let the doctors practice medicine (under the guidance of the fiscally adept). Bring the efficiencies of the for-profit free enterprise system to the healthcare industry, and the healthcare crisis will take care of itself.

Wonkonians versus Gekkonians—a comparison

Wonkonians and Gekkonians seem to have little in common. Wonkonians believe that too much greed is the problem, so the healthcare crisis can only be solved by regulations to hold that greed in check. Gekkonians propose to allow the invisible hand of the market (greed) to solve the healthcare crisis by reducing artificial constraints on the market (that is, by reducing governmental regulations).

A closer look reveals that these two schools of thought have a lot in common; enough to explain why Wonkonians and Gekkonians can often be seen forming alliances in their efforts to reform the system.

Both schools of thought are based on the notion that the healthcare crisis is caused by waste and fraud in the healthcare system. While one school tends to blame the waste and fraud on greed and the other on incompetence, the problem according to both schools is the inefficient use of resources. We've already seen the limitations of the waste and fraud hypothesis. But it is attractive to suppose that enough waste exists in the system to make rationing unnecessary.

By assuming the validity of the waste and fraud hypothesis, both Wonkonians and Gekkonians can assert that the underlying problem is one of how the healthcare system is organized, that is, of who gets to call the shots and which philosophy gets to determine the rules. Neither group questions whether control should be centralized (clearly, it should). The battle is over which central authority should exert that control and whether they should do so through regulatory means or market-based means. There is no questioning, at least publicly, of either the entitlement mentality or the culture of no limits.

Both the Wonkonians and Gekkonians say solving the healthcare crisis requires limiting the capacity of doctors to behave as independent agents. In one case this is to be done by regulatory means to stifle physician greed; in the other it is to be done by the marketplace to eliminate physician inefficiency. But either way the number one priority is to control physicians' behavior. To the extent that controlling physicians' behavior prevents them from being greedy or inefficient, that's good. But to the extent that controlling their behavior prevents them from fulfilling their role as advocates for their patients, that's bad. Very bad.

So each school of thought provides a cover for activities that, if subconscious collusion were not the operational imperative, would be seen for what they are—rationing. Understanding these two schools of thought lets us comprehend the secret language of covert rationing. For rationing behavior is almost always couched in terms of one school of thought or the other.

So far in the race to control our hearts and minds, neither school of thought has clearly predominated. In 1993 and 1994, the heyday of the Clintons' healthcare reform efforts, the Wonkonians were in the driver's seat. Then, when the Clinton plan went down to overwhelming defeat, the Gekkonians rapidly took the fore, and the heyday of private managed care organizations flitted by. Now that the public has soured on healthcare run by the free market, the Wonkonians are making a strong comeback. One school of thought won't vanquish the other any time soon.

But such a horse race scenario is an oversimplification. Many forms of covert rationing are supported by both schools of thought, and the battle has been characterized more by collusion than collision. For the doctors and patients struggling in the trenches, it doesn't much matter which school of thought represents the paradigm of the day. Covert rationing in any guise renders the pursuit of healthcare difficult, frustrating, and dangerous.

The consequences of covert rationing

While devising a fair system of open rationing would be difficult and painful, the consequences of covert rationing are even more terrible.

Consider the most obvious result when healthcare has to be rationed tacitly. Human nature being what it is, interest groups (doctors, hospitals, insurers, biomedical industry, and government) proclaim that the changes in healthcare occurring today are good and represent their single-minded efforts to become more efficient, patient-oriented, and quality-driven. Meanwhile (again, human nature being what it is) those same interest groups compete among themselves for a limited healthcare dollar. This competition is fierce because it is driven not only by greed but also by the threat to professional survival. Next to a threat like this, the healthcare being provided to the public (the entity for which the healthcare system ostensibly exists in the first place) becomes almost an afterthought. So that limited healthcare dollar, instead of being used to bring about the greatest good for the greatest number, ends up in the hands of whichever interest groups are best at playing the game.

But the covert rationing of healthcare is more than just unfair, deceptive, and harmful to individuals; it is destructive to our entire society. By pretending that we are not rationing (and that there is no need to ration), we are bequeathing to our children and grandchildren an enormous, destabilizing fiscal burden.

More important than that fiscal burden are the political and social burdens we are creating for our children. To keep the rationing of healthcare covert, we are engaged in a cascade of compromise and self-deception that threatens the underpinnings of not only our healthcare system but also our American culture. Such self-deception is apparent in every aspect of healthcare: in the restructuring of the business side of healthcare; in the changes in the legal and regulatory climate; in the design, justification, and interpretation of medical research; and ironically, in the growing call for expanded patients' rights. These compromises will have destructive effects that go beyond withholding useful healthcare from some of those who need it. Taken together, these compromises constitute a powerful attack on an ideal that is essential to our American society—the ideal of individual autonomy.

We ought to have learned by now—from the American Revolution to the Civil War to the twentieth century struggles against fascism and communism—that maintaining individual autonomy in the face of the needs of society can never be a settled issue. Each generation of Americans must grapple with this question. (The argument over the Patriot Act, which offers to protect society, but potentially at the expense of abrogating important individual rights, exemplifies this ongoing struggle.)

Healthcare rationing strongly challenges the autonomy of the individual. If we ration, whether overtly or covertly, we must withhold from individuals for the benefit of society. But while it is possible to construct a system of open rationing that balances individual autonomy with the needs of the whole (as we will see later), it is not possible to do so under covert rationing. When we ration covertly we abandon the individual, often as the first step, without any discussion, and without realizing what we're throwing away. This is the ultimate price we pay as a society when we quietly, subconsciously collude with the covert rationing of healthcare.

In the next several chapters we will examine just how it is that Quadrant III healthcare poses such a profound threat to us as individuals and to our society. We'll begin with a survey of the great engine of covert rationing, managed care, as practiced by modern Wonkonians and Gekkonians.

4

Covert Rationing and Managed Care

IF YOU WERE GOING to design from scratch a system for covertly
rationing healthcare, you would need a central organizing concept
like managed care, which everybody can talk about using the same ter-
minology while trying to communicate contradictory ideas.

Defining managed care

Managed care is an administrative philosophy under which certain
management principles that are standard in other industries are
applied to the healthcare industry.

A managed care organization is the bureaucratic entity that applies
the techniques of managed care to a population of actual patients.
Health maintenance organizations (HMOs) and preferred provider
organizations (PPOs) are two types of managed care organizations.
To keep things simple, in this chapter I will arbitrarily use the term
HMO as shorthand for all species of managed care organizations.

Since it is only an administrative philosophy—a technique, a tool—
managed care is value-neutral. It is neither good nor bad, any more
than any other tool is good or bad. What is important is how the tool
is used.

Pure managed care

Managed care is a concept that has been around for decades, developed in academic and intellectual circles by healthcare policy experts,
economists, governmental commissions, and industrial management

experts. In its purest form the idea behind managed care is a simple and useful one—it is to apply management principles that have been used successfully in other industries to the healthcare system, thereby injecting logic, organization, and accountability to what was a bastion of disorganization and inefficiency. There are many industry-derived principles that could be applied to healthcare, but the unifying idea behind most of them boils down to one word: standardization.

Standardization is virtually a synonym for industry. In industry, standardization is the primary means of optimizing the two essential factors in any industrial process: quality and cost.

Let's state this formally as the **Axiom of Industry:**

The standardization of any industrial process will improve the outcome and reduce the cost of that process.

If you had a widget-making factory, you would break your manufacturing process down into discrete, reproducible, repeatable steps and then optimize the procedures and processes necessary to accomplish each step. To further improve the quality of your finished product (or to reduce the cost of producing it), you would reexamine the steps, one by one, seeking opportunities for improvement. You would need to understand the process and you would need to collect data about how well the process works. But with the right information, you could identify a few minor changes to improve the manufacturing process. The beauty in such a system is that you have only to make one change—to the process itself—and every widget that comes off the line after you make that change will be improved.

So standardization is good. It leads to higher quality and lower cost. Conversely, variation is bad. It reduces quality and raises cost.

Proponents of managed care argue that standardization should be just as useful in healthcare as it is in other industries. As medical care has traditionally been individualized, highly variable, and without any semblance of standardization, there must be a huge opportunity to improve the processes of care and to make them both cheaper and more effective. Without a doubt, there is great merit in this idea.

Some benefits of managed care techniques

A good illustration of how industrial principles have been applied to clinical medicine is in the use of critical pathways.

Critical pathways are blueprints for delivering standardized care to patients with specific medical problems. Consider a critical pathway for hip replacement surgery. This is a blueprint of what services the surgeon is to provide for the patient, from the date of hospital admission until the date of discharge (which is, of course, predetermined). The surgeon has a checklist of which laboratory tests to order and when, what medications to administer at which times, and what complications to watch for. The nurse and other healthcare workers involved in the patient's care have their own checklists. They know from the moment of a patient's hospital admission when to take vital signs, when to get the patient out of bed, when to begin physical therapy, and when to provide standardized instructions to the patient before discharge. All this is pre-determined by the critical pathway.

All the while, the care each patient receives under the critical pathway is monitored by a case manager. The job of the case manager (usually a nurse), is to track how well the doctors, nurses, and other healthcare workers involved in the patient's care are sticking to the prescribed pathway. Every deviation from the pathway (for instance, the patient with a hip replacement might begin physical therapy on Day 3 instead of Day 2) is tabulated as a "variance." The idea of tracking variances is not to mete out punishment but to identify areas of the process that need improvement. If too many instances of a particular variance are seen in a critical pathway, then either medical personnel need to be retrained on following the pathway appropriately or the pathway itself should be changed to reflect more realistic expectations.

The case manager is also responsible for tracking the medical outcomes of patients cared for under the critical pathway. If a pathway leads to suboptimal outcomes of care, it needs to be revised. Therefore, a critical pathway is never static. It is a living document that is monitored and revised to produce an ever-improving process of care.

Critical pathways provide at least three benefits that improve the delivery of healthcare.

- Developing a pathway requires that you understand the care process being managed. Before managed care, such insights were rare. Often, when first studying the process, one or more routine clinical practices are identified as being obviously wasteful. So just creating a critical pathway often leads to a rapid improvement in the efficiency of medical care.

- Critical pathways provide a means of standardizing the processes of care. To the extent that healthcare is like other industries, the Axiom of Industry tells us that such standardization ought to be effective in improving outcomes and reducing cost—mainly by assuring that all patients enrolled in a critical pathway receive necessary items of care at the right time and do not receive any unnecessary ones.
- Critical pathways provide an organized means of defining, acquiring, and tracking data related to care. Collection and analysis of data are the keys to improving any repeatable process.

Critical pathways have helped hospitals and physicians achieve the twin goals of managed care—improving outcomes and reducing costs. While critical pathways are only a small part of managed care, they embody the main principles by which managed care aims to tame the healthcare system. People who develop managed care procedures quickly see the benefits of applying these principles. The success of critical pathways has led many in the healthcare field to embrace managed care. Systematically reducing the cost of care while improving the quality of care is an attractive proposition.

Some drawbacks of managed care techniques

There are at least two inherent limitations to the application of industrial management principles to healthcare. The first of these, which escapes many proponents of managed care techniques, is that not all medical processes are suitable for standardization.

The standardization tools of managed care work only when you're dealing with a process that can be broken down into a predictable series of discrete, reproducible tasks that generate reproducible results. In other words, industrial management tools work best when the process of care is similar to the process of making widgets.

Hip replacement surgery tends to be reasonably widget-like. We know that on Day 1 the hip replacement operation itself will take place. We know that hip replacement is usually an elective procedure, so other medical conditions the patient may have will have been stabilized before surgery (and before entrance to the critical pathway); they should not present unexpected problems during the hospitalization. Thus the critical pathway can focus solely on minimizing the risk of complications and speeding recovery. For hip replacement and many other elective surgical procedures, the use of critical pathways has resulted in reduced lengths of hospital stays, less cost, and faster (or at least no slower) recovery.

In contrast, developing critical pathways for non-surgical hospital admissions has proven problematic. For many medical illnesses, neither the diagnostic procedures nor the treatments that may be employed can be predicted or, therefore, standardized. Consider what happens when we try to develop a critical pathway for congestive heart failure (CHF). Patients with CHF may have one or more of a variety of underlying conditions that caused their heart failure in the first place (coronary artery disease, valvular heart disease, viral infections of the heart muscle, and many others); they vary widely in their severity of illness (from mildly ill to moribund); and they often have related complicating disorders of one or more additional organ systems, such as kidney failure or peripheral vascular disease. These factors and others determine what diagnostic and therapeutic maneuvers will be necessary. Knowing only that a patient has been admitted to the hospital with CHF tells you nothing about whether that patient will require cardiac catheterization, angioplasty, bypass surgery, valve replacement, a pacemaker, an implantable defibrillator, a mechanical ventilator, a prolonged and complicated stay in the intensive care unit, or just a couple of diuretic tablets and overnight observation.* No two patients with CHF are alike; and there is no such thing as a standard patient.

For medical conditions like this, in which every patient is unique, managed care techniques are not very useful. The majority of non-surgical hospital admissions fall into this category.

The second inherent limitation in applying industrial management principles to healthcare, and the one that is more pertinent to our discussion of covert rationing, is that in healthcare the Axiom of Industry does not hold true. Standardization does not always improve outcomes and reduce cost.

What makes the Axiom of Industry apply to other businesses but not to healthcare? The answer is:

* While some of these tests and treatments might have their own critical pathways, and while we might thus contemplate enrolling a patient with CHF into various hierarchies of nested critical pathways depending on each patient's individual needs, this approach is generally not feasible. Such individualized, nested systems of critical pathways would be extraordinarily difficult to execute. These subsidiary critical pathways, like the one described for hip replacement, assume that the patient is otherwise stable and free of additional medical problems that would significantly complicate the test or treatment in question (say, cardiac catheterization). Patients presenting with CHF are notoriously uncooperative with managed care theory in this regard, often having multiple disorders that complicate every aspect of their care.

Patients are not widgets. While this fact is obvious to everybody, its implications are not.

If you're a widget maker, deciding between two manufacturing processes is a matter of economics. Nobody expects you to consider the widget itself. The outcome by which you are judged has nothing to do with how many individual widgets get discarded during the manufacturing process or even the quality of the widgets that pass final inspection. Instead, it's the bottom line: how much profit you make in relation to whatever level of quality you put into the widget. So the quality of the widget is not necessarily maximized, instead it's optimized, tuned to the optimal quality/cost ratio as determined by the market forces of the day. This is why, for a widget maker, the axiom holds: standardization, by rooting out variability, reduces the cost of making the widget (whatever quality level you choose). This automatically improves the outcome, because the outcome the manufacturer cares about is profit.

If instead of running a widget company you're running an HMO, the calculus is different. You're supposed to be more interested in how things turn out for individual patients than you are in the bottom line. So an expensive process that yields a better clinical outcome is one most people (patients, at least) would expect you to use, even though it only gets you a healthier patient and doesn't make your money back for you. A process that increases patients' mortality rate by five percent is one you should disregard, even if it is substantially cheaper than the alternative. The clinical outcomes experienced by patients—the measure of success you're supposed to be concerned about—may move in the same direction as costs, or in the opposite direction. But because you're dealing with patients the Axiom of Industry doesn't hold—outcomes and costs do not always move in the same direction.

Pure managed care has given us useful ideas about making healthcare delivery more efficient without diminishing medical outcomes. The principles of managed care are used in most large hospitals in America today and have the potential of even broader applicability. However, contrary to the dogma, these principles are not applicable in all cases, nor do they always yield favorable results.

The two faces of managed care

Managed care—two-faced? No, many-faced. By which I mean the many entities in the healthcare system all mean something different when they use the term "managed care." These meanings are based on the ideas we have just considered, but none conceive of, promote, or apply managed care in its purest form. "Pure" managed care does not exist in the wild.

Fortunately, the most prominent variations in managed care fall into just two major schools of thought; these happen to be those same schools we've already had the pleasure of meeting—the Wonkonians and the Gekkonians.

Wonkonian managed care

Wonkonians believe, you will recall, that the problems in our healthcare system can be traced to human weaknesses (greed on the part of physicians, patients, and corporations). Fixing these problems depends on setting public policy and promulgating governmental regulations. Managed care offers to remove some of the choices humans have to make in delivering healthcare (choices easily colored by greed) and to replace them with externally generated processes and procedures. Philosophically, it's a good fit.

Because Wonkonians like and believe in the ideas behind managed care, the people who conceived of and developed those ideas—academics, healthcare experts, government commissions, economists and editorialists—tend to gravitate to the Wonkonian camp. Wonkonians espousing the ideals of managed care tend to sound like purists. They are proselytizers who believe in applying continuous quality improvement, critical pathways, information management, and other efficiencies of industrial management to healthcare. Because of their obvious sincerity, and because many of their ideas have considerable merit, it is easy for right-minded folks to fall in with this crowd.

What differentiates Wonkonians from true managed care purists is in what they mean by the word "managed." In classic managed care, "manage" refers to the application of management principles such as standardization. To Wonkonians, "manage" means "regulate." Managed care is a convenient tool for advancing their basic belief in policies and regulations to control human behavior. The specific recommendations put forth by Wonkonians have much more to do with establishing a centralized regulatory structure for healthcare than they do with managed care principles. To them, a system of strict regulations has become synonymous with managed care.

Gekkonian managed care

Gekkonians, on the other hand, find that the healthcare system is broken because it hasn't been treated like the business it is. Allow free-
market forces (that is, greed) to reign, and the problems will take care
of themselves.

Accordingly, Gekkonians come at managed care from an entirely
different direction. Historically, they have little claim to the managed care peerage. Gekkonians spent decades decrying managed care
as socialist heresy. "Freedom and competition" is their battle cry, and
managed care smacks too much of social engineering.

Since the 1980s, however, Gekkonians have co-opted the term
"managed care" and changed its meaning. As managed care techniques
derive from industrial management principles, they hold, managed
care is actually a child of the open marketplace. Thus, Gekkonians
seem to be saying, what managed care is really about is applying the
principles of free enterprise to the business of healthcare.

Managed care to Gekkonians is dog-eat-dog, compete until you
die, for-profit healthcare. Any actual relationship between Gekkonian
managed care and classic managed care is incidental. (Sometimes standard managed care techniques can be useful, but only if they give you
a competitive advantage.)

Managed care is a means of establishing stronger regulations on one
hand and a means of maximizing profits on the other. Wonkonians
and Gekkonians are both prominent today, and both groups are
actively and loudly advancing their respective points of view. A lot of
the turmoil we have seen over the past decades can be explained by the
competition and interplay as they each try to advance their visions for
American healthcare.

In the next few chapters we will see how the Wonkonians are
employing their concept of managed care in their continuing efforts to
control the American healthcare system. But for more than a decade
it has been the Gekkonians—armed with their chief weapon, the
Gekkonian HMO—who have held center stage. Gekkonian managed
care will be the main emphasis of this chapter.

But first a brief history of American healthcare—observing how
the American healthcare system has drifted, across the healthcare
landscape as defined by the GUTH—will help us to place into bet-

ter perspective the reasons Gekkonians became ascendant in the mid-1990s, will help us understand why their flight path is now looking more parabolic than orbital, and will prepare us for the re-ascendancy of Wonkonians.

A brief history of American healthcare

The guild building era

Such modern ideas as capitation (the providing of medical care for a fixed annual fee) and the corporate practice of medicine (medical practices controlled by companies, not by doctors) are older than we might think. American companies pioneered the contracting of medical services before the beginning of the twentieth century. This innovation came from industries such as railroads and lumber, whose operations often took place in isolated areas, so medical care for their employees otherwise would not have been available. Some companies went so far as to build and operate their own hospitals and staffed those hospitals with physicians who were paid out of the company payroll. By the early 1900s, contract medicine was commonplace in the United States and was conducted by many kinds of organizations—not only by companies (both large and small), but also by multitudes of fraternal orders and lodges, which began offering subscription medical services to their members. Soon the federal and local governments were also contracting for physician services on behalf of their employees, prisoners, and wards of the state.

Organized medicine looked on these developments with great alarm. The mission of organized medicine was to foster an environment under which their physician members could practice their profession scientifically and ethically while maintaining favorable fees. Contract healthcare placed too much control in the hands of third-party payers, thus threatening all three goals of profit, quality, and ethical standards.

In response, in the early 1900s organized medicine went on the offensive, claiming both the scientific and the moral high ground. The practice of medicine, they asserted, was based in the sciences. Therefore, the allegedly poor working conditions suffered by contract practitioners precluded their upholding the high scientific standards to which physicians aspired. And thus contract medicine was bad medicine.

Contract medicine violated the sacred relationship of trust between physicians and their patients; that is, it wrecked the doctor–patient relationship, according to these same critics. Such a relationship requires patients and physicians to contract directly with one another, without intermediaries. Any other party (such as an employer or the state) inserting itself into this relationship would end up dividing the loyalties of the physician and thus violating the nature of this sacred trust. Contract medicine and state-controlled medicine were therefore unethical.

Medical organizations lobbied both the general public and state legislators with the notion that it was in society's best interest to prevent middlemen from inserting themselves between physicians and their patients. Physicians who practiced contract medicine were held out as being something less than true physicians, and before long they had trouble joining their local medical societies; at the time, this made it next to impossible for them to purchase malpractice insurance or gain hospital privileges. Many state legislatures passed laws making most contract medicine illegal.

By the 1920s, organized medicine had beaten third-party payers. The medical profession had successfully created a guild; that is, physicians had established a monopoly over an economic realm, allowing competition to occur only within that protected sphere. Outsiders would have little to say about how the practice of medicine was conducted.

The economic golden era

From an economic standpoint, an ideal healthcare system is one in which patients pay directly for their medical care. In such a system, patients freely choose their own physicians and, together with their

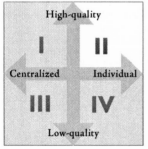

physicians, make all medical decisions, mindful that any costs are theirs to pay. Cost controls are automatic. During the first decades of the twentieth century and into the 1930s, this ideal system existed in the United States. Given that doctors at the time had very little to offer in terms of expensive (or effective) therapies, and patients' expectations were (appropriately) low, the purchasing decisions, relative to the options available, were of high quality. For a decade or two, the U.S. experienced ideal Quadrant II healthcare.

The medical golden era

This economic equilibrium began to falter in the 1930s and deteriorated rapidly in the years following World War II. The first kink in the connection between physicians and their patients occurred during the Great Depression, when hospitals began to suffer from patients' inability to pay their bills. Over the initial objections of physicians, financially stressed hospitals prevailed on state legislatures to legalize the insurance schemes that evolved into Blue Cross. To assuage the moral indignation of physicians, the Blues were set up as nonprofit, provider-oriented insurance organizations.

"Provider-oriented" meant two things. First, Blue Cross (and later Blue Shield) did not attempt to tell physicians how to practice medicine. Physicians were free to practice as they saw fit, and the Blues paid the bills on a fee-for-service basis. Second, the boards of trustees of local Blue Cross and Blue Shield organizations were loaded with prominent local physicians and hospital administrators.

Not only did this system preserve the direct physician–patient relationship, it also paid the bills more reliably than did patients themselves. The Blues' boards of trustees traditionally chose reimbursement methodologies that guaranteed doctors regular and favorable increases in revenue. The system worked so well that soon physicians accepted the formation of private health insurance companies, as long as those companies followed the same general guidelines as the Blues.

Health insurance proved to be so popular among both patients and doctors that, during the wage and price controls of World War II, companies began offering it to their employees in lieu of higher wages. After the war, American labor unions began to demand that employers provide health insurance as a benefit of employment. The government liked this idea too, and, in order to encourage it, Congress changed the tax laws to make providing this benefit attractive to employers. In this way, employer-provided health insurance became a tax-deductible business expense and rendered the health insurance many of us receive a public expense instead of a business expense.

Without this tax break, companies would have to recoup the cost of employee health insurance in the normal way, by increasing the price of their products. Consumers, with their purchasing decisions, would then decide how much of that healthcare burden was economically reasonable. When the cost of products became too high, sales would fall, and by this mechanism the amount of money businesses spend on health insurance would reach a natural ceiling.

But because employer-provided health insurance costs are tax-deductible, companies don't have to raise the price of their products—at least, not nearly as much—to cover these expenses. Instead, much of the cost is passed off to the general population, which must then either pay more taxes, or accept a further increase in the national debt or both. Either way, the checks and balances of the marketplace have been circumvented, and overall spending on healthcare can grow relatively unchecked.*

* Despite this arrangement, businesses today are unhappy about skyrocketing health insurance premiums. If their tax-deductible insurance expenses are growing at a faster rate than their revenues, as they often are, eventually companies will become unprofitable. And tax deductions are only useful if you are making a profit. So sooner or later market forces do apply here; but by making employee health insurance tax deductible, we have made sure it's much later.

The federal government became more directly involved in paying for American healthcare with the institution of Medicare and Medicaid in 1965. By 1970 much of the healthcare in the United States was being paid for by the American taxpayer. Taxpayers had to cover the tax breaks given to companies that provided their employees' health insurance and also had to support Medicare expenditures through payroll taxes. Because you can only tax the people so much, the rising cost of healthcare began to accrue to the national debt.

But for physicians and their patients, the system seemed nearly perfect. While patients were free to choose doctors and hospitals, and while the physician–patient relationship remained largely free of outside influence, somebody else was paying the bills. There was a dissociation between providing or consuming healthcare and paying for it. The era of Quadrant IV, Tooth-Fairy healthcare was in full blossom.

This economic arrangement did two things that spelled its doom. First, it allowed the no limits mentality to flourish—the notion that the best possible care should be provided to everybody and that where healthcare is concerned, there are no limits. It created expectations that ultimately could not be met.

Second, this system fostered the development of the medical-industrial complex. As any medical advance that seemed useful would be paid for, powerful corporations arose that were dedicated to meeting the bottomless demand for medical advances. The pharmaceutical companies, hospital suppliers, and medical device companies began turning out a stream of expensive technology. Ironically, given that this whole system had evolved from physicians' attempts to shield them-selves from corporate influence, these corporations used their market-ing clout to influence the decisions, the practice patterns, and even the demographic distribution (such as patterns of specialization) of the medical profession.

The unlimited expectations of patients and physicians, coupled with the never-ending meeting (and stimulation) of those expectations by industry, created a positive feedback loop. The more healthcare the doctors and patients got, the more they wanted. The more they wanted, the more the medical–industrial complex was happy to provide. It was inevitable that those paying the mounting healthcare costs (employers and the government) would reach the breaking point. While the sys-tem that prevailed during this golden era of Quadrant IV healthcare came to be regarded by American physicians and their patients as the norm and even as a birthright, that system is clearly an unsustainable aberrancy. At some point the mounting costs of no limit healthcare had to generate its own backlash. The system had to implode.

The era of healthcare reform—Wonkonians get their chance

Recognition that such a healthcare system could not be sustained did not begin with the Clintons. Employers and the government became alarmed with rapidly rising healthcare expenditures as far back as the 1960s and 1970s. During our great national debate on healthcare reform in the early 1990s, few seemed to remember that President Nixon had proposed a sweeping national healthcare plan more than twenty years earlier. (Yes, Nixon was a Wonkonian.) Nixon's plan, like the Clintons', fell victim to the groups most entrenched in the medical–industrial complex: hospitals, doctors, medical device and pharmaceutical com-panies, and the insurance industry. (Watergate also had something to do with the demise of Nixon's plan.)

The failure of Nixon's reform plan was followed by two decades of more gradual, stepwise efforts to bring healthcare spending under con-trol. Many of these changes were driven by Congress, whose efforts to regulate healthcare were considered legitimate, because Congress provided healthcare funding through Medicare and Medicaid. By forc-ing regional planning for expensive medical facilities and by more carefully reviewing the practices of physicians, Congress hoped to slow the increase in healthcare spending. Both Congress and the courts acted to increase competition within the medical marketplace, on the theory that competition reduces costs (and it does—in almost any other economic realm). Thus, legal barriers to advertising and, more important, barriers to the creation of HMOs were gradually withdrawn. While doctors chafed at these efforts (grumbling about middlemen between themselves and their patients), they still got paid, so their complaints were muffled.

But such stepwise reform efforts had little effect on overall healthcare spending. From 1970 until the early 1990s, as we have seen, the proportion of the GDP spent on healthcare increased from 7.3 percent to approximately 13 percent; and in dollars healthcare spending increased tenfold, from $74.4 billion to nearly $752 billion annually.

By the beginning of the 1990s, healthcare spending reached the crisis level. Things were so bad that when the Clintons came into office and went about launching their comprehensive Wonkonian plan for healthcare reform, they initially found an enthusiastic ally in what should have been their natural enemy—the Gekkonian insurance industry.

The dynamics of this uneasy alliance are fascinating. The insurance industry supported the Clintons' wide-ranging reforms because those reforms promised them a vast new market—the millions of heretofore uninsured Americans whose premiums would be paid, presumably, by the government. The Clintons, in turn, needed the support of the insurance industry to have any prayer of passing their reform plan. So Wonkonians and Gekkonians allied themselves in the name of healthcare reform, each with their own agenda (Wonkonians—comprehensive regulations; Gekkonians—profit), and each meaning something different by "managed care."

In this light, the etymology of the term they coined for their joint endeavor—managed competition—is instructive. "Managed competition" embodies the chief concerns of both camps. "Managed," ostensibly from the term "managed care," carries the connotation the Wonkonians attach to the word; here, managed means regulated. "Competition" represents the interests of the Gekkonians; it implies a for-profit, market-driven sort of healthcare. So "managed competition" means something like "regulated free markets." This oxymoron reflected the unnatural alliance between Wonkonians and Gekkonians; it was clear that the alliance would not hold.

And of course, it didn't. It fell apart when the insurance industry began reading the massive regulations the Clintons produced and found much they didn't like. (Among other things they found regulations that would plug profitable loopholes traditionally enjoyed by that industry.) They turned on the Clintons and spent millions introducing us to Harry and Louise (a "typical," presumably Gekkonian, American couple who, in commercials and print ads, discovered various appalling provisions of the Clinton plan). The rest is history.

The rise of the Gekkonians

While the collapse of the Clintons' reform plan caused a sudden deflation of expectations, the fiscal crisis remained. Awareness of that crisis had been heightened by the Clintons' campaign to reform healthcare, and nobody (except some of the doctors) entertained the delusion that we could go back to business as usual. Everybody could see that traditional Quadrant IV healthcare was no longer feasible.

As it turned out, a savior awaited. That savior was the same insurance industry that had first built up and then scuttled national healthcare reform. Only now the insurance companies had reformulated themselves into HMOs, had decked themselves out in Gekkonian raiment, and had fully assimilated the language of managed care.

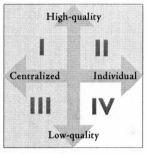

And here is what they said: "Citizens! We all— employers, patients, physicians, hospitals, manufacturers and insurers—have just dodged a bullet. Thanks to us, the frightening socialist reforms of the Clintons have been soundly defeated. But where does this leave us? We stand now between Scylla and Charybdis, between the specter of nationalized healthcare on one hand, and the continued profligacy of traditional fee-for-service medicine on the other. And we cannot countenance either. But here," the Gekkonians continued, "is a third way. A painless way, based on the sound principles of managed care, open markets, and free enterprise. Let healthcare become a business like any other business, and the mar-

ket forces will find ways not only to cut costs but also to improve quality, and with no government intervention."

The offer, in other words, was to turn healthcare over to the business
professionals, and let them harness the efficiencies of the marketplace
to solve our problems. Because we're Americans and we know the benefits of capitalism, and because the other choices we faced looked even
worse, we all said, Go for it. And with that decision, we said goodbye to
Quadrant IV and stepped into Quadrant III, led not by Wonkonians
but Gekkonians.

The next few years saw the fastest transformation our healthcare
system has ever undergone. While most of the changes were real, pal-
pable, and material, the biggest transformation of all was a philosophical one.

For all their faults, Wonkonians have held to the notion that the
basic purpose of healthcare is to maximize the public good. This is
what gives government the authority to regulate healthcare. Only the
government can guarantee that the various interest groups will provide
a public benefit. (The flaw in this argument, for those of us who are
suspicious of Wonkonians, is that regulatory bureaucracies often wind
up becoming the biggest, nastiest interest group of all.)

What Gekkonians gave us in the 1990s was a brand new first premise. The primary purpose of healthcare, they said, is not to increase
public benefit. How could it be, when healthcare is merely a business
like any other business? What we should be striving for is to build a
well-run business. Since well-run businesses are beneficial to the community, in the end we can expect plenty of benefits to go around. But
the fact remains that healthcare is a business. And the primary purpose of business is to make money.

The contemporary HMO

HMOs are perplexing institutions. Brought into being as an antidote to the inefficiencies and misaligned incentives attributed to fee-
for-service medicine, HMOs have pioneered the use of many of the
best features of managed care in clinical practice, including critical
pathways, continuous quality improvement, and scientifically-based
medical decisions. Early HMOs emphasized health maintenance—as
their name implied—stressing good health habits and disease preven-

tion instead of concentrating solely on the treatment of acute illnesses. These not-for-profit entities were regarded by most healthcare professionals (and, one suspects, most patients) with bemusement, tolerated as yet another social engineering experiment of little consequence, an eccentric aunt puttering about the attic of the healthcare homestead.

That began to change in the mid-1980s, when Gekkonians became interested in HMOs as a way into the healthcare marketplace. For-profit corporations began to take over HMOs. By the time they had routed the Clinton healthcare reform efforts, Gekkonians were ready, in most major American cities, to accept the huge numbers of patients who began flooding into their for-profit HMOs.

Both for-profit and not-for-profit healthcare organizations have always had to be concerned about where the money is coming from. Forget that, for even a moment, and you're toast, no matter what manner of good works you may perform.

What's new for contemporary HMOs is that making money is no longer something to be whispered about or a topic unsuitable for public discussion or a necessary evil. Making money is now more than okay. It's expected, celebrated, and rewarded; it's become why HMOs exist in the first place. In fact, making money is the means by which HMOs will save the American healthcare system. And the better they are at making money, the better they are for society. This new paradigm is uniquely American. Every other western nation has bent the market to accommodate the needs of healthcare. We are bending healthcare to accommodate the needs of market. And it's drastically affected the way HMOs operate.

To see the effects these Gekkonian-style HMOs are having on doctors, patients, and American culture, let's look at the evolution of an imaginary but typical modern-day HMO called For the Patient (FTP).

Portrait of a Modern HMO

It's 1995; Clinton healthcare reform has just gone down in flames, and it's a new era for HMOs—HMOs like FTP. FTP, established in 1992, has already gained a foothold in eight cities along the eastern seaboard. Following the original business plan, FTP was taken public last year.

But FTP is in trouble. Earnings, and consequently stock prices, have been stagnant. Enrollment has not met expectations; the physicians on FTP's panel (most of whom are new to managed care) have resisted changing their patterns of practice; and it's been difficult to get hospitals in the FTP system (some of which have been rivals for decades) to cooperate with one another. The shareholders are restless, and in response the board has just fired the old CEO (a physician and one of FTP's founders) to bring in a hard-nosed businessman who will know how to put things right.

That man is Gregory Gekko (distant cousin to Gordon). He doesn't know much about healthcare, but he's not intimidated. The last CEO knew plenty about healthcare, and look where it got him. Besides, Gekko didn't know anything about greeting cards either before he developed a tiny greeting card company called Greetings Schmeetings into a multibillion-dollar corporation that's giving Hallmark a run for its money. What Gekko does know is business.

Gekko begins with the two steps that must always be taken when building a business: First, define your customers. Second, define the scope of your business (that is, decide what it is you do to make your customers happy). Only then, knowing both your customer base and your scope of business, can you decide how best to maximize your profits.

Who are FTP's customers?

To Gekko, making money is everything—but not because conservative Republicans have recently swept Congress or because it's the new paradigm for healthcare. Making money is everything to Gekko because that's what the stockholders of FTP have hired him to do. Gekko knows that when his judgment day comes, those doing the judging will be the shareholders of FTP. He knows from experience that he will have some latitude and flexibility regarding the tactics he uses to make that money, but ultimately he has to please those shareholders. Keeping in mind who his *personal* customers are, Gekko carefully considers who might be the customers of his company—of FTP.

Gekko knows this is where the last CEO made his big mistake. He'd talked about his primary customers being the patients enrolled in FTP and their doctors. It wasn't until his final share-holders' meeting that he'd finally gotten it. Of course, it was too late for him by then.

Obviously the primary customers of any business are the people who decide to purchase whatever product the business is selling. In this case, those would be the individuals who decide whether or not to use FTP as their health plan. Gekko knows that patients don't really purchase health insurance, nor do their doctors significantly influence those purchasing decisions. Patients and doctors are important on the spending side of the equation, since they determine how much of FTP's money will be frittered away on delivering healthcare. They will have to be dealt with. But they don't buy insurance.

The people who make the purchasing decisions are the human resource executives and benefits officers in companies that provide health insurance for their employees. To FTP, these purchasing agents are all-important; they will determine Gekko's success or failure. He knows he has to pull out all the stops to make these individuals feel favorable toward FTP. Gekko is confident in this regard; he knows many techniques, subtle and otherwise, that he can use to that end.

What is FTP's scope of business?

This is also pretty straightforward for Gekko. FTP's main business is to take in lots of money in the form of health insurance premiums and then try to keep as much of that money as possible. The rest of the insurance premium money, the money FTP doesn't get to keep, must be held on to and invested for as long as possible. The best part is that, unlike a bank, FTP doesn't have to pay any interest on the money it holds.

In return for this opportunity, FTP must arrange for the provision of healthcare to the individuals for whom the insurance is paid. But providing healthcare is not how FTP will make its money—it's one of the costs of doing business. It's the price FTP must pay for access to all those insurance premiums. How FTP should go about providing the necessary healthcare to its enrollees is an open question for Gekko. There are a lot of ways to do it, and he's not married to any of them. The only bounds he sets for his executives are that whatever methods FTP uses to dispense healthcare must be legally defensible, must minimize or mitigate any opportunity for negative publicity, and must be sufficiently acceptable to its customers—those benefits officers.

As his ultimate goal is to make money for the shareholders, Gekko also understands that he needs to be alert to any low-risk investment opportunities—aside from high-grade government and corporate securities, of course—for turning all that cash flow into profit.

The bottom line is that to be successful, Gekko must maximize the inward flow of cash (health insurance premiums) and minimize the outward flow of cash (healthcare payments). Much of his effort will have to be targeted toward these two goals.

Maximizing the inward flow of cash

To maximize the amount of money flowing into FTP in the form of insurance premiums, Gekko must do several things. He needs to expand FTP into more localities as fast as possible, to increase the number of businesses FTP can sell to. He needs to create an aggressive sales team who can market, enlighten, persuade, cajole, schmooze, entice, bribe, seduce, blackmail, or threaten the benefits officers of those companies to offer FTP as a health insurance option to their employees (as the sole option, whenever possible). And he needs to charge as much for his insurance products as the market will bear.

Keeping premiums high

Optimizing the cost of his health insurance premiums is pretty simple. Gekko must lower his premiums enough to induce employers to switch to FTP, but not a penny lower. Because high-priced indemnity insurance plans are still active in all the cities in which FTP operates, all he has to do is to beat their prices by a little bit. So Gekko sets his rates to a fixed proportion—ninety percent—of the indemnity rates, and he's in business. Whenever the indemnity plans are forced to increase their rates, FTP automatically gets a raise, too.

Gekko understands that the reason everybody's pushing HMOs in the first place is that they're supposed to reduce the cost of healthcare. And most people assume that what HMOs charge for their premiums is tied somehow to that lower cost of delivering care. Gekko just shakes his head. Why would people assume that? Why would anyone expect Gekko, a businessperson, to pass his savings on to the consumer (unless doing so results in a competitive advantage)? Businesses are supposed to make as much profit as they can. That's how it works. To do anything else would be unfair to FTP's shareholders and fatal to Gekko's career.

With all the promises from Gekkonians in the mid-1990s about how their HMOs would save money for the healthcare system, this last point deserves some emphasis. Despite the aggressive cost-cutting measures taken by HMOs (which now enroll over eighty percent of insured Americans), the health insurance premiums paid by employers haven't fallen. Except for a few years during the mid-1990s when the inflation rate for insurance premiums dropped to below five percent, premiums have increased by double digit amounts in most years. But with the drastic cuts in services being made by HMOs and the resultant lowered costs, shouldn't we have seen a sizeable one-time saving in healthcare spending? Where did it go?

Gekko has already answered our question. The dollars that HMOs squeeze out of the system are not returned to the payer in the form of reduced premiums; nor are they plowed back into the healthcare system in the form of improved or widened services; rather, they are invested for maximum returns, which are then pocketed by the HMOs in the form of administrative costs, bonuses for top executives, and profit for the shareholders.

Typical HMOs end up spending around eighty-five percent of their collected premiums on actual healthcare, a proportion shareholders and analysts refer to as the medical loss ratio. That medical loss ratio had better not climb. In 2002, when Aetna was found to be spending as much as 90.5 percent of its money delivering healthcare, the Wall Street analysts and shareholders went ballistic, and inside of Aetna heads rolled. Keeping premium dollars out of the medical arena is critically important for HMOs.

Growing FTP: acquiring community assets

Growth is required to maximize the inflow of cash. Gekko decides that the fastest way to grow FTP is to acquire major healthcare facilities (hospitals and nursing homes) in all its key cities of operation, and he begins doing so. Along the way, Gekko stumbles upon a gold mine. It is a gold mine not directly related to FTP's scope of business, but it's close enough, and the shareholders love it.

The first time Gekko acquires a community hospital for FTP, he notices that within a week of the transaction the price of FTP's stock rises by five percent. What he has just done, he realizes, is to cash in on a publicly-owned asset. So Gekko tries it again, and this time the stock rises by seven percent. Gekko's head spins. This scheme threatens to become such a windfall that Gekko momentarily worries that it might overwhelm the presumed actual business of FTP. The payoff promises to be so astounding, however, that he decides not to worry about it.

Gekko is right. It's a great scam, and completely legal to boot.

Nonprofit hospitals existed in the first place because their communities decided they were needed for the public good. Accordingly, these hospitals were established under the nonprofit laws, which required them to function primarily under a charitable philosophy. Over the decades and in return for their service to the community, these hospitals operated under the public largesse, in the form of their blanket tax-free status, their ability to raise tax-free bonds, and their ability to raise tax-free charitable contributions. Their boards of trustees, made up of prominent members of the community, were charged with guarding the accumulated public value represented by those institutions.

The widespread transfer of not-for-profit public assets (such as a community hospital) to for-profit corporations (such as an HMO) was a major unnoticed healthcare story of the 1990s. It was fueled by the Gekkonian notion that for-profits are inherently more efficient in providing healthcare than charities. Such transfers only occurred at the urging of the community hospital's board of trustees and had to be overseen, depending on local regulations, by either the state insurance commissioner or the state attorney general. That state official, if he or she approved the conversion, was expected to assign a formal dollar value to the hospital. The HMO then had to reimburse the community for that amount, usually by establishing a charitable foundation.

It is a procedure that might be acceptable in theory. In practice, all too often the hospital's board of trustees permitted, or even encouraged, a low valuation for their hospital. State insurance commissioners seemed congenitally unable to establish an accurate value for nonprofit hospitals. In doing those valuations, they considered only tangible property values. They ignored (and neither the hospital's board nor the HMO insisted on pointing out to them) the value of many of the assets owned by the hospital such as trademarks, reputation, name recognition, provider contracts, and subscriber lists. The commissioners didn't insist on going through a competitive bidding process or conducting a formal market valuation. In fact, only the hospital's value as a charity, and not as a business, was considered. For some reason insurance commissioners also seemed happy to do the negotiations behind closed doors, and with no public disclosure.

> Within a year Gekko has established a routine for acquiring community hospitals, and it works like this. First, the hospital's board of directors see fit (when necessary, induced by stock options or offers of directorships in FTP) to under-represent the value of their institution to the insurance commissioner. The insurance commissioner then approves the transfer to FTP at a low valuation. After the hospital becomes a hard asset of FTP, its true value is established by the market, as reflected in the price of FTP's stock. Almost invariably, that value is orders of magnitude greater than the value set by the insurance commissioner. So, without doing a thing to improve the quality of care or to reduce the cost of care, FTP's market value soars—and all at the expense of the public.
>
> It's a win-win. During Gekko's first two years at the helm of FTP, not only does the company's stock go through the roof, but also Gekko acquires key medical facilities in all the cities where FTP operates (now expanded to fifteen). He finds he is able to influence the healthcare markets in most of those cities and consequently control the behavior of even the most recalcitrant of physicians and benefits officers (who suddenly find they have to

deal with FTP whether they want to or not). The health insurance premiums, always optimally priced, are pouring in to FTP at a twenty-five percent annual rate of growth.

Minimizing the outward flow of cash

Having lots of health insurance premiums flowing in the front door is nice, but it will be of limited value to FTP if that money ends up flowing out the back door to buy healthcare for subscribers. Gekko has to minimize the cost to administer actual healthcare. He knows this will be a challenge; the reason HMOs have a mandate to run healthcare is that no other method of reducing costs has worked. But he is confident. The key element that was missing before has now been supplied—the profit motive. What a wonderful way to concentrate the mind! He is sure he can find ways to cut costs.

Furthermore, the healthcare crisis itself will be helpful to him, in that it gives him cover. The need to trim the cost of healthcare is an excuse to make cuts that might otherwise be unacceptable. And the mandate not to reduce the quality of care gives him an excuse to keep his premiums as high as he can. (If we cut our premiums, he says, quality will suffer.) Confident that he has a lot of latitude, Gekko develops strategies for minimizing his cost of doing business.

Cost-minimizing strategy number 1—economies of scale

FTP's large size has benefits in addition to increasing the inflow of dollars. It gives Gekko opportunities to capitalize on the economies of scale. He negotiates favorable purchasing agreements with all the major vendors. He works to reduce pharmacy costs by having the major pharmaceutical houses bid to have their drugs included on the limited FTP drug formulary (a list of drugs approved by FTP). And he streamlines the management of each of his new hospitals as they come on line, firing layers of old-fashioned administrators and replacing them with streamlined management teams made up of his own people, using standard FTP operating policies and procedures.

Cost-minimizing strategy number 2—avoiding unnecessary risk

A glance at the dynamics of the HMO industry is enough to convince Gekko that the biggest risk he faces is sick patients. They are extremely expensive these days. The sickest ten percent of the population account for over seventy percent of all healthcare spending, and one really sick subscriber can wipe out the potential profit from twenty, thirty, or even fifty healthy subscribers. Sick patients are to be avoided like the plague.

There are two obvious ways to avoid the sick. First, don't sign them up. Second, if you do have to sign them up, make it unpleasant for them to stay with you.

The system Gekko has inherited helps immensely. Because FTP's insurance products are only available through employers, only employed people can sign up for FTP. And employed people are, on average, far healthier than unemployed people. There are good reasons for this. In most of the cities where FTP operates, a substantial proportion of the unemployed do not have jobs precisely because of some chronic illness, disability, or addiction. And because employers are loath to employ the obviously ill, there's a screening process that takes place before anyone becomes eligible for FTP. You can't buy prescreening like that at any price, and Gekko's getting it for free.

Not all of Gekko's options in this regard are passive. Several of FTP's new hospitals run specialty centers that are counterproductive—two hospitals have congestive heart failure centers, and five have cancer centers. Why should he support clinical programs that go out of their way to attract patients with chronic (and therefore expensive) illnesses? Gekko orders his medical directors to figure out how to make these programs profitable within six months or shut them down.

FTP's new size gives Gekko some clout where it counts. When he learns that Congress is considering legislation that would require insurers to make health insurance available to people who are between jobs, he directs FTP's high-paid lobbyists to keep any such bill from having teeth.

Despite his best efforts, Gekko realizes, FTP will get its share of patients with chronic illnesses. He'll deal with these simply by allowing layers of obstacles to form between those patients and the care they need. Gekko realizes he doesn't have to ask anyone to create such barriers—they'll form naturally within any bureaucracy. What he needs to do is to let the system bog down in red tape for the ill while working hard to keep the system squeaky clean for healthy subscribers.

It won't be long before the chronically ill begin switching to other plans out of sheer frustration—preferably back to indemnity plans so their premium rates (and thus FTP's) will keep rising. Even better, the healthy (who are receiving benefits like free memberships to health clubs) won't know what the malcontents are complaining about—FTP seems pretty good to them. As a result, when FTP does its periodic consumer surveys, at least seventy to eighty percent of its subscribers will rate its service as good to excellent.

A survey in 2000 by the Kaiser Family Foundation and *Consumer Reports* showed that while sixty-four percent of Americans gave their health plans an A or B grade, the sickest twenty percent reported having major problems getting the care they need. The most common complaints were denials of care, difficulty getting in to see a doctor, and billing problems. "These results are not good news for consumers," said Peter Lee, president and CEO of the Pacific Group on Health. On the other hand, these results are "good news for consumers," said Susan Pisano, spokesperson for the American Association of Health Plans (AAHP). I guess it all depends on whether the consumers you're talking about are the ones who are healthy or the ones who are sick. It is not surprising that the AAHP identifies with the needs of the former.

Health plans seek to attract only healthy patients. The practice of attracting only healthy patients is called skimming or cherry-picking, and it's an art. HMOs make a lot of money by enrolling healthy young families and avoiding the old or chronically ill. In the mid-1990s, when indemnity insurance plans were still common, skimming actually made money for the HMOs twice—once by enrolling only patients who probably will not need medical care; and again by driving the sick into traditional indemnity plans, thus causing the premiums of those plans to rise and pulling up the HMO's premiums automatically.

Nowhere was the practice of skimming more profitable for HMOs than in the government's push in the mid-1990s to get Medicare patients into HMOs. A Medicare HMO during that era got paid a flat amount per enrollee. If it spent less in delivering healthcare than it took in, the HMO kept the difference. The amount Medicare HMOs received was set at ninety-five percent of what it costs to care for a Medicare patient on a fee-for-service basis, which at the time was about $5,000 per year.

HMOs were smart enough to figure out what Congress apparently couldn't—cherry-picking is especially profitable with Medicare patients. If HMOs could recruit from the healthiest seventy-five percent of Medicare patients (who use only nine percent of the Medicare health dollar), the sickest twenty-five percent of patients then would continue using fee-for-service plans, thus driving costs for those plans through the roof. The HMOs continued to receive ninety-five percent of those higher premiums.

HMOs had to work harder to cherry-pick Medicare patients (since employers didn't do the dirty work for them), but they were up to the task, and it was worth the effort. The public recruiting of Medicare patients at the time was telling. We saw HMOs advertising enrollment drives in affluent suburbs, or at country clubs, or on the third floor of a building without elevators. Medicare HMOs assiduously avoided the less affluent parts of town. They not only avoided recruiting patients in such locations, they (and non-Medicare HMOs for that matter) also avoided contracting with doctors whose offices were located within a couple of bus transfers of those areas. (This is an added benefit if you're trying to covertly ration healthcare; it punishes doctors who choose to work in economically deprived areas.)

The Medicare HMO scheme worked well (for the HMOs) until the late 1990s, when the government finally noticed that the for-profits were skimming all the healthy patients and leaving the sick ones for standard Medicare. They changed the rules to remedy this practice— and within three years virtually every for-profit HMO had abandoned the Medicare program.

If you can't cherry-pick the healthy patients any more, you can still try to frustrate the sick. The practice of discouraging the use of expensive services, and thus making healthcare particularly inconvenient for the ill, has been openly discussed as a legitimate technique among healthcare managers. A 1994 article in *Journal of Healthcare Marketing* is particularly interesting in this regard.* This article praises several useful techniques that HMOs have developed for discouraging the use of (or "demarketing") costly healthcare services:

> Decreasing accessibility to services ... can be accomplished by "managing" the information distributed to patients regarding services available and how to access them. For example, an organization might excessively promote less-costly preventive procedures ... and repress information about other elective and/or expensive services. In addition, providers can strategically locate and number specific services to make them easy (e.g., primary care) or difficult (e.g., specialists) to utilize. Furthermore, lag periods ... also serve as containment strategies. Lags may be affected by the need for referrals, limited number of contracted specialists, restricted or inconvenient appointment availability, and increased office-visit waiting periods.

* Borkowski NM. Demarketing of health services. *Journal of Healthcare Marketing* 1994;14:12.

We see once again that institutionalized waste and red tape are an essential part of covert rationing. While Gekko is willing to streamline the internal processes that affect the efficiency of FTP itself and is not against improving the convenience factor for healthy subscribers, he will, at best, let processes that affect services for sick patients bog down in bureaucratic inefficiencies and, at worst, actively establish road blocks to adequate services.

Cost minimizing strategy number 3—controlling the physicians' behavior

One night shortly after becoming CEO, Gekko has a nightmare. A doctor and a patient are sitting together in the privacy of the doctor's office, and the two of them are deciding how much of Gekko's money to spend. As they ponder their options, all they talk about is what the *patient* wants or needs. Then, the decision at last made, the doctor takes out his pen and with a few strokes bends the will of the vast medical–industrial complex—and mobilizes Gekko's money—to suit his patient's needs.

Gekko awakens in a sweat and considers his dream. He realizes that all you had to do was to multiply the one encounter he'd dreamed about by the 1.5 million similar encounters that take place every day, and you'd know why healthcare is so expensive. It frightens Gekko to think that this is how his money is being spent. But the fear motivates him powerfully, and focuses him on what he has to do to control his expenses.

He has to control the behavior of his physicians. There is no way he can allow them to carry on as if the patient is their only concern. When FTP physicians are counseling their patients, deciding how much of FTP's money to spend, they've got to consider something other than just the patient. They've got to consider the needs of FTP.

Gekko knows there are many, many ways to accomplish this. Some involve instilling loyalty in the physicians, others instilling fear. Some involve subtle intimidation, others heavy-handedness. Gekko can pull no punches on this one. This, he knows, is where the money is. He decides to use every means at his disposal to become an unseen presence in that office with the doctor and the patient. He's got to become the doctor's primary customer; keeping Gekko happy must become the doctor's number one concern.

Controlling the flow of patients

Physicians are nothing without their patients. So the first thing Gekko must do is wrest control of patients away from the doctors in each city. Purchasing key community hospitals is a major step toward this goal, but Gekko leaves nothing to chance.

So he mixes himself a martini, puts his feet up, and dictates a first draft of an eighteen-month plan, aimed at nothing short of bringing the physicians to heel:

THE FTP 18-MONTH PLAN

Phase 1 (Months 1–6): Open the gates. *Allow any willing licensed physician in the area to join FTP's physician panel. Actively and aggressively recruit all the largest and best known physician practices. Purchase a few key practices, if necessary, to break any physician resistance to joining FTP.*

Phase 2 (Months 7–12): Get control of the patients. *Armed with an impressive physician panel that promises not to limit the choice of any patient, aggressively market FTP to all large and moderate-sized businesses in the area. By the end of month 12, FTP should be offered to every employee of every company employing 250 or more in each area of operation. Undercut prices of every other insurer in the market, if necessary, to achieve this goal. On Day 1 of month 13, FTP should control at least 30 percent of all insured patients in key medical practices.*

Phase 3 (Months 13–18): Collect the data, begin making the cuts. *Track how much of FTP's money is being spent by every FTP physician. Then publicly drop from the FTP panel several prominent and highly visible physicians who are deemed to be spending too much on patient care.*

Note: The letter sent to the dropped physicians should not give a cause for termination. It should simply thank them for their services and say those services will no longer be required.

Note: This step will be most effective if those physicians dropped from the panel are not only well known to their colleagues but also lose a substantial proportion of their long-time patients as a result of their being dropped.

It's a good plan. It is designed to rapidly and efficiently assume control of the physicians' means of livelihood—their patients— and in practice Gekko is pleased to find that it most often accomplishes this goal before the doctors even realize what is going on. The plan is vital to the mission of FTP, and it works well (although in three cities it takes up to twenty-four months to complete).

Once the plan has achieved its goals, Gekko institutes Phase 4. Phase 4 lasts forever.

Phase 4 (Month 19 and beyond): Turn the screws. *Let the FTP physicians know what is expected of them.*

A) Revise the terms of their contracts with FTP. New contracts will lay out terms of capitation and associated incentives and disincentive, and will add nondisclosure language.

B) Begin a quarterly review of each practice, showing physicians in detail where they are spending dollars and comparing their expenditures both to target values and to the expenditures of their peers.

C) Continuously reinforce who is in charge. Periodic issuance of without-cause termination notices to selected physicians will be important. Handing out occasional but highly visible performance awards will also be helpful in this regard.

In other words, now that Gekko owns the physicians, it's time to let them know what their new boss wants.

Controlling the flow of dollars

Before Phase 4 of his plan begins, Gekko continues paying his physicians on a discounted fee-for-service basis (they get paid for every service they provide, at a somewhat lower fee schedule than for Medicare). But for any HMO during the 1990s, the pot of gold at the end of the rainbow is capitation. And Gekko institutes capitation with great relish during Phase 4.

Under his capitation plan, FTP primary care physicians (PCPs) get paid a fixed amount per month for every FTP patient they follow in their practice. No matter how much or how little medical care they provide for that patient, the PCPs get paid only the capitated amount. But Gekko doesn't actually pay them the full capitated rate up front—they get only ninety percent. He keeps the last ten percent as a "withhold," which he fashions as an additional incentive.

At the end of the year, if FTP meets its financial goals and the PCP meets certain performance requirements, Gekko distributes the last ten percent. If not, FTP keeps the money. It is possible, of course (if FTP's financial goals are exceeded and the physician's performance is rated excellent), for the PCP to receive a bonus in addition to the ten percent withhold. And Gekko sees to it that at least a few PCPs get such a bonus each year, just to let his physicians know that such a thing is within the realm of possibility. Capitation fee schedules are renegotiated each year with each PCP, based on how well the PCP has done in the previous year.

It's a shame Gekko's number crunchers can't yet figure out a way to capitate specialists as well, but so far it's too complicated. The accountants cannot guarantee him that he'd make money capitating specialists. Some day they'll have sufficient data to pull it off, but for now he continues paying his specialists on a modified fee-for-service basis. Gekko knows he needs alternative measures to control the behavior of the specialists.

The performance measures that determine whether a PCP does or does not get the ten percent withhold at the end of the year are a vital part of Gekko's plan. There are a few token quality performance measures that monitor whether the doctors are aggressively treating hypertension and screening for high cholesterol and the like. But Gekko wants to make sure his doctors know what he really means by performance, so he doesn't try to disguise the fact that the bulk of FTP's performance measures have to do with fiscal performance.

Each quarter, a dark-suited FTP representative (a "practice consultant") visits each PCP with a performance report. The performance report accounts for every dollar that FTP has had to spend during the past quarter on patients enrolled in the PCP's practice.

"Your patients cost us an average of $439 apiece during the past quarter, Dr. Smith," the practice consultant might say. "That compares unfavorably with the mean of $348 achieved by your peer PCPs, and even less favorably with the target of $294 that would be required for you to receive your portion of the year-end withhold. Now, Dr. Smith, let's examine this report in more detail to see if we can figure out where all that money is going."

So Dr. Smith and the helpful practice consultant look things over. They notice that Dr. Smith referred ten patients to cardiology practices during the past quarter. The Valley View Cardiology practice ended up spending an average of $6,247 on the five patients Smith sent them, but the Cormatic cardiologists only spent $4,593 taking care of the other five. They both agree that substantial savings could have been realized by referring more patients to Cormatic, and fewer to Valley View.

"Of course," the practice consultant says, "we would never tell you how to practice medicine."

"Of course," Dr. Smith replies.

It is a thing of beauty. Look what Gekko has accomplished here. By rapidly gaining control of physicians' means of livelihood (access to patients), he is able to dictate the terms of their surrender.

Those terms put fiscal pressure on doctors at several levels.

Because they are paid a capitated rate, there is financial pressure on the PCPs to keep patients out of their offices. Office overhead is often figured on an hourly basis, so the more time a patient spends in the office (that is, the more office overhead that patient consumes) the less profit (or the more loss) the physician realizes on that patient. Under many capitation rate schedules, more than two office visits per patient per year will result in a net loss for the PCP. This is why many doctors now take great pains to head off office visits by requiring patients to go through a screening process before letting them in the door.

HMOs themselves sometimes pitch in to discourage patients from visiting doctors' offices, humanely relieving their doctors of some of the burden. In 2002 Kaiser Permanente was accused by a disgruntled nurses' union of paying bonuses to clerks in three northern California call centers for limiting the medical services provided to patients who called in with medical problems. They charged that Kaiser had set up a quota system that paid these minimally trained clerks bonuses of two to four percent of their salaries in return for not making doctors' appointments, for not transferring calls to a registered nurse for further evaluation, and for keeping the average call time under four minutes. When the story made the news, Kaiser admitted the story was true but said that now they had stopped (leaving one to wonder whether, instead of paying bonuses to the clerks to get them to do their jobs well, the company might have reverted to more traditional and less humane incentives such as threats, terminations, and arbitrary scheduling practices).

HMOs do not directly control patients' visits to medical specialists—patients are referred to specialists by their PCPs. So to control expenditures by specialists, the pressure needs to be applied to the PCP. This is done by holding the PCP personally accountable for whatever money the specialist ends up spending on a referred patient. These specialist-ordered expenditures will affect the PCP's end-of-year bonus, and will affect the next year's capitation rates.

Because doctors really do want to take good care of their patients, most PCPs will refer when they think it's necessary. But to whom do they refer? In the old days, they referred to the specialists they thought gave the best care, or who were the most congenial, or who invited them to the best golf outings, or who were their brothers-in-law. The new fiscal incentives are so powerful that they tend to override any of these considerations.

> FTP   For the Patient (imaginary HMO)
> HMO   health maintenance organization
> PCP   primary care physician

This is how HMOs control specialists indirectly: A cardiologist whose referrals have fallen drastically is all ears when the friendly FTP practice consultant shows up in her office with facts and figures. Learning that she is spending a lot more money than her peers in providing patient care (and that her referring PCPs also have been provided with the same data), leaves her with two choices. Either cut out some of the services she is providing or go out of business.

Gekko's operational plan has at least one other major benefit. Visualize what happens, if you will, when a patient with a chronic illness shows up for the first time in the office of a PCP. Most likely the PCP immediately has visions of hundred-dollar bills flying out the window. He gets paid no more for delivering care to that sick patient (who may require office visits every month) than he does for a healthy eighteen-year-old he will not see at all. And, odds are he'll end up having to refer the patient to at least a couple of specialists during the course of the year. The PCP has already seen his income fall by more than ten percent each of the last two years and has had to lay off office personnel to boot. He can't afford to absorb any more cuts.

So, is he happy to see that patient? Or is he frustrated and maybe even angry—at the patient, at the system, and at himself? It would only be human nature to begin sending the patient subtle messages that indicate she's not really welcome. During office visits the physician is more likely to seem disinterested, distracted, or rushed—off-putting. He may be a little less accommodating when she needs to schedule an appointment; he may drag his feet when she sends him a stack of disability applications to fill out. He may be a little slower than necessary to return her calls. And after a while, the patient is likely to get the message and switch PCPs or, better yet, switch health plans altogether.

By appropriately incenting his physicians, Gekko has thus established an effective adjunct to his cherry-picking program. His physicians want just as badly as he does to avoid the sick; and by their words, actions, and deeds they are able to directly discourage the more expensive patients from staying with FTP.

Making the destruction of the doctor–patient relationship legally binding

Gekko is happy with the results of his eighteen-month plan, but he wants to reinforce and formalize the message he has successfully delivered to FTP's physicians. He wishes to make that message legally binding. When it is time for him to rework his physician contracts, Gekko asks his attorneys to come up with language that does just that, and they are happy to accommodate him:

"The physician agrees not to take any action or make any communication with patients or patients' families, potential patients or potential patients' families, employers, unions, the media, or the public that would tend to undermine, disparage, or otherwise criticize FTP or FTP's healthcare coverage. The physician further agrees to keep all proprietary information such as payment rates, reimbursement procedures, utilization-review procedures, etc., strictly confidential."

Gekko likes the language. It is plain and straightforward. His physicians, completely without choice, sign the new contracts with nary a peep of complaint. Gekko has made an assertion to his doctors. He has said, "You work for me, and me alone. You're all mine." His doctors, by their legally affixed signatures, have acknowledged that assertion.

Gekko has sought a place at the table with FTP doctors and their patients, and now he has it. In fact, he is at the head of the table.

What Gekko has just done is to add a gag clause to his physician contracts. The final insult to a doctor's professional integrity, a gag clause prohibits the doctor from disclosing certain types of information to his or her patients. The forbidden information is likely to be material to the patient's ability to accurately assess the doctor's medical advice, and therefore the lack of that information may affect the patient's health. So gag clauses are a threat to patients.

What the gag clause represents—by the fact that HMOs used them with impunity and physicians signed them with little more than a whimper—is a formal death certificate for the physician–patient relationship. It officially and legally certifies that the doctor's first loyalty is to the integrity and reputation of the HMO, which supersedes any loyalty or duty that might exist toward the patient.

Gag clauses attracted a fair amount of criticism in the late 1990s, from the standpoint that it's not nice to gag physicians from telling their patients what they need to know. Little has been said about the implications of HMOs having had the audacity to include gag clauses in physician contracts in the first place or of physicians quietly and timidly signing them by the tens of thousands.

In response to the concerns over gag clauses, the Government Accountability Office (GAO) more recently conducted a study to assess their continued prevalence in HMO contracts. The report concluded that gag clauses are no longer a problem, and for the most part they don't exist any more.

The reason gag clauses don't exist is that the HMOs, feeling the heat, have converted them to business clauses. Business clauses require the signer (usually an employee) to agree not to disparage the business, not to encourage clients to use some other business instead, and not to break confidentiality with the business. In other words, business clauses are gag clauses somewhat reworded and then relabeled.

In this manner, HMOs have asserted that, since they are a business, they have a right to the same protections as any other business. And if assertion of those business rights require the business's contractors (doctors) to forego previous arrangements and understandings (the doctor–patient relationship), well, that's business. The GAO, apparently, was swayed by this argument.

Various proposed Patients' Bills of Rights require striking gag clauses from HMO–physician contracts. Presumably (now that they are just business clauses), that has already been accomplished. But even if all such clauses—whatever they are called—are struck from every contract today, the damage has been done.

For when HMOs asked physicians for a declaration of loyalty that superseded all other loyalties, physicians gave it. Removing gag clauses from contracts at this point doesn't change the fact that, when asked, physicians signed. Once a dog learns to heel, you can get rid of the leash—the dog still heels just fine. The HMOs have more than made their point.

Just a second. What about outcomes? What about quality?

Well, what about them? Nobody in our FTP vignette has any incentive to know about outcomes—except as they may be incidentally useful as a marketing tool.

Gekko doesn't have any reason to care about clinical outcomes. His outcome is measured by his profit. So as long as he's making money, his outcome is good—and data on clinical outcomes would only serve to threaten what is now a nice, clean picture. Unless pushed, he sees no reason to invest his resources in collecting such data.

What about Dr. Smith—the PCP who has to decide whether to refer his patients with heart problems to cardiologists in the more expensive Valley View group or those in the less expensive Cormatic Group? Wouldn't he want to know which group has the better clinical results? Certainly he would, on a professional level. But subconsciously, he realizes that if he had that data, it might give him the wrong answer—there's at least a good chance that the more expensive group might turn out to achieve better results. That would certainly complicate his referral decisions.

And what about the cardiologists of the thrifty Cormatic Group? Do they really want outcomes data? Well, why should they? They're already getting the referrals.

Doctors in the profligate Valley View Group are the only ones who have a good reason to care about clinical outcomes; if they turn out to have more favorable outcomes, it might help to exonerate their expensive ways. But even if they take the time and expense to examine the outcomes they achieve in their own practices, there is no way for them to get the comparative data from competitive groups.

So, while there is plenty of talk about outcomes in the Gekkonian HMO world, when you analyze the mechanics, it is difficult to find anyone slogging away in the trenches who really wants to know about them.

But surely somebody wants to know about quality. What about the patients? What about the employers who are paying the bills?

Gekko knows about patients. When patients are faced with a choice between an HMO that's "free" or an indemnity plan that might cost them an extra fifty or hundred dollars a month, he knows they're going to pick the HMO. And while they're picking it, they want to feel good about it. They deeply, sincerely, and desperately want to hear that they're making a good choice. They want to hear what a high-quality HMO they're being forced to join. And that's where quality and marketing come together. To Gekko, quality *is* marketing.

This is why HMOs over the past few years have gotten away from advertising (and implying ready access to) their fancy, state-of-the-art, high-tech services. Instead, they've gone all fluffy, emphasizing warmth, concern, and caring, through filtered lenses and soft music. When you join our HMO, it's like joining a family. What a good choice you've made.

Okay, you might reply, but what about employers? Don't they want to offer high-quality healthcare to their employees? Well, sort of. What most of them really want is to offer adequate healthcare without losing their shirts on it.

My own eyes were opened on this issue several years ago when I attended a retreat, sponsored by my hospital, that featured a panel discussion by a group of prominent local employers. When asked how they go about assuring themselves that the health coverage they buy for their employees provides high-quality care, the captains of industry responded thusly: "We make widgets, we don't assess healthcare quality. We don't know how, and we don't want to know how. So we've got to be practical about it. To us, quality means quiet. As long as we don't hear more than the average number of complaints from our employees, the health coverage we provide is, by definition, good enough."

Men and women like Gekko long ago figured out what their paying customers (the businesses that purchase health insurance for their employees) want. And because of what his customers want, Gekko can define quality as keeping the volume of complaints down to an acceptable level and keeping FTP out of the newspaper.

Efforts are being made on several fronts to measure quality in healthcare, and some of these efforts are having an impact. But these efforts are not originating with Gekkonian-style HMOs, or even from healthcare providers.

FTP—twelve years later

The end game is near for Gekko, and none too soon, because running FTP for twelve years has aged him. Continuing to grow his company throughout this time has been a real challenge. The preponderance of FTP's growth once came from expansion into new cities and especially from the acquisition of public assets. But it's long since become impossible to find new areas in which to expand, and worthwhile community hospitals ripe for takeover are no longer growing on trees.

For the last five years, Gekko has been able to continue FTP's growth cycle by acquiring smaller HMOs every eighteen months or so, and in doing so he eventually developed a national presence for FTP. He's even become a regular on CNBC. But even that means of growth is now drying up. Smaller HMOs that would be suitable acquisition targets have become hard to find.

The time has finally arrived when Gekko has to try growing FTP's revenues solely by providing healthcare to patients. This has turned out to be harder than Gekko ever thought it would be. Despite the fact that he continues to turn up the heat on his physicians—cutting their reimbursement schedule every year and raising the bar for getting their end-of year payouts—FTP's revenue is stagnant and even shows signs of dropping.

HMOs have long since penetrated the healthcare market so thoroughly that, in most of FTP's cities, the indemnity insurance plans are no longer players. This means FTP isn't competing against indemnity plans anymore; instead it's competing against other HMOs. It's hard for Gekko to keep his premiums as high as he'd like. In a couple of cities, FTP has gotten into some nasty bidding wars.

And now that the large majority of Americans are already enrolled in HMOs, cherry-picking the healthy enrollees has become virtually impossible. Even making the chronically ill feel unwelcome is no longer effective, since most sick people have finally realized that one HMO is pretty much like another. There's no point in their changing health plans any more.

Patients are becoming more vocal, as are Congress and the state legislatures, about HMOs conducting themselves dishonorably. Gekko fears that one or more of the various proposals on a Patients' Bill of Rights may end up taking away even more of his prerogatives for making money.

Then there are the rumblings Gekko is hearing in high places about how for-profit healthcare is robbing society of its precious healthcare premiums. It may still be a way off, but Gekko now thinks that someday for-profits will be outlawed and the government will take over the whole shebang. That wouldn't be fair, but Gekko's a realist. He doesn't insist on providing fairness, nor does he insist on receiving it. This is business, after all.

His run as CEO of FTP has already lasted far longer than he had ever thought it would. He has set himself up for a platinum parachute when the time comes for him to retire, but even now he is imagining grander exit strategies. For instance, perhaps he will be able to engineer an acquisition of FTP by one of the two or three even larger HMOs. Gekko would do quite well under such a scenario. If he's really thinking expansively, he can see himself playing a key role in negotiating the final buyout of FTP and all the other remaining for-profit HMOs by an even more massive and even more affluent entity—that is, by the feds.

HMOs—the end of the line?

No, not really. But I personally wouldn't buy any stock in FTP. I believe HMOs will be around for a long time. But I also believe that the heyday of the for-profit, Gekkonian-style HMO is coming to an end.

Considering the demographic facts of life outlined in Chapter 2, it is inevitable that society will find it unconscionable for these organizations to continue siphoning off large proportions of the healthcare dollar for profit—especially when it is debatable whether they are contributing anything substantial to the actual delivery of healthcare. Sooner or later, we will become indignant about the for-profits.

My guess is that the for-profit HMOs will fade from the scene of their own accord, before the rest of us get exercised enough to do the job ourselves. Gekko has shown us why.

There is a natural life cycle to for-profit HMOs. In their early years, their meteoric rise was attributable not to their efficient management of healthcare but instead to their rapid growth and subsequent consolidation and to the acquisition and privatization of public assets. As the opportunities for rapid growth dry up, as the opportunities to select the most desirable enrollees fades, and as public officials, government agencies, and the general public become wise to their ways, Gekkonian HMOs are finding their traditional methods for making money no longer feasible.

As is the case for FTP, few for-profit HMOs have ever done well financially by managing the healthcare of their subscribers. My prediction is that they will ultimately find it so difficult to make a profit in this way—at least enough profit to keep their shareholders happy— that they'll eventually get out of managed care on their own.

This is especially likely when you consider that the Wonkonians have never gone away—they're still there, still as active as they can be while waiting for their chance to assume their rightful, regulatory control of the healthcare system. Imagine the for-profits—seeing that their days are numbered—whispering in just the right places that, for the right price, they would be willing to consider selling their business to the government. It wouldn't be the first time the government assumed control of a formerly powerful industry, nor would it be the first time the owners of that fading industry would get one final windfall for their troubles. Remember the railroads?

If I'm right, we the taxpayers will get one last chance to contribute to the welfare of Gekko and his brethren. If so, perhaps we should consider it a reasonable price to pay for bringing the era of the for-profit Gekkonian HMOs to a close.

The meaning of the Gekkonian era

The demise I've just predicted for the Gekkonians may be a bit premature, but let's still conduct a postmortem.

The positives—incremental efficiencies

On the positive side, the Gekkonians have focused the attention of everyone in the healthcare system on the issue of costs. Today, in any healthcare organization, no purchase of any sizeable item is made without first considering how much the item is needed, calculating the full cost of ownership, and defining who will pay for the expanded services made possible by the new item. This is a radical departure from just a few years ago, when hospitals often purchased high-cost equipment of marginal value just to keep up with their rivals across town.

Similarly, the fiscal pressures brought to bear on doctors and hospitals by the Gekkonians have resulted in many true improvements in efficiency. This is because when the providers are squeezed by the payers, not all the cutbacks they make are in useful or worthwhile services. A lot of wasteful endeavors are cut too. When providers are forced to cut back, they try to eliminate the inefficiencies first.

So the Gekkonians have driven our healthcare system to become leaner, meaner, and more in fighting trim than it was before. We may have made the same changes eventually even without the Gekkonians, but it probably would have taken longer.

The negatives—facilitating covert rationing

On the negative side, the Gekkonians have expanded our capacity for covertly rationing healthcare.

HMOs are *supposed* to ration

That HMOs ration healthcare is beyond question. Indeed, in 2000, the U.S. Supreme Court ruled that HMOs are *supposed* to ration healthcare.

The case in point was *Pegram et al v. Herdrich*, in which the Court heard the complaint of a Ms. Herdrich, whose appendix ruptured after her HMO doctor—who was under financial incentives to spend less money—delayed the diagnostic tests she clearly needed. Justice Souter wrote the Court's unanimous opinion in favor of the HMO, declaring that rationing healthcare was the very point of HMOs, and that Congress had a twenty-seven-year history of passing legislation encouraging HMOs to do just that. If Herdrich (or anybody else) doesn't like that fact, Souter said, they need to petition Congress, not the federal courts.

Souter invoked the GUTH in all but name in writing this opinion. He especially stressed what we've called the First Corollary: When HMOs can take in only a fixed amount of money from premiums, thus creating a centralized pool of funds, but are at risk for having to spend unlimited amounts of money on their subscribers' healthcare, there must be a system of rationing in place. It's just math.

Justice Souter further implied that patients themselves have not been entirely innocent casualties of secret rationing by HMOs. Patients who abandoned their more expensive fee-for-service insurance for cheaper HMOs should have known what they were getting into and should not think of themselves as blameless victims. Ms. Herdrich learned this the hard way. As healthcare expert David Mechanic has said,

> Enrollment in an HMO is really an agreement between the enrollee and the plan to accept a situation of "constructive rationing." ... For a lower premium, more comprehensive benefits, or both, the consumer implicitly agrees to accept the plan's judgment as to what services are necessary.*

* Mechanic D. Trust and informed consent to rationing. The Milbank Quarterly. 1994;72:217.

Patients may not consciously realize that they've made this agreement, but the healthcare economists, academics, HMO directors—and the Supreme Court—realize it. Accordingly, patients and their health have become fair game.

Faced with the mathematically necessary, congressionally legislated, Supreme Court sanctioned, patient-acquiesced-to, but socially unacceptable mandate to ration healthcare, what is Gekko to do? He's got to ration covertly.

Whether or not Gekko really understood (or cared) that he was advancing the cause of covert rationing is irrelevant. Whatever he did or didn't think about it, that's clearly what he was doing. His most blatant covert rationing endeavors were the extensive efforts to exclude expensive patients from the healthcare system. More subtle were the pains he took to pry all those not-for-profit healthcare institutions out of their fundamentally charitable charters and launch them into the wild, wooly world of for-profit healthcare. But the most far reaching was his campaign to destroy the doctor–patient relationship.

Destroying the doctor–patient relationship

Destroying that relationship was a requirement for Gekkonian managed care, and the Gekkonians accomplished it with devastating effect. Their efforts have left the medical profession in disarray and physicians' formerly clear-cut ethical mandates in tatters. As a result, the behavior of individual doctors and of their professional organizations as they try desperately to reassert old values or establish new ones—or simply explain what the heck they are doing—have been bizarre. Such behavior would be comical if the implications were not so profound.

Item 1. In a survey conducted by the American Medical Association's Institute for Ethics and published in the April 12, 2000, issue of the *Journal of the American Medical Association*, thirty-nine percent of American doctors admitted that they sometimes or very often manipulated reports to their patients' health plans so their patients might gain coverage for needed medical care. These manipulations included exaggerating the severity of the patients' condition, changing the billing diagnosis, or reporting symptoms the patient did not have. And seventy-two percent admitted using one of these tactics at least once in the past year. More than a quarter said that gaming the system was necessary in order to provide high quality care to their patients, and fifteen percent asserted that it was ethical.

This survey elicited a firestorm of criticism against the cheating doctors. Ethicists called for doctors to stop applying "insular" ethical norms and to begin using the norms that professional ethicists have long established against cheating health plans. Similarly, the AMA and the American College of Physicians have published strongly worded statements opposing the manipulation of reimbursement rules. And the federal government has made such "misstatements" to health plans a federal crime, punishable by huge fines, jail terms, and loss of license.

Item 2. Another survey, published in the July/August, 2003, issue of *Health Affairs*, reported that nearly one-third of American doctors admit that they routinely withhold from their patients pertinent information about optimal medical treatments, because they suspect the patients' health plans won't cover those treatments. The always amazing Susan Pisano, spokesperson of the AAHP (the group representing the very health plans that are pulling out all the stops to make sure that doctors do exactly what this study confirms they are doing), told the *AMA News* at the time that AAHP officials "actually find it difficult to believe that that's going on." Meanwhile, the authors of the study, pointing out that gag clauses no longer exist, could only conclude (with seeming surprise) that doctors are "rationing by omission" on their own volition.

These two surveys reveal some of the confusion and frustration being felt by doctors as a result of HMO rules, and the guidance they're getting from their professional organizations as to what to do about those rules. How are they to square those rules and that guidance with their obligation to always do what's best for their patients? What's a doctor to do, for instance, when a patient needs a treatment but they're pretty sure the health plan won't pay for it? There are only three choices:

+ Tell the health plan whatever you must in order to get the needed treatment for the patient.
+ Don't tell the patient about the treatment since they can't get it anyway.
+ Tell the patient about the treatment they need, and then tell them they can't have it.

The most straightforward thing for doctors is to choose Door Number 3—just tell the truth. After all, a patient has a right to know what medical treatment he needs, whether or not he's allowed to have it. Informing a patient that the health plan won't pay for the needed treatment gives him useful information—it lets him know that his health plan is not adequate to his needs and gives him an opportunity to respond appropriately to that information. For instance, a patient might appeal to the health plan directly, seek intervention by his local Congressperson, or ask his employer (who is the HMO's true customer), to intervene on his behalf. He can even raise the funds to pay for the therapy himself.

What patients actually do when doctors choose Door Number 3, however, is to beg, demand, threaten, implore, and plead for the doctor to do something to fix things, since after all, it is the doctor who started the problem in the first place by insisting that this forbidden therapy is the only one that will do. So, the moment doctors choose Door 3, they are placed under incredible pressure to go back and choose again—Door Number 1, their patients are communicating to them, is actually the correct choice. This reason, plus wanting to avoid all the anguish and drama that follows telling the truth, leads doctors who are inclined to lie to health plans (and thus risk angering the entities that determine their ability to make a living, not to mention committing a federal crime), to choose Door Number 1 in the first place. If doctors are not inclined to risk their livelihoods and freedom by deceiving health plans, they will probably simply default to Door Number 2—rationing by omission.

The above two items reflect the proportion of doctors willing to admit which group they routinely lie to—health plans or patients. Most of the other doctors, one suspects, would just rather not say.

> **Item 3.** In 2000, the AMA filed an amicus brief with the Illinois Supreme Court on behalf of a Dr. Portes, asserting that doctors have no duty to inform their patients when HMOs have given them financial incentives to withhold medical care. Apparently a patient of Dr. Portes died of a heart attack shortly after the doctor allegedly refused to refer him to a cardiologist. As it turned out, the patient's health plan apparently had agreed to pay the doctor's medical group sixty percent of any funds not used on referrals to specialists. A lower court in Illinois had found that Portes had a duty to disclose this financial relationship to patients, since it might clearly impact their interpretation of his medical recommendations, and Portes appealed. In this appeal, the AMA sided with the doctor.
>
> The AMA said in its amicus brief that the obligation imposed on doctors by the lower court amounted to an "insurmountable burden," since it was hard for doctors to keep track of all the

sundry ways that HMOs might induce them to behave in this way or that way, and besides, the need to disclose would impinge on the doctor's valuable time with the patient and therefore disrupt the doctor–patient relationship. Interestingly, the AMA's own Council on Ethical and Judicial Affairs (CEJA) had previously written that, "physicians must assure disclosure of any financial inducements that may tend to limit the diagnostic and therapeutic alternatives that are offered to patients . . . ." In explaining why its amicus brief differed from the opinion of its own Ethics Council, the AMA explained that its CEJA standard was just an ethical one and not a legal one.

So what we have here is:
1. An HMO induces doctors to withhold medical care
2. A doctor acts on that inducement
3. As a result, predictable harm comes to a patient
4. After which, the doctor and the AMA whine that he shouldn't have to inform patients of his financial incentives because
5. To do so would harm the doctor–patient relationship
This is all just too precious for words.

Commonly used covert rationing techniques have relegated even the most straightforward of the medical profession's ethical precepts to the status of a "nice-to-have," instead of a standard to be maintained, embraced, and fought over when threatened. While various ethical panels may still voice the proper sentiments, in the real world those sentiments are the first to go.

Item 4. The AMA recently conducted yet another study documenting that the medical insurance industry has become overly dominant within the healthcare system, leaving "doctors and patients . . . at a severe disadvantage." The AMA's solution, of course, is to renew its lobbying efforts to get Congress to legalize a doctors' union, so physicians can engage in collective bargaining with HMOs, the better to advocate for their patients. A union is the only way doctors are likely to gain enough power to help their patients, the AMA maintains.

As a former card carrying member of the United Steelworkers of America, I well understand how important unions can be for wage earners who must deal with an all-powerful employer. But unions can be effective only to the extent that they demand unquestioning loyalty to the union. It's the only way the union can guarantee the solidarity it needs when it engages management in collective bargaining. Only union solidarity can render their one and only weapon—the strike—credible as a threat, and that solidarity must be maintained at all costs, by violence if necessary.

This, of course, is a problem when we talk about unionizing the professions. Professionals by definition have a primary obligation to their "customers," be they clients, students, or patients, and that obligation is supposed to supersede any other. Professionals cannot be primarily obligated to their clients and at the same time primarily obligated to their union. For a doctors' union ever to be a threat to an HMO, that union must be inviolate in the minds of its physician members, who must be willing to do harm to patients, if necessary, through a work stoppage or slowdown, if that's what it takes to bring the HMO to heel. For the AMA to lobby for such a thing, however reluctantly, is a further illustration of how damaged the doctor–patient relationship has become.

So what's happened here? What's happened is that both patients and doctors have been marginalized within our healthcare system. The individual doctor and individual patient, together, no longer make up the nuclear unit of healthcare. Doctors and patients have been separated from one another and reduced to ciphers, to mere commodities in the healthcare marketplace.

When a commodities trader is dealing in pork bellies, he's only concerned about buying and selling, thus maximizing his profit on large quantities of pork bellies. Concern for the careful handling of the individual pig never crosses his mind.

If it becomes too difficult to follow ethical precepts, just change them

The physician's change in focus from the individual to the group is more than just tacit. Until recently, professional codes of ethics still held the physician's primary responsibility to be toward the individual patient. But in the late 1990s, after a few years of being exposed to Gekkonian

HMOs, many healthcare experts and even ethicists began to propose explicitly that this ideal be changed. A 1998 article in the *Annals of Internal Medicine* had this to say about the physician's traditional role:

> It is untenable for the medical profession to continue asserting an idealistic ethic that is contradicted so openly in clinical practice. ... We propose that devotion to the best medical interests of each individual patient be replaced with an ethic of devotion to the best medical interests of the group [of patients] for which the physician is personally responsible.*†

After kicking this sort of idea around for a few years, three prestigious medical societies finally published a new definition of medical professionalism.‡ This new statement of a physician's ethical obligations added to the time-honored principles of (a) primacy of the welfare of the individual patient; and (b) patient autonomy—the two precepts that required doctors to always make their patients' needs their primary concern—a third precept: (c) social justice. Under social justice, doctors are now exhorted to work for the "fair distribution of healthcare resources," based on "wise and cost-effective management of limited resources."

There's nothing wrong with working for social justice, of course. Social justice is important. Even doctors should care about it. But when they are seeing a patient who has come to them for help, that patient—and not social justice—should be their primary concern. They should not cheat or lie for that patient, not even to rapacious Gekkonian insurance companies. But within the rules of engagement (rules the patient has signed up for) they should see that the patient gets whatever medical services are medically indicated. Doctors should not be placed in the position of having to "fairly distribute limited healthcare resources"; of having to decide which patients are worthy of being offered available services and which are not; of having to weigh the needs of society against the needs of their individual patient and decide, for each patient, which is to predominate; of having to ration at the bedside. But this is precisely

* Hall MA, Berenson RA. Ethical practice in managed care: a dose of realism. *Annals of Internal Medicine.* 1998;128:395

† That is, the doctor should ration at the bedside to attempt to optimize the outcome for the population of patients in the physician's practice. Instead of competing against society for rationed medical services, Hall and Berenson would have patients compete only against the other patients in their doctor's practice. This suggestion was not adopted by the medical societies—a shame, because if it had been, doctors would receive a lot more baked goods and hockey tickets from their patients than they do today.

‡ Project of the ABIM Foundation, ACP-ASIM Foundation, and the European Federation of Internal Medicine. Medical Professionalism in the New Millenium: A Physician Charter. *Annals of Internal Medicine* 2002;136(3):243..

what the new professional ethical standards provide for. For the first time, doctors have been given explicit ethical cover for covertly rationing healthcare.

This change in ethical standards would not be necessary if we conducted healthcare rationing under a system of open, society-approved rules, where everybody knew where they stood. Under such a system doctors could still advocate entirely for the individual patient, doing whatever they could for that patient under society's explicit rules for rationing, much like a lawyer, pulling out all the legal stops for a client.

This new "social justice" precept is only needed to provide comfort to doctors who have to ration covertly and who might be bothered by this clear violation of their traditional duties to individual patients. "Sure I'm violating precept a," they can now tell themselves, "but I've got to do that to abide by precept c." If doctors can avoid too much introspection and self-analysis—not a problem for many of us—this new precept may take away some sense of guilt. But as long as doctors are withholding care from patients who need it, without telling them and perhaps without telling themselves, no new revision of ethical principles can rescue them.*

* Social justice, while not one that can be managed from the bedside, is nonetheless an important ethical precept. The appropriate way to apply the precept of social justice will be discussed in Chapter 9.

The Gekkonian legacy

When (if) Gekkonians finally withdraw from the field, they will leave doctors, patients, and our healthcare system very different from the way they found them. They will leave us more cost-aware and somewhat more efficient. But they also will leave us much readier to sacrifice the individual for the sake of the group. And, with our principles thus subtly softened (or flagrantly redefined) by Gekkonians, the inexorable escalation in healthcare costs will lead us to far more blatant violations of individual rights and individual welfare than any we've seen to date.

5

Covert Rationing and the Regulators

W E HAVE SEEN GEKKONIANS in action; and we have looked at how Gekkonian-style health plans have corrupted the ethical standards of the medical profession and coerced doctors to move away from doing what's best for their patients and toward keeping the health plans happy. By now we're feeling sympathetic toward the Wonkonian notion that our healthcare problems would best be resolved not by free market economics but by better federal regulations or by a government takeover of healthcare.

Wonkonians have not been sitting idly by, wringing their hands in despair and wishing things had turned out differently. This past decade or so has been busy and often fruitful for them; they have been setting up laws, regulations, processes, and bureaucratic structures that will enable them to hit the ground running when their time comes again. And it is coming.

But when their time does come, Wonkonians threaten to do at least as much damage to our healthcare system, to the doctor–patient relationship, and to individual autonomy as Gekkonians. We have seen how much harm Gekkonians were able to do in a short time by seizing control of the doctor's ability to make a living. Wonkonians have that same weapon and more. Not only do Wonkonians have direct control over the doctor's professional viability but they can also threaten physicians with financial ruin and even imprisonment. Wonkonians have the potential of directing the physician's behavior in ways Gekkonians can only fantasize about. We should be asking ourselves, as we contemplate the day when Wonkonians emerge from the shadows and resume

their place as the *ultimate* central authority in the healthcare system,
How will they use that power?

Wonkonians have not been shy about flexing the new regulatory
muscles they have pumped up in recent years, and in the process they
have given us some clues as to how they might behave once they're
fully back in control. These clues should be chilling not only to doctors but also to patients. They are most apparent in how Wonkonians
have handled their chief regulatory initiative over the past decade—an
initiative for which we want to cheer them on—rooting out fraud from
the healthcare system.

The antifraud imperative

In his 1994 State of the Union Address, President Clinton, still fighting for passage of his Health Security Act, declared that our healthcare system "is riddled with inefficiency, with abuse, with fraud, and
everybody knows it." This line gained him a huge bipartisan round of
applause. And why shouldn't it? Everybody hates healthcare fraud.

The mandate to get rid of fraud in the healthcare system is a powerful one. Everyone agrees that healthcare fraud is an inexcusable
crime and that perpetrators of such fraud should be tracked down and
prosecuted.

Until the early 1990s federal programs like Medicare were pretty
lax about fraud detection and did not have the will, the funding, or
the systems in place to detect it and prosecute it. It was relatively easy
for unscrupulous individuals to get away with even the most obvious
fraudulent practices. Scam artists, organized crime syndicates, and
drug-related money launderers saw the $400–500 billion doled out
each year by Medicare as a huge pot of unguarded money. This laxity
with public funds is inexcusable, and efforts to get tough with fraud
should be—and have become—a priority.

Why fraud sells

Fraud is dishonest, deceitful, and illegal. And there are other good reasons healthcare fraud provokes a visceral reaction in most of us. For
one, fraud is expensive. The government argues that of all the hun-

dreds of billions of dollars they spend each year on healthcare, ten percent is siphoned off by fraud.* When the costs of healthcare are skyrocketing, anything that diverts money out of the healthcare system is reprehensible.

But there's an even more compelling reason for much of the angry talk about fraud—namely the idea that if we don't root out this fraud, *we may have to ration healthcare.* This notion follows from the fact that there are only two ways of reducing the amount of money we spend on healthcare: eliminating waste and inefficiency (for example, eliminating fraud) and rationing. So if we don't want to ration, we'd better find lots of fraud to eliminate.

Because fraud and rationing are inversely related (the more fraud we find, the less rationing we'll have to do), we need to find fraud under every rock. We are more than ready to believe there is a lot of fraud out there and more than ready to use drastic measures to find and punish the perpetrators. This gives the authorities tremendous latitude as they decide which activities constitute fraud and which do not and as they decide what steps they must take to get rid of it. Accordingly, fraud has become the Wonkonians' focal point for instituting aggressive regulatory action in healthcare.

For physicians, this scenario has ugly overtones. For there's a substantial difference between trying to identify and root out real fraud and trying to find as many activities as possible that can be characterized as fraud because the more fraud you find the better off society is. Wonkonians' antifraud efforts have often looked more like the latter than the former.

* This oft-quoted ten percent figure, despite its now-iconic status, is suspect. It originated with a 1992 General Accounting Office report, which identifies the estimation that fraud accounts for ten percent of healthcare costs as a gross estimate, as not coming from any actual data but instead from an average of the educated guesses made by an undisclosed number of unnamed individuals. But at least the guesses are said to be educated, so we will go with it.

Interpreting Wonkonians' intentions

How you interpret government antifraud activities over the past several years depends on your outlook and prejudices. An individual who is inclined to view government as essentially benign and well-meaning can look at those antifraud activities and conclude that in general they have been reasonably constrained. One who is inclined toward the opposite view of government can look at those same activities and see things that are deeply disturbing.

I am going to argue that, even if you are inclined toward the former view, you need to take into account the Fourth Corollary of the GUTH—that covert rationing corrupts everything it touches. For the antifraud imperative presents to Wonkonians opportunities for abuse that, under a covert rationing paradigm, become irresistible.

My view of Wonkonians' antifraud activities is influenced—though, I submit, not invalidated—by my personal experience. The following story shows how Wonkonians are capable of behaving, and—in the interest of full disclosure—it gives you some indication of my frame of mind as we explore together the implications of their antifraud imperative.

Your author becomes radicalized

One afternoon in June of 1994, I was summoned to a meeting by a vice president of the hospital where I worked at the time. Meetings, especially unannounced ones, are the bane of employed physicians; but this one, I was led to understand, was mandatory.

I found the meeting room filled with high-ranking hospital administrators, hospital attorneys, and my clinical chairman. A gathering of luminaries such as these, especially on short notice, was rare. As I walked into the room all eyes were on me. I knew all these people; they'd been my friends and colleagues for years. We'd been fighting the healthcare wars side by side. But now they studied me as if seeing me for the first time.

"Who died?" I asked, just to break the ice.

"To be determined," responded one of the lawyers.

They got right down to business. The chief hospital attorney explained: The federal government, in the guise of the Office of the Inspector General (OIG), had launched a major investigation of allegedly improper Medicare billing practices related to the use of investigational implantable cardioverter defibrillators (ICDs) in the late 1980s. This investigation, I was told, had begun as a whistleblower lawsuit out on the West Coast, and the feds were now expanding their inquiry. The OIG had just subpoenaed records from approximately 120 of the largest hospitals in the country that implanted ICDs. We were one of the 120.

Now I understood why I was here. As chief of cardiac electrophysiology, I was involved in research with the ICD; this was one of the major endeavors of my career. The ICD is designed to prevent sudden death in patients whose cardiac disease makes them susceptible to such an event. Once implanted, the ICD recognizes the sudden heart rhythm disturbances that can cause nearly instant death and automatically delivers a shock to the heart to restore it to a normal rhythm. It is a remarkably effective device and was obviously so from the very beginning. For this reason, as long as I had access to these devices I (and most electrophysiologists) felt morally obligated to offer them to any eligible patients who were at high risk for sudden death.

So now I understood why I had been summoned to the meeting. What I didn't understand was why the government thought we'd done anything wrong.

"We shouldn't have any problems there," I said. "You'll recall that we looked into the legality of billing for ICDs back in '87 when I first started working here. And Medicare said it was okay." As an employed physician, with the hospital billing for my services, I'd had enough concern about billing Medicare for investigational devices that I'd insisted the hospital get clarification from our Medicare intermediary (the local agent and representative for Medicare) on the matter.

One of the attorneys answered. "That's right. The Medicare intermediary indicated at the time that there was nothing illegal about billing for the ICDs but couldn't guarantee they'd pay for them. As it turns out, they've paid for each one we've implanted and never questioned our using them."

"Then what's the problem?"

"Medicare now says we've been in violation by sending the bills," the lawyer replied. "There's apparently an obscure instruction in the intermediary's guidebook that prohibits billing for some investigational devices."

"But we got clearance from the intermediary," I said.

"And that's the defense we'll take. The intermediary itself didn't know about this rule. But unfortunately, Medicare operates a little like the IRS. If you call the IRS with a tax question and they give you bad advice, it's your fault if you follow that advice. The fact that the Medicare people were unaware of their own rules and apparently told us the wrong thing doesn't absolve us."

"So what's the worst case scenario?" someone asked. "That we'll have to pay all the money back?"

"The monetary penalties are much worse than that," intoned the CFO. "We're looking at over 100 investigational ICDs that the good doctor here has implanted," he said, glaring at me. "And at about $25,000 each, that's a pretty penny right there. But the OIG is also talking about a $10,000 fine per incident, plus triple damages, so we're really looking at several million dollars we can't afford. What's worse, the fact that the OIG joined the whistle-blower's actions suggests that they're going to claim we *intentionally* violated Medicare regs—which could mean jail time." He was looking at me again when he said "jail."

"Don't worry," a vice-president said to me sympathetically. "We're all in this together. We'll help you as much as we can."

"What do you mean, *you'll* help *me*?" I said. "I just work here. *You* do all the billing, keep everything you collect, and pay me a paltry salary."

"Like I said, we're all in this together. But those bills do go out under your name, Dr. Fogoros. As far as Medicare is concerned, they're your bills." As I've since learned, when the federal government begins pointing its finger, it's customary for everybody to dive for cover.

For the next two years my life was plagued by a series of complex machinations—legal probes and parries—made in response to the OIG's investigation of our supposedly fraudulent submission of bills. I won't bore you with the details—I'll just hit a few highlights.

First, my hospital threw in with two dozen other large hospitals from all over the U.S. that were also affected by the OIG's subpoena, and together we hired a fancy inside-the-beltway law firm that specialized in healthcare law. These attorneys ultimately determined that the obscure regulation the OIG was invoking against us had itself been illegally promulgated and therefore should not be enforceable. Accordingly, our hospitals sued Secretary of Health and Human Services (HHS) Donna Shalala, in federal court to prevent her from enforcing this obscure, previously unknown, and (we held) illegal rule. "We have maybe a fifty–fifty chance of winning this suit," I was told by one of our attorneys, "but it won't be settled for years."

While all this was going on, the subpoenaed hospitals also lobbied Congress to act on the essential unfairness of it all. Look, the hospitals said, we've got one agency of the federal government (Medicare) coming after us for doing research that had been duly approved by another agency of the federal government, the Food and Drug Administration (FDA). We need laws to make government agencies behave consistently. When the FDA approves clinical research, Medicare should allow patients to avail themselves of that approved research. Finally, in November of 1995, Congress passed just such a law. "So we've won!" I exulted when the hospital attorney called me with the good news. "Not exactly," was the reply. "The OIG prevailed on Congress not to make the law retroactive. So the OIG is still coming after us for what they say we did in the 1980s."

CEO   chief executive officer
CFO   chief financial officer
FDA   Food and Drug Administration
HHS   Health and Human Services
ICD   implantable cardioverter defibrillator
OIG   Office of the Inspector General

Then, in January of 1996, the government launched a new attack. Senator Roth, chair of the Senate Finance Committee, decided it would be in somebody's best interest to have a showcase hearing, highlighting the grievous crimes against Medicare being promulgated by avaricious physicians and institutions like me and mine. So the Permanent Subcommittee on Investigations sent subpoenas to the CEOs of several hospitals from the OIG's list of 120, mandating that they appear before that committee on Valentine's Day (heart day) to answer questions regarding the allegations that we'd committed Medicare fraud in our use of the ICD. It was to be a real circus—covered on C-SPAN, with major networks in attendance and lots of national publicity. The works.

Immediately, there was a mad rush to have the subpoenas quashed. All the hospitals from states whose senators were members of the Finance Committee managed to be excused from appearing. At the end of the day, only four hospitals remained. Mine was one.

I was sure my career had ended. My family, friends, patients, and colleagues were about to see the CEO of my hospital appearing before a hostile Senate committee answering questions on the

Medicare fraud that I supposedly had committed. I knew it didn't matter that I hadn't done anything wrong.

I spent two days in Washington helping the fancy beltway lawyers prepare our CEO for his testimony. I failed miserably in my emotional pitch to be allowed to testify in his stead (the CEO had been subpoenaed, not me; besides, anyone who seemed eager to testify before Congress must be crazy enough to get us in trouble). But at least I managed to convince the CEO that we should take a hard line with the subcommittee. After all, we had truth, righteousness, ethics, and possibly even the law on our side. We shouldn't allow ourselves to be intimidated.

Each witness was to be permitted to read a statement into the record before the questioning began. Our attorneys had prepared a ten-page statement that was vague, wishy-washy, filled with legalese, and as nearly as I could tell, didn't deny wrongdoing as much as it promised we'd be more careful next time.

So I prevailed on the CEO to ignore this lawyered-up document and instead use a one-page statement I wrote for him, saying:

- We implanted investigational ICDs in Medicare patients because they were at high risk of dying without them, and to withhold such life-saving devices when they were available to us would have been unethical and would have constituted malpractice.
- Before implanting the investigational ICDs, we obtained approval for their use through the FDA.
- Before billing for the investigational ICDs we asked for and received clearance to do so from our Medicare intermediary.
- The records and documents we sent Medicare in support of our billing for these ICDs clearly indicated that the devices were investigational, and yet Medicare reimbursed us each time, over a period of several years and without questioning our actions or our bills.
- The regulation Medicare is now invoking was unknown to us during this period and also, apparently, unknown to the Medicare intermediary.
- In any case, as we have asserted in federal court, that regulation was illegally promulgated, and is therefore not a legal rule.

- Congress has agreed that regulation to have been at least an ill-advised one, as evidenced by the fact that Congress recently passed legislation that now renders that regulation illegal, whatever its previous legality.
- If they now assert that our actions constitute fraud, then the message the OIG, Medicare and the Senate subcommittee is sending to the public is that doctors and hospitals are expected to discriminate against the elderly and will be called to task by the federal government if they refuse to do so.
- Thank you for your attention.

The hearing was indeed quite a show. The whistleblower himself was the first witness, and he entered the chamber wearing a hood to hide his face, sat behind a screen, and spoke with his voice electronically distorted. This was the first time in history, I was told, that a witness had appeared before Congress disguised in this way, except in hearings featuring Mafia turncoats, drug lords, and the like. The implication, I presume, was that I and my fellow cardiac electrophysiologists were no less evil or potentially violent than other, more famous sorts of felons and that if we learned this guy's identity his life wouldn't be worth a nickel.

Then it was us perpetrators' turn to testify. The CEOs of the other three subpoenaed hospitals, after reading their lengthy, lawyerly, and seemingly contrite statements into the record, were grilled mercilessly by the Senators of the subcommittee. Our CEO was the last witness. Once he read our brief but much more aggressive statement, the Senators seemed not to have any substantial questions for him. His testimony was over almost before it had started. Our hard line had paid off.

One more blessing occurred on that day. Somebody apparently found some Whitewater documents that weren't supposed to have existed, so ten minutes before the hearing, C-SPAN pulled out and went running down the hall to televise the Whitewater doings. All the other news media went with them. Our hearing, despite the big build-up, the dramatically disguised whistleblower, and the fact that it was Valentine's Day, barely made the news. The lack of national news exposure (and as a result, the lack of local news coverage) spared my reputation and that of my hospital.

Then finally, later in 1996, a federal judge ruled in our favor in our suit against HHS; the regulation Medicare was invoking, the judge ruled, had indeed been illegally promulgated. The OIG still didn't give up, but in the end offered a settlement deal to the hospital for a mere million or two, which, by this time, was less than we had already spent defending ourselves; and nobody would have to admit to wrongdoing or go to jail or have a criminal record.

So, thanks to a few smart people and a few lucky breaks the whole episode seems to have had a happy ending. Right?

I'm not complaining. It could have turned out a lot worse. And the whole ordeal provided me with enough amusing anecdotes to last a lifetime. But having the federal government coming after me for more than two years was an eye-opening experience.

As I saw it, the rightness of my actions seemed completely obvious. I had used those ICDs because my high-risk patients needed them, and from every indication their usage was legal and proper. But in the service of my patients, I (through my representative and billing agent, the hospital) had failed to discover a vague, obscure, and difficult-to-interpret regulation—one that also had escaped the notice of the Medicare intermediary in whose guidebook the rule appeared. As a result I had been caught up in the great Wonkonian antifraud initiative.

For over two years I was never be sure what would happen to me. For days at a time, usually just after a round of legal punches and counterpunches, there was little else I could think of. (Would I lose my job, my career, my reputation, all my worldly possessions—would I go to jail?) I was of little use to anybody—family, colleagues, or patients.

It all turned out fine, but the reason for the favorable outcome wasn't that the OIG agreed my actions had been appropriate and nonfraudulent. It was that our lawyers had found a legal technicality in the government's own actions. Had it not been for this fortuitous discovery, who knows what might have happened?

So I've seen a side of the antifraud imperative that most doctors have not, and I'll admit to a robust paranoia on the subject. The way it looks from here, Wonkonians—at least sometimes—are willing to go to great lengths to prove just how rife with fraud is our healthcare system, and once they set their sights on an alleged perpetrator, are pleased go to great lengths to bring that supposed perpetrator down.

At least sometimes they're willing to base their prosecution on bad rules that are poorly written, illegally promulgated, and hidden away in obscure manuals; they're willing to ignore the fact that the alleged perp had relied on advice from the government's own agents before proceeding; they're willing to summon that perp before a televised, circus-like inquisition to be publicly humiliated for actions that, just a few months earlier, they themselves had passed explicit laws to endorse; and they're willing, when all legal justifications for their persecutions have vanished, to demand a cash payment before they'll go away. At least, that's how it looks from here.

It is not my position that Wonkonians have been engaging in an orgy of illegitimate antifraud activities over the past dozen years or more. I am sure they have not. Indeed, most of the antifraud activities the OIG has undertaken have been legitimate and useful. I understand that any get-tough government initiative—whether it be antifraud or anti-terror—has to have teeth, and that it is natural that a few innocents will get bitten. I admit that my frightening experience may represent the collateral damage that happens whenever the sovereign power finds it necessary to wield its great hammer in the public interest.

But forgive me if I believe the experience I have just related represents instead a glimpse into Wonkonians' methods of intimidating and controlling doctors who would otherwise keep doing whatever they'd like with the government's money. If I am correct, then the unpredictability, arbitrariness, doggedness, and absurdity of government actions in my own case are not accidents but are essential to Wonkonians' goal of keeping their prey completely off balance and in their thrall. If I am correct, then we should be able to find evidence that this example is part of a recurring pattern of behavior.

The Regulatory Speed Trap

Wonkonian philosophy is not exclusively practiced by liberals and Democrats. Nixon behaved like a Wonkonian. And the first easily recognizable application of Wonkonian antifraud methodology occurred during the Reagan administration, in its crackdown on the defense industry.

When the Reagan Justice Department began its attack on fraud in the defense industry, that industry was slow to realize what was happening to it. The industry did not understand for a year or two that the government had suddenly become serious about regulation. Business as usual had become felonious behavior. Federal prosecutors pursued activities that had formerly been tolerated. They applied federal statutes—such as mail fraud and money laundering statutes—that were originally aimed at stopping racketeers and drug pushers. By the time the defense industry awoke to the danger—and began to protect itself by instituting expensive compliance programs and spending millions on lawyers, consultants, and accountants—the government had won criminal convictions against more than sixty firms and individuals.

The government recovered a lot of money that it said had been misused. But the defense industry simultaneously began spending huge amounts of new money on regulatory compliance, and that cost was passed back to their customer, the same government they had paid fines to. How much money the government actually saved is open to question.

There was fraud in the defense industry, and it needed to be investigated and prosecuted. Is there less corruption now? Probably. But the famous $450 hammer incident that set the whole thing off resulted from a silly accounting practice rather than graft. The Army paid only $5 for that hammer. The other $445 was a standard unit charge for administrative overhead that Army bookkeepers routinely added to many items they purchased. Likewise, a good bit of the fraud and abuse that was uncovered during the government's crackdown on the defense industry was not fraud in any real sense; it was misinterpretation or ignorance of regulations or just ignoring regulations that didn't make much sense in the first place.

The methods used in the crackdown on fraud in the defense industry establish an easily recognizable pattern that is being repeated in the healthcare antifraud campaign. I call this five-step pattern of behavior the Regulatory Speed Trap:

1. Over a long period of time, regulators promulgate a confusing array of vague, disparate, poorly worded, obscure, and mutually incompatible rules, regulations, and guidelines.

2. Individuals or companies, having to provide a service despite hard-to-interpret regulations, render their own interpretations (usually with assistance from attorneys, consultants, and the regulators themselves), and act according to those interpretations.

3. By their apparent concurrence with (or at least by their failure to object to) the providers' interpretation of the rules, over time regulators allow de facto standards of behavior to become established.

4. After substantial time passes, regulators reinterpret (or "clarify") the ambiguous regulations in such a way that the de facto standards now constitute grievous violations.

5. Regulators aggressively prosecute the newly felonious service providers.

This Regulatory Speed Trap is an easily recognized modus operandi for Wonkonians (whatever their political party). It is one of the chief methods by which they are attempting to gain control of the healthcare system.

Basic to the Regulatory Speed Trap is an underlying set of complicated and contradictory rules and regulations. Government regulations tend to evolve away from clarity and toward complexity, so this is a given. Societies have survived despite complex regulations only because bureaucrats have traditionally allowed de facto standards to form under their purview, thus preventing paralysis and allowing society to function within reasonable bounds.

What Wonkonians have discovered is that the tangle of vague regulations underlying this normal way of doing business gives them the means to an end that otherwise might be unachievable. Under a system of complex and contradictory regulations, everyone is always guilty of something. By enforcing strict new interpretations of inherently confusing and traditionally ignored rules ("Here is what we meant all along, and you should have known it"), they can press their own agenda.

Wonkonians have equipped themselves with a new set of crimes, a new and robust bureaucratic infrastructure, and the new sources of funding to use the Regulatory Speed Trap to its greatest effect.

The new antifraud regulations

One of the things that frightened doctors most about the Clintons' failed Health Security Act in 1994 was the draconian program it proposed for combating healthcare fraud. It offered a definition of fraud arguably broad enough to encompass almost every practitioner. And the punishment it offered for perpetrators of fraud ranged from massive monetary penalties to doing hard time. So the largest sigh of relief when that bill was defeated emanated from doctors, who thought the threat of overzealous punishment for innocent mistakes had passed.

The "accountability" in HIPAA

Physicians were dismayed—at least, those who were paying attention—when the Health Insurance Portability and Accountability Act of 1996 (HIPAA) resurrected many of those same antifraud measures, lifting large blocks of language from the Clintons' original plan and making them the law of the land. HIPAA today is thought of mainly as a bill to control the privacy of medical records. But as the title of the bill itself indicates, "accountability"—a euphemism for fraud control—was one of the major emphases of the bill (the "portability" of health insurance was pretty much a complete bust).

The HIPAA legislation included a mandate for the Department of Justice (DOJ) to make healthcare fraud a top priority. This the DOJ has done; only violent crime has a higher priority today. Some of the more notable antifraud provisions of HIPAA follow.

Creation of new federal crimes related to healthcare

HIPAA created a new series of federal crimes, together called "healthcare fraud." It is a federal crime to defraud healthcare benefit programs—any benefit program, not just Medicare. Defrauding healthcare benefit programs may be accomplished by theft or embezzlement, obstructing a criminal investigation of healthcare offenses, making false statements or misrepresentations relating to healthcare matters, using the mail in the act of doing any of the above (mail fraud), or processing the proceeds gained from doing any of the above (money laundering). These crimes are punishable by up to ten years' imprisonment or up to life in prison if a patient dies as a result of fraudulent activity.

In addition, HIPAA gives prosecutors sharp teeth for pursuing alleged fraud cases. They can subpoena virtually any financial and medical records in existence and can immunize individuals who supply the records (to assuage their reluctance to breach physicians' or patients' confidentiality). They can freeze all the assets of anyone suspected of healthcare fraud. The number of times that gun-toting, windbreakered federal agents have actually burst into physicians' offices, frightening both office staff and patients nearly to death, to confiscate all medical records and thus put the doctor out of business while they investigate possible fraud, is probably small—but it has happened at least a few times. When it does happen it makes headlines in professional publications and thus a big impression in the medical community—which may be precisely the point.

New monetary penalties for civil offenses

HIPAA provides for robust monetary penalties for civil offenses. Violations of healthcare regulations—especially those related to billing irregularities—may be considered for both criminal and civil charges. Monetary penalties include up to a $10,000 fine plus up to three times the dollar amount for each item "overbilled." Since doctors commonly submit thousands of small bills each year, the penalties sought over a six-year statute of limitations period can amount to many tens of millions of dollars—thus creating a powerful incentive to settle with the government at the first sign of an investigation.

Creation of a coordinated antifraud program and account

The bureaucracy created by HIPAA to find and prosecute healthcare fraud includes three separate programs.

* The Health Care Fraud and Abuse Control Program (HCFAC), administered by the Attorney General and the Secretary of HHS, coordinates fraud and abuse activities across all levels of government and has become the major antifraud bureaucratic entity under HIPAA.
* The Medicare Integrity Program allows HHS to contract with private companies to engage in fraud control activities, including the auditing of physicians and institutions. These companies, which exist for this sole purpose, naturally want to assure the renewal of their contracts when the time comes. It therefore behooves them to find lots of fraud.
* The Beneficiary Incentive Program offers monetary incentives to patients who turn in their doctors for defrauding payers. Patients who think their doctors ought to be willing to shade the truth to help them get the care they need should be aware of this: Doctors know that if they accede to such requests, those same patients can then turn them in to the government for big cash rewards. This program gives doctors a more powerful reason to be wary of their patients than the threat of malpractice suits.

HIPAA also creates, for the first time, a dedicated funding source for fighting fraud, called the Health Care Fraud and Abuse Control Account, which is part of the Medicare Part A trust fund. Penalties and other funds collected by the antifraud program are deposited back into this account. Officially, the fraud control system does not get to keep what it collects. Providers have always suspected otherwise, believing that strong financial incentives exist for the antifraud bureaucracy; but the government has always denied it. Nonetheless, the funding for the antifraud bureaucracy comes out of the same trust fund into which antifraud recoveries are deposited.

The False Claims Act

While HIPAA provides strong weapons for the antifraud initiative, it is not the major weapon wielded by Wonkonians. An even more powerful and practical weapon is the False Claims Act (FCA).

The FCA provides for legal action against government contractors—such as doctors, hospitals, or health plans—who knowingly present a false claim to the government. The definition of "knowingly" in this case is broad and includes situations where the alleged perpetrator "should have known" the claim was false. Further, prosecution under the FCA does not require a specific intent to defraud. All it takes to become a target is not knowing something the government decides you should have known.

A false claim suit can be initiated either by the government or by a private citizen (known as a *qui tam*, or a whistleblower). The *qui tam* provisions of the FCA were originally enacted during the Civil War to protect the government from buying bad gunpowder and were largely forgotten until the 1980s. At that time, *qui tam* provisions were resurrected, strengthened, and given new emphasis in the False Claims Act to bolster the DOJ's crackdown on the defense industry. When healthcare fraud became important a few years later, whistleblower suits were actively encouraged as a way of discovering new sources of healthcare fraud. *Qui tam* actions can be joined by the federal government, and successful *qui tam* actions usually are.

The FCA provides powerful incentives for suing providers—in *qui tam* suits, the whistleblower gets to keep up to fifteen percent of whatever damages and penalties are collected. And the penalties are high. The FCA specifies penalties of $5,500 to $11,000 per claim. As doctors and hospitals typically submit hundreds or thousands of claims, if a submissions practice is found to be fraudulent under the FCA, penalties can run into tens of millions of dollars.

The *qui tam* suit has proven popular and lucrative. An entire industry has sprung up to service these suits—a simple Google search on *qui tam* turns up a host of law firms that specialize in these actions. Whistleblowers often turn out to be disgruntled employees, ex-spouses, or competitors seeking either revenge or quick riches. The penalties are so onerous and the cost of defending oneself so high that *qui tam* actions often trigger rapid and lucrative settlements.

How are the antifraud regulations being used?

Anyone inclined to criticize the antifraud activities of the government as overzealous runs into a problem right away: The existence of healthcare fraud is undeniable, it is inexcusable, and vigorous efforts to eliminate it are appropriate. The provisions of HIPAA and the FCA can easily be viewed as giving prosecutors the weapons they need to go after the criminals who are robbing all of us.

One way to examine whether the antifraud campaign is doing good or doing evil is to look at how these regulations are applied. Are they being used to seek out and destroy those providers who are guilty of fraud (the intentional and willful effort to procure funds illegally)? Or are they being used as a Regulatory Speed Trap, to hound and intimidate the honest practitioner who is confused about the regulations but who wants to avoid even the appearance of impropriety? If our healthcare system were operating anywhere but in Quadrant III, where covert rationing is king and where controlling physician behavior is Job One, we would see the regulations used to prosecute true fraud. We are operating in Quadrant III, though; and too often we see the Regulatory Speed Trap in action.

> **DOJ** Department of Justice
> **FCA** False Claims Act
> **HCFAC** Health Care Fraud and Abuse Control Program
> **HHS** Health and Human Services
> **HIPAA** Health Insurance Portability and Accountability Act
> **OIG** Office of the Inspector General
> *qui tam* whistleblower

Lack of clarity, and lack of desire for clarity

If the objective of an antifraud campaign were to eliminate fraud from the system, then the enforcers would want the rules and regulations to be simple and clear enough that honest, well-intended people would know how to behave.

Admittedly, this is easier said than done. It is the nature of regulations to become more complex over time. "Thou shalt not kill" is a pretty straightforward regulation, but civilization cannot leave it alone. After a few thousand years we find ourselves factoring in issues such as warfare, capital punishment, late-term (or early-term) abortion, frozen embryos, withdrawal of life support, physician-assisted suicide, the insanity plea, the definition of brain-death, and cloning. Soon, deciding (in a regulatory sense) whether it's okay to kill or even whether one is killing becomes next to impossible.

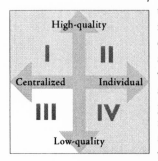

So it is unfair to indict Wonkonians for not giving us a simple code that clarifies all healthcare regulations. Healthcare is a muddy field of endeavor, and the regulations that have evolved to govern healthcare are even murkier than, say, banking regulations.

On the other hand, especially when they're talking about punishing violators with massive financial penalties or jail, it *is* fair to expect Wonkonians to clarify specific areas of regulatory confusion. They should act as if they are interested in helping the essentially honest to stay on the straight and narrow, not in entrapping them.

When Congress was deliberating about HIPAA in the mid-1990s, the only fraud-related provision that produced significant debate was the stipulation that the government should provide "guidance" to providers regarding the legality of certain proposed activities. Under this contentious provision, providers could seek advice prospectively from the OIG on, for example, what constitutes prohibited remuneration or whether a proposed partnership structure meets safe harbor provisions under the anti-kickback law. Providers would be saying, in other words, We don't want to break the law; we want to be solid citizens. Here's what we propose to do. If we do this, will we be in compliance with the law?

The Clinton administration, the DOJ, and the OIG vociferously opposed this proposal. Their objections were based on the fear that issuing opinions before the fact would impinge on their ability to subsequently prosecute cases. In other words, clarifying the regulations would lead to more compliance and therefore less fraud to uncover. In the end, the advisory opinion requirement became part of HIPAA.

But President Clinton called for rapid repeal of these provisions just a few days after signing the bill into law. Wonkonians do not consider the clarification of healthcare regulations to be a worthwhile endeavor. Instead, any requirement to do so is seen as being burdensome and counterproductive to their true goal.

Providers counting on these advisory opinions to keep them out of trouble are likely to be disappointed. In practice, submitting a question for an advisory opinion to the OIG is time-consuming and expensive, and when the reply is finally obtained it can be less than helpful. The OIG routinely stipulates, for instance, that its opinions are binding only for the individual entities requesting the particular opinion in question and cannot be relied upon by any other individual or entity; that its opinions are stipulated to be strictly limited to the facts described therein and apply only as long as all of the material facts have been fully, completely, and accurately presented and the arrangement in practice fully comports with the information provided; that no other party may introduce any advisory opinion into evidence in a legal proceeding; that no other federal or state agency is bound by these opinions; and that an advisory opinion cannot be applied to any other arrangements which appear similar in nature or scope. Finally, as the kicker, the OIG reserves the right to reconsider the questions and issues raised in its advisory opinions at any time and modify or terminate those opinions retrospectively.

The regulators do not seem interested in giving providers a line of sight to regulatory compliance.

How effective is the new antifraud bureaucracy?

There are no metrics by which to judge the effectiveness of the antifraud regime. There are ways to estimate the number of fraud cases brought and the amount of money collected by the fraud control activities. But because we don't know the true baseline level of fraud, judging the impact on the overall amount of healthcare fraud is not possible.

Effectiveness of HIPAA antifraud measures

The number of civil filings and criminal indictments more than doubled (from approximately three hundred cases to nearly seven hundred cases) in the first five years after HIPAA became law.

Periodically and in accordance with federal regulations, the GAO performs an audit of HCFAC. In its most recent report,* which covers fiscal years 2002 and 2003, the GAO notes that HCFAC gave themselves credit for saving the healthcare system $19.9 billion in 2002 and $20.8 billion in 2003 as a result of their antifraud activities. However, the GAO's audit could only account for savings of $1.5 billion (2002) and $3.9 billion (2003). Thus, HCFAC had exaggerated its own effectiveness by an order of magnitude. Further, the GAO notes in its report that while it had previously asked both the HHS and the DOJ to formally notify Congress of the fact that HCFAC's own reports have not been accurate or timely, HHS and DOJ had thus far declined to do so. (If physicians had taken accounting liberties anything like those taken by the regulators themselves, they would be paying triple damages and negotiating plea bargains to stay out of jail.)

* Health care fraud and abuse program: Results of review of annual reports for fiscal years 2002 and 2003. GAO-05-134. Washington, D.C.: April, 2005.

In summary, the HCFAC effort has resulted in a doubling of legal filings against providers and in the recovery of an additional few billion dollars a year. Is this good? Sure it is. Is it a resounding success? Given that, officially, ten percent of the $1.2 trillion we spend on healthcare is supposedly wasted on fraud, recovering a couple of billion here or there does not seem all that impressive. If it were sufficiently impressive, perhaps the HCFAC folks might not have felt compelled to inflate tenfold the savings they actually generate.

Effectiveness of the False Claims Act

How much has the FCA saved the healthcare system? As many FCA actions take the form of lawsuits brought by private citizens and are litigated by private law firms, a lot of the proceeds are not returned to the healthcare system. The FCA industry, however, has seen robust growth. While in 1991 only $70 million was recovered in *qui tam* lawsuits, by 2001 $1.6 billion was recovered; the majority of this recovery came from suits related to healthcare fraud.

The FCA appears to have become the government's vehicle of choice for prosecuting healthcare fraud cases, either by initiating actions themselves, or joining *qui tam* suits brought by individuals. A notorious and illustrative FCA action was the Physicians at Teaching Hospitals (PATH) audit. This example nicely illustrates the methods the government is willing to use and the attitude they display as they pursue fraud claims.

The PATH audit—a case study

In mid-1996, Medicare adopted a new set of regulations governing how physicians should bill Medicare for services performed in conjunction with medical residents (medical trainees) in teaching hospitals. These regulations stipulated that, to legally bill Medicare for a service provided to a patient, an attending physician must either provide that service directly or be physically present when the resident physician performs the service. The regulations spelled out strict requirements for how the attending physician must document that physical presence in writing.

At almost the same time, the OIG announced a nationwide audit to determine how well physicians at teaching hospitals complied with those rules—the Physicians at Teaching Hospitals (PATH) audit. The PATH audit would cover the six-year period (the entire statute of limitation period) from 1990 through 1995.

You can see the problem: The audit was to be conducted to check compliance with rules that had not yet been promulgated.

Before 1996, the rules governing when a teaching physician could bill Medicare for patient services were extremely ambiguous. The most authoritative document before the new rules was Intermediary Letter 372 (IL372), written in 1969. IL372 appeared to require the physical presence of the attending physician for billable services only "when a major surgical procedure or a complex or dangerous medical procedure is performed." Regarding the required documentation of billable services, IL372 was ambiguous. One paragraph states that adequate notes documenting these billable services could be "either written or countersigned by the supervising physician." However a different paragraph in the same letter says that billable services must be "substantiated by appropriate and adequate recordings entered personally by the physician . . . ." (This discrepancy is one example of how even a single regulatory document can give conflicting advice on a key issue.)

Over the years the ambiguous nature of these documentation requirements was acknowledged by teaching physicians, medical schools, and the government, all of which talked about (some day) initiating clarification efforts. But life must go on, so a de facto standard of behavior was established. In most teaching institutions that standard was as follows: For routine (that is, non-surgical and non-complex) services performed by residents, it was okay to bill as long as those services were clearly overseen by an attending physician. Further, the attending physician's countersignature of the resident's note was considered adequate evidence of such oversight (and of acceptance of legal responsibility for the resident's actions).

This de facto standard was adopted not only as a matter of convenience but also as a vital part of the teaching process. In training good physicians, it is important to allow trainees some degree of independence—with oversight by an experienced clinician. A resident must learn to assess patients' problems and to reach tentative clinical decisions on his own. Committing those assessments and decisions to writing (in the form of a progress note in the patient's medical record) forces him to consider the important clinical parameters and to summarize the patient's clinical problems, the objective findings, the assessment, and the plan for diagnosis and therapy. The attending physician, after performing her own assessment of the patient, then discusses the case with the resident and reviews the resident's progress note. If there is a deficiency in the resident's analysis, it is corrected. If there is a discrepancy of opinion regarding the diagnosis or the management of the patient, the discrepancy is discussed and a resolution negotiated (the attending physician has the last word). The attending physician's countersignature of the resident's note (most often with an addendum that makes corrections or underscores issues of importance) indicates that all of the above has occurred.

For decades this was an effective method both for patient care and for optimizing the training of physicians. The de facto standard was adopted not only because it appeared to comply with IL372 but also because it was philosophically the right thing to do.

When the new regulations became effective in June of 1996, the resident's independence was significantly reduced. Under the new guidelines, the attending physician has to be present for even routine patient services. Further, only the attending physician's own progress note can legally describe those services. The need for the attending physician to write her own extensive progress note (essentially duplicating the resident's note) devalues the efforts of the resident and reduces the attending physician's motivation (and time) to carefully critique the resident's efforts. This requirement dilutes the opportunity for teaching and learning. But rules are rules, especially when violating them constitutes a federal crime. While most teaching physicians disagreed with these new regulations, at least they understood them clearly.

The obvious problems with the PATH audit were that it applied these newly clarified regulations retrospectively, to events that took place during a time when the existing rules were ambiguous and unclear, and the new rules require actions entirely different from the de facto standards that had been used in the nation's best teaching institutions for decades before 1996.

The audit model used in the PATH initiative, therefore, was the Regulatory Speed Trap. The first four steps of the Speed Trap were successfully completed with the publication of the new 1996 regulations:

1. Formulation of ambiguous regulations
2. Over decades, establishment of de facto standards
3. Long-term tacit acceptance of those de facto standards by the appropriate federal agencies
4. Sudden reinterpretation ("clarification") of the ambiguous regulations

Up to this point, the motives of the regulators might still be viewed as benign. It was only the aggressiveness of the retrospective application of the new regulations (the fifth and most telling step of the Regulatory Speed Trap), that revealed the true motivation of the OIG.

That aggressiveness became apparent immediately. The first audits occurred at the University of Pennsylvania and Thomas Jefferson University. After conducting these audits, the OIG extracted settlements from these two prestigious institutions of $30 million and $12 million, respectively. While these universities paid a lot of money to settle, they did so—as they themselves made clear—only because they faced the possibility of crippling fines, having submitted millions of claims over the six years in question, that were subject to fines of up to $11,000 each, plus triple damages. Settling, even at extortionate rates, was their only option.

The size of these settlements grabbed the attention of the medical academic community, which then sat stunned as the OIG explained its plan for the broader PATH audit (both in writing and in a chilling videotape that was distributed to academic medical centers). Those plans were intimidating.

The OIG said that all academic centers in the U.S. would be audited during the next year or so under the PATH initiative. Medical centers would have a choice between two methods of conducting the audit, neither of which was attractive. "PATH 1" would involve the office of the OIG itself conducting an on-site audit. The potential danger here, the

OIG pointedly warned, was that many times federal auditors notice things—peripheral issues aside from the main event—and one thing will lead to another. Once federal auditors arrive at an institution, the OIG implied, no telling what other Medicare violations they will find, or when they will leave. "PATH 2" would allow the teaching hospital, at its own expense, to engage an external auditing firm that is acceptable to the OIG. However, the hospital electing this method would surrender certain legal and accounting privileges (including the attorney–client privilege) and would be required to have a representative of the OIG present at all meetings related to the audit.

Whether a hospital elected PATH 1 or PATH 2, approximately 100 patients' charts would be audited from each hospital. The error rates in billing (based on the new standards retrospectively applied) would be determined from this sample and extrapolated across *all* the billing that the hospital had done during the six-year period in question to calculate the total amount overbilled. (Any underbilling that might be discovered during the audit would not be taken into account.) The False Claims Act would then be invoked to allow the OIG to recover up to three times the calculated amount the hospital had overbilled during this six-year period. Because the total amount a hospital would owe the government under this process was huge, many institutions, the OIG suggested, might want to consider an early settlement, just as the two index institutions had done.

Step 5 of the Regulatory Speed Trap was thus fulfilled.

The Association of American Medical Colleges (AAMC) and other organized groups appealed to reason and asked the OIG to desist. Two former Secretaries of HHS (Bowen and Sullivan) wrote in a letter to Rep. John Porter (R-IL) about the unfairness of the PATH audit, "Really since the inception of the Medicare program HHS has had a difficult time in setting forth a bright line standard that could be used to separate the services provided by an attending physician that are strictly teaching in nature and those that involve care to a specific patient. ... Given the contorted history of [IL372] through the years, it would appear to be an unlikely candidate for an OIG investigation."*

In a 1997 response to the president of the AAMC, Harriet Rabb, general counsel of HHS, said, "The standards for paying teaching physicians under Part

* Background Paper— Physicians at Teaching Hospitals (PATH) Intitative. American Medical Association and Association of American Medical Colleges, October 20, 1997

B of Medicare have not been consistently and clearly articulated by HCFA over a period of decades."* However, she then went on to defend the PATH audit, which continued unabated.

If anyone working in a teaching institution at the time had any doubt about Wonkonians' pursuit of healthcare fraud, the PATH audit should have clarified those doubts. The feds were not fooling around. They went out and got themselves the weapons, as well as the public support to use those weapons, and then they set about using them, brazenly, arrogantly, and aggressively. Their goals seemed to be to extract as much money as they could from providers and to intimidate as many doctors and hospitals as possible. Wonkonians were saying, effectively, You think Gekkonians are running things? Think again.

* Letter from Harriett Rabb to Jordan J. Cohen, MD, President of the AAMC, and P. John Seward, JD, Executive Vice President of the AAMC, July 11, 1997, www.aamc.org/advocacy/library/teach-phys/corres/1997/oig711.htm accessed March 18, 2007.

Physicians didn't know to whom they were supposed to sell their patients out.

Post–PATH

In 1998, as a result of the PATH audit, the American Hospital Association (AHA) sent a letter of desperation and surrender to the Secretary of HHS and the OIG, noting that almost 5,000 hospitals were already under siege by federal law enforcement and investigative personnel and pleading for a temporary cease-fire on FCA-based whistleblower actions. The climate of accusation and allegation, the AHA said, was out of control. They asked for a six-month moratorium on further actions under the FCA and offered to use the time to initiate a joint effort with the government to institute voluntary compliance programs and to establish clear criteria for distinguishing simple errors from genuine fraud. They were asking for relief from entrapment, and they wanted the new rules explained to them so they could avoid taking any actions that could be construed as fraud.

When federal investigators had gone after the defense industry in the 1980s, using the same FCA powers, they first conducted enough prosecutions to get the industry's attention, then squired the industry through the development of an adequate compliance program, then moved on to something else (many of these investigators moved on to healthcare, as a matter of fact). In 1998, the government had now reached that same point with the healthcare industry. They had gotten the attention of the alleged perpetrators of fraud, and these malefactors were now begging for the same type of relief the defense industry had been given.

If the real motivation of Wonkonians was to reduce fraud in healthcare and not to establish a system where they could find as much fraud as they wanted to, they would have again declared victory at this juncture and helped the providers learn to become better citizens. In 1998, however, the response of the government was a flat No. The OIG responded by vociferously attacking the AHA's request, indignantly claiming that to accede to their wishes would cripple the government's antifraud initiatives.*

* Testimony on The False Claims Act by Lewis Morris, Assistant Inspector General, HHS. Before the Committee on the Judiciary Subcommittee on Immigration and Claims, April 28, 1998, http://www.hhs.gov/asl/testify/t980428b.html, accessed March 18, 2007.

The AHA didn't give up. They next lobbied Congress for relief and found sympathetic members of the House of Representatives willing to sponsor a bill that would prevent HHS from abusing the provisions of the FCA. As a result, later that year the OIG reversed field and issued a set of best practice guidelines on implementation of FCA actions.

These guidelines do not have the force of law; they are just guidelines that HHS may or may not choose to follow. But the guidelines achieved their purpose, which was to induce the House to drop the bill that, if enacted, would have limited the power of HHS. Since that time, large-scale federal initiatives as egregiously abusive as the PATH audit have not occurred. Wonkonians began lying low, but too late to keep objective observers like you and me from seeing their real intentions. The infrastructure and regulations that enabled the PATH audit remain intact and can be picked up again when the time is right.

E&M guidelines—the new frontier

The PATH audit affected only a small minority of physicians and institutions. Most physicians are not faculty at teaching institutions, and most gave only passing attention to the events surrounding this episode. The remainder of American doctors got their wake up call a few years later, when the Medicare introduced its new evaluation and management (E&M) coding rules. The new rules, which went into effect in

1999, have made every practicing physician eligible for the regulators' scrutiny.

The E&M coding rules apply to the documentation that doctors are required to produce in support of their Medicare billing. Medicare billing codes are divided into five levels, each associated with a different amount of reimbursement. The E&M documentation rules are supposed to help physicians select the proper level for the billing codes they submit. Every note written in the Medicare patient's medical record now must comply with E&M standards. If the subsequent billing code is not supported by a medical note that is compliant with E&M standards, the physician may be charged with healthcare fraud.

These rules were ostensibly designed to reduce the opportunity for fraudulent billing, but their complexity magnifies a doctor's risk of committing inadvertent documentation errors and thus of being fingered. The E&M rules consist of forty-eight pages of dense prose and are complicated and hard to follow. Physicians, when they first encounter them, find them time-consuming, confusing, frustrating, insulting, and difficult to correlate with the five permitted levels of billing under Medicare.

Writing a medical progress note used to be an art. These notes should be brief and to the point, so that a physician caring for the patient at a later time can skim through the medical records and focus on key events. The notes should not be cluttered with extraneous or irrelevant data.

The new E&M rules require medical notes to be packed with extraneous information related to the history, physical exam, assessment, and plan. For example, the physical exam portion of the note must be written in accordance with one of four levels of complexity ("problem focused," "expanded problem focused," "detailed," or "comprehensive"). Documentation of each of the four levels of complexity must comply with requirements that read like a take-out menu. For example, for a detailed physical examination, the note must document "at least two bulleted elements from each of six areas/systems OR at least twelve bulleted elements in two or more areas/systems." The "areas/systems" are a list of body systems such as cardiovas-

AAMC Association of American Medical Colleges
AHA American Hospital Association
E&M evaluation and management
FCA False Claims Act
HHS Health and Human Services
IL372 Intermediary Letter 372
OIG Office of the Inspector General
PATH Physicians at Teaching Hospitals

cular or respiratory, and the "bulleted elements" are lists of pieces of the physical examination that must be written down, such as "femoral arteries (e.g. pulse amplitude, bruits)."

For each patient, each day, the physician must assemble a progress note based on scores of pages of similar instructions. These documentation requirements are time-consuming, often taking an hour or two a day out of a doctor's available time with patients.

Worse, they are confusing and difficult to follow. Choosing the proper billing code, for instance, depends on the level of the history taken, the level of the physical exam, and the level of complexity of the medical problem—and all those levels depend on which elements you've selected from which menu. This complexity is unfortunate, because an error can land you in jail.

The E&M documentation guidelines do not lend themselves to ready interpretation or application, and the government knows it. In a study conducted by the OIG, a sampling of Medicare's own carriers were asked to use E&M guidelines to code five hypothetical patient office visits. None of the five visits were coded the same way by the eight Medicare carriers tested. According to the study report, this result "illustrates carrier difficulty in understanding the visit codes."*

Fortunately for the carriers, misapplying the E&M codes does not place them in jeopardy of a federal healthcare fraud rap. That's only for doctors.

Whether the E&M guidelines are well understood or not, the physician is left with a medical progress note that is less than useful. It is filled with all sorts of extraneous, federally-required phrases from complex checklists that make it inherently difficult to read. A colleague trying to sort out what the physician really thinks is going on with the patient, from the morass of three bulleted elements from Column A and twelve bulleted elements from Column B, will have a challenging time doing so. But a bureaucrat auditing billing patterns will have everything laid out for him just as he wants it—and apparently that's what is important. These new-style medical notes are great for accountants and fraud investigators and are especially useful for computer-assisted fraud-detection data-mining expeditions, but they are terrible for patient care.

* C. Anderson Hedburg, MD, Chair, Medical Service Committee, American College of Physicians, letter to Tom Scully, Administrator, CMS "ACP Response to CMS Preliminary 2003 Medicare Improper Payment Report," http://www.acponline. org/hpp/improper_pay.htm, accessed March18, 2007.

The hue and cry from the physician community against the E&M rules, during the late 1990s and early 2000s, was loud and clear. To mollify the angry medical community, in 2001 the Secretary of HHS appointed a special advisory commission to review the E&M plans. That commission, citing the factors I have just outlined, concluded that the E&M guidelines were counterproductive to good patient care, and in June of 2002 voted twenty to one to recommend abandoning the guidelines altogether. For a few glorious days, doctors thought the E&M ordeal might finally end.

But HHS and the OIG declined to follow the advice of their own commission; or rather, they temporized. The oppressive E&M guidelines have therefore remained in full force, with a promise that simpler, fairer guidelines would be developed some day. This simplification has yet to happen.

In the meantime, the OIG is pressing forward with audits and prosecutions based on the existing E&M rules. One noteworthy example: The government brought criminal charges against a family doctor in Montana, alleging medical coding irregularities. But the government's own expert, hired to review the doctor's billing records and support the prosecution, concluded instead that the prosecutors were holding the doctor to standards that weren't in force at the time the bills were submitted (sound familiar?) and even offered to testify in favor of the doctor. The government switched tactics, dropping criminal charges and instead initiating a civil suit against the doctor for $37 million. Unlike most doctors caught in the Regulatory Speed Trap, this one chose to fight instead of settle. She was finally cleared, but not before spending $300,000 out of pocket in legal defense fees.*

In addition to targeted investigations like this one (more accurately, to fuel them), the Centers for Medicare and Medicaid Services (CMS, formerly HCFA) has initiated a more general program called Comprehensive Error Rate Testing (CERT), wherein doctors' billing records are randomly examined for appropriate documentation. In 2005, CERT, which is conducted by a private government contractor, examined over 160,000 randomly collected medical claims. CMS has stated its intent to ask the CERT contractor for lists of doctors whose records

* Paul Rosenzweig, Senior Legal Research Fellow, The Heritage Foundation, testimony on "Sentencing and Enforcement of White Collar Crimes," Subcommittee on Crime and Drugs, Committee on the Judiciary, U.S. Senate, June 19, 2002, p. 9.

and documentation aren't up to snuff, so they may "consider further action." The way the doctors see it, now anyone can be targeted at any time.

Frightened by instances like the one from Montana, many doctors have apparently adopted the tact of systematically downcoding their Medicare bills, in the attempt to immunize themselves from the accusation of fraud. Some feel that if they consistently bill for Level 2 E&M services (with Level 5 being the highest-paying) they will take the penalty of receiving lower payments than they deserve in return for not having to worry about following all those noxious E&M guidelines precisely and also avoiding government scrutiny. This, these doctors reason, should be considered a victory by the government, since it will be paying out less than the doctors rightfully deserve. However, the Medicare has decided that this practice also constitutes a fraud—the fraud of "clustering." As stated in its Compliance Program Guidance for Individual and Small Group Physician Practices, released on September 25, 2000, clustering constitutes strong evidence that a doctor may not be applying the E&M guidelines as they are intended and constitutes evidence that the doctor may be upcoding what ought to be Level 1 services. (In practice, a Level 1 service is such a trivial patient encounter as to constitute a relative rarity. Doctors who cluster at Level 2 are downcoding, not upcoding.) A doctor whose billing records show an insufficiently diverse distribution of claim levels are now considered to be clustering and may become a target for a formal audit. Doctors can't win, they can't break even, and now they can't even get out of the game—unless they *really* get out.

Individuals who are having a hard time finding doctors willing to accept Medicare patients tend to blame the avarice of physicians. I am not denying that some, maybe many, physicians are avaricious. But avarice is *not* the primary motivation for doctors to avoid the Medicare program. Trying to steer clear of the fraud trap that Medicare has become—thanks especially to the E&M guidelines—is a much more compelling reason.

Many doctors who choose to stay engaged with Medicare have had to expend tremendous efforts to comply with the E&M documentation guidelines. A large and lucrative industry has sprung up to produce courses of study that teach doctors how to deal with these guidelines, and many wise physicians have forsaken a large part of their continuing medical education in order to learn to become better accountants. As a result, the latest CMS report on the CERT program* shows that improper Medicare payments (as judged by compliance with E&M guidelines) was only 5.2 percent in 2005. This figure is down from 14.2 percent in 1996.

To the extent that this reduction in "improper pay-ments" represents an actual reduction in waste and abuse, this result is good. However, given the clinically counterproductive nature of the E&M guidelines themselves, another way of looking at these results is that doctors have caved in (under intense pressure) to this intrusion in good patient care. Such a capitulation is not surprising. For physicians to accede to the oppressive E&M guidelines, as demanded by Wonkonians, is the analog of their acceding to gag clauses, as demanded by Gekkonians. It is another sign of their inability to honor the doctor–patient relationship and remain viable as practitioners at the same time.

* CMS Media Affairs, "Medicare Reduces Improper Claims by Half," CMS News, November 10, 2005

The criminalization of healthcare

It is important to reduce fraud in the healthcare system; and to fight that fraud effectively, the kind of power the government has gathered to itself is reasonable and necessary. There can be little doubt that the Wonkonian antifraud initiative has reduced the amount of actual fraud in healthcare. But it is evident that when all that federal power is applied within an environment of covert rationing, the primary objective—fighting fraud—is sometimes relegated to a secondary status to the goal of intimidating and controlling those who work in the healthcare system—and even of hastening the looming bankruptcy of that system.

Many who work in the healthcare industry—like those who worked in the defense industry in the 1980s—have been stunned by what the government regulators consider fraud and by the lengths to which they are willing to go in prosecuting that fraud. In an effort to avoid committing inadvertent fraud, the healthcare industry is now spending billions of dollars on compliance efforts, efforts complicated by regulations that are exquisitely opaque, constantly changing, and retrospectively applied. The money being spent on reducing this compliance risk ultimately comes from health insurance premiums, which means that a good bit of this money is being siphoned away from the care of patients. Whether the antifraud initiative is adding to or removing dollars from actual healthcare is open to question.

That their antifraud efforts may be inducing the waste of even more healthcare dollars plays into the hands of Wonkonians. Forcing doctors, hospitals, Gekkonian health plans, and the biomedical industry to spend billions on compliance programs (especially because such expenditures do not eliminate the risk of being hit with a fraud accusation) and making it ever more difficult for doctors to participate in Medicare (thus creating growing numbers of angry Medicare patients) will only hasten the day when the whole system is so bankrupt and broken that government-controlled healthcare seems like the only viable option.

Wonkonians have demonstrated their zeal for using the Regulatory Speed Trap to bring physicians under their sway. To the extent that the public and Congress continue cheering them on, there is little reason for them to stop. While they pushed things a bit too far with the PATH audit (to the extent that they briefly awoke the interest of Congress), they seem to have calibrated their activities more effectively since then, and it is unlikely they will allow their pursuit of physician fraud to accelerate to orgiastic proportions, at least for the foreseeable future.

They are being more subtle than that. When a shark preys on a school of mackerel, it does not allow its feeding to become so frenzied as to disperse the school. It makes quick, terror-inducing strikes, grabs a few fish, then retreats, allowing the mackerel to re-form into a semblance of piscatorial serenity. Sharks and Wonkonians think long-term.

Physicians are resolving themselves to a mackerel-like mentality: The shark probably won't get me. But it's always out there, and it's always hungry. It will continue to strike now and then, viciously and at random. I'll try to stay in the middle of the school, away from the edges, and do nothing to draw attention to myself. And I'll always be alert for it, always watching, even as I try to fulfill my mackerel needs.

Maybe you're thinking, Nuts to the doctors. Couldn't happen to a nicer bunch.

Doctors have—by their historically exuberant embrace of a runaway Tooth Fairy healthcare system and, more recently, their wholesale abandonment of the doctor–patient relationship—lost much of their moral authority. The ostentatious and avaricious behavior of many doctors, the fraudulent behavior of some others, and the inability or unwillingness of the profession to police itself have lent plausibility to the government's fraud argument. Doctors had best not rely on the sympathy of the public to escape excessive antifraud activities.

The reason the public should be concerned is not what is happening to doctors. They should be concerned because of what is happening to them. What can more effectively separate the interests of doctors from the interests of their patients than the threat of a career-ending federal conviction, loss of all personal assets, and hard time in a federal prison? When patients are discussing their chest pain with their doctors or asking advice about mammograms, avoiding fraud is not what they want the doc to be thinking about. How should a physician decide whether or not to offer a medical service he believes is needed but that he suspects the insurer won't pay for? In the old days a disagreement with the payer over such a service might result in, at worst, a few unpleasant telephone exchanges and having to return a contested payment. Now it might result in federal charges. Reasonable discretion dictates that the doctor withhold the medical service.

The physician's wariness of the regulators is not an occasional thing, either. It is becoming an ever-present and pervasive concern; as important to every healthcare decision as avoiding the scrutiny of the IRS is to every financial decision. The major impact of the E&M regulations, in fact, is to guarantee that the physician spends time thinking about how to avoid a fraud rap during every encounter with a patient. It's the law.

Once again we see the futility of trying to avoid the rationing of healthcare by eliminating waste and fraud. Whether these efforts are made through market forces or through federal regulations, the result is to increase (not decrease) rationing. Just as the HMO coerces physicians to withhold services by threatening the loss of income or the loss of jobs, the antifraud initiatives coerce physicians to withhold services by threatening crippling fines or jail terms. Either way, physicians must relegate the needs of patients to a secondary position to mollify a master who can ruin them if they behave otherwise.

First Corollary

Left = Rationing

Second Corollary

Covert rationing requires Quadrant III.

Third Corollary

Covert rationing destroys the doctor–patient relationship.

Fourth Corollary

Covert rationing corrupts everything it touches.

6

Covert Rationing and Medical Science

THE COVERT RATIONING BEHAVIORS we have examined so far are straightforward and easy to spot, once you look for them. For patients seeking healthcare and doctors trying to provide it, in fact, those behaviors are getting hard to ignore.

In this chapter and the next, we will consider avenues of covert rationing that are more subtle but potentially more dangerous to our society. That the ideals of scientific inquiry (discussed in this chapter) and patients' rights at the end of their lives (discussed in the next) can be co-opted to abet covert rationing seems startling—at least until we recall the Fourth Corollary of the GUTH, which informs us that covert rationing corrupts *everything* it touches. The extent to which we allow such ideals to be corrupted speaks volumes about the depths of our determination to conduct the rationing of our healthcare covertly.

Science and covert rationing

For over three hundred years, Western tradition has held science to be an objective, dispassionate, data-driven discipline, above the influence of emotion, politics, religion, or prejudice. Science uses logic, observation, experimentation, and mathematics to discover the Truth about our physical universe.

But the practice of science is a human endeavor, much more an art than most would like to admit. People decide how scientific questions are framed, which data are collected to answer those questions, and how those data are analyzed and interpreted. The subjective nature of the human mind cannot be removed from scientific inquiry, and so science, like any human endeavor, is subject to the whims of human politics, passion, and bias. While complete objectivity is the ideal, it is not an ideal that is always met, even under the best of circumstances.

Practicing science under a system of covert healthcare rationing does not constitute the best of circumstances. If science can be distorted to explain, justify, and promote the activities of covert rationing, neither Gekkonians nor Wonkonians will hesitate to use it that way. Neither of these groups is marked by a tradition of science, and we shouldn't expect them to hold the ideals of science any more sacred than they hold the ideals of the doctor–patient relationship.

In subverting science to the cause of covert rationing, Wonkonians have taken the lead and Gekkonians have followed. The federal government includes agencies—particularly FDA and CMS—charged with evaluating the scientific evidence that justifies the use of specific medical therapies and deciding whether and when doctors can use those therapies. Grants from the National Institutes of Health influence the general research agenda of the medical academy and determine who gets to conduct that research. So Wonkonians have a lot of say about which medical science gets done, how it is done and by whom, and how it is interpreted.

Why Wonkonians need to abuse science

The last two chapters may have left the impression that Gekkonians control doctors by manipulating their ability to earn a paycheck and Wonkonians are limited to controlling them through the threat of a fraud rap. Actually, Wonkonians have more to say about physicians' incomes than Gekkonians do. The government *directly* determines how much doctors are paid for treating Medicare patients. And, because many private health plans tie their physician reimbursement schedules to Medicare's fee schedule, the government indirectly determines how much doctors are paid for the rest of the patients they see.

Medicare fee schedules are determined by complex and cumbersome rules that are designed to generate some dandy Regulatory Speed Traps and thus to intimidate doctors. Recently Medicare has tied these fee schedules to the so-called sustainable growth rate (SGR) formula, which relates physicians' fees directly to the projected GDP. This latest gambit has been particularly galling to physicians, because the number of Medicare patients they see and the extent of care those patients require have nothing to do with the GDP. According to the SGR formula, physicians can expect a twenty-six percent cut in payments between 2006 and 2011, when the demand for Medicare services will be exploding.

Just about everybody is frustrated with the current Medicare reimbursement scheme. Doctors are frustrated for obvious reasons. Wonkonians are frustrated because, despite their efforts, Medicare expenditures continue to skyrocket. Clearly, something else must be tried.

That "something else" is a new methodology for physician reimbursement that is gaining traction in both CMS and Congress. This new methodology is based on scientific principles, specifically on evidence gathered from randomized clinical trials (RCTs). As such, it is hailed as a breakthrough that will significantly improve the medical care delivered to Medicare patients. And it will also reduce costs. It is called Pay for Performance.

Pay for Performance

Pay for Performance is a system of reimbursement in which "clinical practice guidelines" will be developed by Medicare, based on the principles of evidence-based medicine, to establish uniform standards for the treatment of various medical conditions. The compensation doctors receive will be based on how well they comply with these guidelines.

CMS was first authorized to conduct demonstration projects with the Pay for Performance methodology in 2003, and eight such projects are currently underway. Without waiting for the results from these demonstration projects, Congress has already taken steps to make Pay for Performance the law of the land, and CMS administrators have endorsed the rapid and widespread expansion of Pay for Performance. This

CMS   Centers for Medicare and Medicaid Services (formerly HCFA)
FDA   Food and Drug Administration
GDP   gross domestic product
GUTH   grand unification theory of healthcare
RCT   randomized clinical trials
SGR   sustainable growth rate

methodology has not yet been widely implemented, but every indication is that soon will be.

We should note three things about Pay for Performance:

+ It doesn't replace the current complex, centralized reimbursement rules; it adds another layer of regulatory control. Whatever else Pay for Performance does, it does *not* simplify regulations or reduce overhead; so it does not refocus physicians' attention away from fraud avoidance and back toward patient care.

+ While it is touted in some quarters as a revolutionary way to improve the quality of healthcare, Pay for Performance is essentially a repackaging of strategies that have been in use by managed care organizations for decades. It is similar to the "critical pathway" initiatives described in Chapter 4. The major difference between critical pathways and Pay for Performance guidelines is that the former are devised, implemented, monitored and adjusted locally, usually by healthcare providers themselves, whereas the latter are handed down to providers by Medicare and are not amenable to the continuous, data-driven process improvements that are the hallmark of real critical pathways (and, for that matter, of industrial processes in general). Far more than critical pathways ever did, Pay for Performance threatens to reduce medical practice to making ticks on a centrally dictated check list.

+ Pay for Performance allows federal bureaucrats to dictate the practice of medicine directly.* The feds will do this, they assure us, by strictly adhering to the principles of science. But their chief objective is to cut Medicare costs. In circumstances where the science indicates that *more* money ought to be spent, it is easy to predict that something will have to be done about the science.

* This authority is a clear violation of the Act that established Medicare in the first place, which states, "Nothing in this title shall be construed to authorize any Federal officer or employee to exercise any supervision or control over the practice of medicine or the manner in which medical services are provided ... ." Social Security Act, §1801, Title XVIII

Why Pay for Performance would be a bad idea even if the science were legitimate

Medical science is being corrupted in the cause of covert rationing. Pay for Performance is important in this light because it formalizes the authority of Wonkonians to interpret medical science for doctors.

But here is why Pay for Performance would be a bad idea even if it did not rely on distorted medical science.

It is based on a false assumption

Like critical pathways, Pay for Performance relies on the Axiom of Industry—the standardization of any process improves outcomes and reduces cost. While *quality* and *outcomes* are the buzzwords used publicly to explain the importance of the Pay for Performance initiative, the real motivator driving this effort is cost reduction. The Axiom of Industry identifies reduced costs with better outcomes—they become one and the same. So central planners devising clinical guidelines for Pay for Performance can tailor those guidelines to reduce costs, then invoke the Axiom of Industry to claim improved outcomes.

But Pay for Performance is subject to the same limitations that plague other managed care techniques. Because patients are not widgets, the Axiom of Industry does not apply. Standardizing a care process to achieve the best clinical outcomes can greatly increase costs; and standardizing a care process to achieve lower costs can degrade clinical outcomes. The individuals devising the care guidelines are going to have to make a choice between high-quality outcomes and lower cost. (See Chapter 4 for a fuller discussion of the limitations of managed care techniques.) There's nothing evil about this—it's just the way it is. The evil is in using these methodologies to ration covertly, claiming that the goal is to optimize clinical outcomes while designing guidelines to optimize costs.

They say performance but mean compliance

When Wonkonians talk about Pay for Performance, what do they mean by "performance"? In the demonstration projects authorized by Medicare, eighty percent of the quality indicators used to monitor the effectiveness of Pay for Performance measure compliance with the prescribed processes of care; they do not measure clinical outcome.* This should not be a surprise. Bureaucracies are absorbed with processes (their lifeblood), not with outcomes. Doctors' Medicare reimbursements under Pay for Performance will be based on how well they comply with guidelines

* "CMS HQI Demonstration Project: Composite Quality Score Methodology Overview," March 26, 2004. http://www.cms.hhs. gov/HospitalQualityInits/downloads/HospitalCompositeQuality ScoreMethodologyOverview.pdf, accessed March 22, 2007

instead of how well their patients fare with their medical care. When you make compliance the chief quality indicator, compliance *becomes* performance.

The problem with guidelines

Care guidelines—standardizing the processes and procedures of medical care—are helpful in many cases, particularly where the patient's medical condition is well defined, there are no confounding medical complications, and the care process has been demonstrated in RCTs to improve the clinical outcome in patients like the one the doctor is treating.

But patients often show up with a more complex condition than a single, isolated, well-defined medical problem. Twenty percent of Medicare patients have at least five chronic medical conditions, and more than half are taking at least five prescription medications.* Clinical research often yields inconsistent or incomplete results (patients not

* Tinetti ME, Bogardus ST, being widgets). Such equivocal results can be applied Agostini JV. Potential Pitfalls of in the clinical arena, if at all, only after informed inter- Disease-Specific Guidelines for pretation. Choosing the best course of action in these Patients with Multiple Medical less-than-straightforward cases therefore involves a Conditons. *New England Journal* combination of clinical judgment and educated guess- *of Medicine* 351:2870, December work—and is necessarily subject to some form of bias. 30, 2004 The question is whose judgment, guesswork, and bias ought to guide the treatment—the physician's or a remote bureaucrat's? The answer to this question, I realize, is not straightforward for everyone, but I believe most people would rather leave it to their doctors. The representation made repeatedly by proponents of Pay for Performance— that the right medical decisions in most clinical situations can be predetermined objectively and at a distance—is simply wrong.

When Pay for Performance guidelines are developed by bureaucrats whose chief concern is cost reduction, they immediately become a vehicle for covert rationing. As we saw in Chapter 5, *guidelines* quickly become *rules*, and the failure to follow rules under Medicare is construed as healthcare fraud, a federal crime. The need to follow such guidelines will erode whatever might be left of a physician's autonomy, specifically their freedom to apply their own experience and clinical judgment to the needs of an individual patient. Instead, doctors will be expected to blindly apply received knowledge. Worse, Pay for

Performance guidelines will limit a patient's choices regarding care. A patient may elect not to receive the therapy recommended by the guidelines (and duly parroted to them by their well-performing physician), but in many cases they will not be offered the opportunity to choose a different therapy unless that alternative therapy is cheaper or their doctor is willing to risk defying the government.

The fundamental flaw with Pay for Performance

The basic conceit of Pay for Performance is to imagine that the art of clinical medicine can be reduced to a set of steps, guidelines, or rules—that is, that it can be reduced to a process—which can then be centrally monitored, enforced, and controlled, thus yielding a superb end product. While this notion is attractive to Wonkonian bureaucrats, it cannot work.

Imagine that the government, having determined that food is as important as healthcare, were to decide to pay for elderly people (thanks again, AARP!) to enjoy one meal per day in a restaurant of their choice. As the government would instantly become the biggest purchaser of restaurant services in the world, they would assume the authority to regulate restaurants to assure quality while controlling costs. To this end, they would develop a Pay for Restaurant Performance scheme.

In trying to sell us on their Pay for Restaurant Performance idea, Wonkonians would assure us that every restaurant would become the equivalent of a Lutèce, because standardized processes would optimize restaurant quality (while, as an added benefit, reducing costs). People who don't buy all of the government's claims but still think pay for restaurant performance is a good idea might admit that the Lutèce promise is over the top; but still, if all restaurants became the equivalent of an Olive Garden or even a Denny's, on average society would be better off than it is today. What these reasonable people fail to realize is that even the quality of your average Olive Garden or Denny's requires a sense of ownership, pride, drive, and personal satisfaction in a job well done on the part of owners, managers, and workers. If you dishearten those individuals by taking away their financial incentives for hard work and their authority to make local decisions; burdening them with complicated rules they must follow to the letter; and threatening to fire, fine, or jail them for the slightest deviation from those rules, you won't have a Denny's any more. To experience what kind of restaurant you would end up with, try dinner some night in the cafeteria of your average VA hospital.

Even if the science is left alone, Pay for Performance is a bad idea.

But Pay for Performance can't leave the science alone

"Pure" Pay for Performance is founded on a noble-sounding principle—that scientific studies will reveal best medical practices and enable the development of guidelines to optimize medical care. It is plain, however, that the real reason CMS and Congress are latching on to the idea of Pay for Performance is that it is supposed to become the Next Big Thing for controlling the cost of healthcare.

But you can't both follow the science to wherever it might lead and also guarantee that costs will be reduced, because—especially in the era of high-tech medicine—the best medical care might be the most expensive. You either have to admit that you can't always follow the science because that would be too expensive (you would have to engage in openly rationing healthcare) or you have to twist the science to get it to say what you need it to say (so you can continue rationing covertly). Given these two choices, you have to twist the science.

By endorsing Pay for Performance, Wonkonians have announced their willingness to institutionalize the corruption of medical science. A full-blown Pay for Performance reimbursement scheme has not yet been implemented, and so we have not yet seen such broadly institutionalized science abuse. What we have seen are enough examples to see what is coming. These examples range from the misapplication of statistics to precedents of thought and of deed that, carried to their logical extremes, would threaten not only medical science but society itself.

Abusing the science

The Cult of Randomization

The "evidence" used in evidence-based medicine and that forms the backbone of Pay for Performance comes from RCTs. An RCT is a medical study that takes a group of patients who might benefit from a certain experimental treatment, and randomizes those patients into at least two subgroups. One subgroup gets the experimental treatment, and the second subgroup (the control group) does not. The control group receives some alternative treatment—either a placebo or some non-experimental therapy that represents the current standard of care. By comparing the outcomes of these two groups, you can estimate, to a known degree of certainty, how well the experimental treatment works.

The problem with other kinds of clinical trials—the non-randomized ones—is the lack of a control group, that is, the lack of a group of similar patients treated at the same time with an alternative therapy or placebo. Non-randomized clinical trials often just give a group of patients the therapy being studied, then measure the outcomes achieved with that therapy. No direct comparison is made with patients treated differently. Using a non-randomized trial to decide whether a treatment works depends on one's ability to assess the expected outcome had that treatment not been used. Judging such expected outcomes (usually by invoking historical data) often introduces significant statistical bias into the analysis.

On the other hand, randomized trials allow you to directly compare two different therapies in two similar groups of patients. The effect of the experimental therapy can be directly estimated against a control. RCTs are almost always better than non-randomized trials for judging the benefit of a therapy.

RCTs are not just the backbone of Pay for Performance. They form the backbone of the entire regulatory process in healthcare. Any company that wants to market a new medical product first has to prove the safety and efficacy of that product to the FDA through the use of an RCT. Then, even if the FDA approves the product, Medicare won't pay for it unless the results of the RCT satisfy their separate review process.

> CMS   Centers for Medicare and Medicaid Services (formerly HCFA)
> RCT   randomized clinical trials
> SGR   sustainable growth rate

Physicians have become strongly conditioned to believe that RCTs are the only legitimate method for validating new medical therapies. And indeed, RCTs have revolutionized modern healthcare. As a cardiologist, I can vouch that RCTs are largely responsible for the incredible reduction we have seen in mortality from acute myocardial infarctions over the past two or three decades (a drop from nearly twenty percent to well under five percent). This improvement would not have been possible without RCTs. This same sort of success story with RCTs has been written scores of times in clinical medicine over the past few decades.

Because of these successes, many thought leaders in medicine have concluded that RCTs are not only helpful but also *required*. These authorities have reduced the statistical technique of randomization to a Cult of Randomization, which comes complete with its own dogma:

If it's randomized data, it's good data.
If it's not randomized data, it's bad data.
If you disagree, you're a heathen.

The Cult of Randomization can stifle scientific dissent. Those who criticize the need for a particular randomized trial, even when their criticism is based on sound scientific principles and logic, expose themselves as scientific heathens—and their opinions are immediately rendered worthless.

Much of the abuse of science that accompanies covert rationing stems from the Cult of Randomization, where RCTs are vigorously defended—often by well meaning individuals trying to protect what they see as a scientific imperative—from barbarians who would criticize the use of a particular RCT for any reason.

So what's the harm in a randomized trial?

Doctors should have to be talked into RCTs, not talked out of them. Here are four reasons physicians should be skeptical when somebody suggests performing a randomized trial.

1. *Randomized trials are expensive and time consuming.* Randomized trials require an extraordinary and sustained effort. They often cost millions of dollars to perform and usually take several years to complete. To conduct a large RCT, you have to: assemble a group of potential investigators from institutions around the country or around the world; hold several long and often argumentative meetings to hash out the study design, which results most often in a design that represents a compromise of several positions and satisfies nobody completely; establish a data-coordinating center, statistical analysis center, and safety-monitoring committee; find sources of funding; sell the final study design

to enough investigators to actually conduct the study; monitor the conduct of the study at each site to assure the safety of enrolled patients and that data is completely gathered; monitor the results to decide when endpoints of the study have been reached; and finally, analyze, interpret and report the results of the trial. To organize such a trial is a huge undertaking, one that can consume a substantial proportion of an individual's entire academic career. Many people would not make that kind of investment; those who do will want the question being studied by the randomized trial to be seen by the medical community as an important one. It is easy to see why, after expending all this effort, critics of such a trial will not be welcomed with open arms.

2. *Randomized trials are not always necessary.* Contrary to dogma, randomized trials are not necessary to answer every important question in medicine. Penicillin was readily found to be useful in the treatment of syphilis, strep throat, and streptococcal pneumonia without randomized trials. The need to perform surgery on gunshot wounds to the chest was established without requiring a randomized trial (in which a control group of gunshot victims, presumably, would be randomized to non-surgical therapy). In these examples, the result of alternative therapies was so obviously bad, and the result of the test therapy was so obviously better, that RCTs were not needed. Indeed, they would have been unethical.

3. *Randomized trials do not eliminate statistical bias.* Clinical trials are supposed to teach us something about the use of a treatment in a particular population of patients. The treatment is tested in a representative sample of patients (whether in a randomized or non-randomized fashion), and the results are then assumed to be applicable to the larger population. The most you can gain from any clinical trial is a statistical inference, not absolute proof. Well-designed RCTs can often provide a more accurate statistical inference than you could have gotten from a non-randomized trial. But one thing you are *not* doing with an RCT is distinguishing truth from falsity.

The misconception that RCTs automatically produce Truth is based on the idea that randomization eliminates statistical bias. It does not. The major statistical benefit of an RCT (and also the major threat) is not that it eliminates bias, but that it systematizes bias, enabling the designers of the trial to control that bias. Decisions made when designing an RCT determine the direction of statistical bias, and thus, often, the outcome of the trial. Let's see how this is so.

From a statistical standpoint, the most fundamental decision that must be made when designing an RCT is whether the trial is to be a fastidious or a pragmatic one. A *fastidious* trial enrolls and randomizes only a narrowly defined subset of patients. If we were designing a fastidious RCT to examine a new treatment for patients who have survived cardiac arrest, for instance, we might limit our study to cardiac arrest survivors over forty but under seventy-five years of age who have had myocardial infarctions at least three months previously as well as depressed cardiac function and a history of congestive heart failure, with at least one hospitalization for heart failure in the past year. By limiting enrollment to this kind of narrow subset, fastidious trials have more scientific validity than other kinds of RCTs; the treatment being tested is nearly the only difference between two randomized groups of extraordinarily similar patients.

The major hitch with a fastidious trial is that after the trial is completed, the results can be legitimately applied only to the narrow group of patients who meet the same selection criteria as the subset enrolled in the trial. The results cannot safely be extrapolated to broader groups of patients. This limitation is not just a rule (rules can be changed); it is a law of nature. As all other kinds of patients have been systematically excluded from the fastidious study, it is invalid to apply the results to those patients.

The biggest practical problem with fastidious trials is that they cost as much in time and money as any other RCT, and when they are finished they've addressed only a tiny subset of patients. (Fastidious trials are often especially expensive and time-consuming to conduct, because fewer screened patients meet all the enrollment criteria, and the effort required to enroll sufficient numbers of patients is correspondingly large.) If you want to apply the same therapy to some other subset, you have to

conduct another RCT. Fastidious trials advance medical knowledge in a slow and piecemeal fashion.

On the other hand, an investigator can design a *pragmatic*
RCT. Pragmatic trials allow a broad cross-section of patients
with the condition being studied (for example, all survivors of
cardiac arrest) to be enrolled. A pragmatic study more nearly
reflects the practice of medicine, and its results tend to be more
generalizable to broader populations of patients.

The inherent problem with a pragmatic RCT is that subsets
of eligible patients may respond in a distinctive manner to the
therapy being tested—and a pragmatic trial usually offers no
way of identifying these subsets. Instead, a pragmatic trial yields
the average response to a therapy in a relatively heterogeneous
population of patients.

If there are subsets of patients that respond differently to a
therapy, as there frequently are, then whether one designs a fastidious or a pragmatic RCT will determine the outcome of the
trial. The dichotomy of fastidious versus pragmatic amounts to
a Heisenberg uncertainty principle for RCTs. The more fastidious an RCT, the less generalizable the results. The more pragmatic an RCT, the less one learns about applying those results to
specific individuals. When you design an RCT, therefore, you're
choosing, whether you realize it or not, which kind of bias you
are building into the study.

The failure to understand this basic dichotomy explains one
of the common mistakes made with RCTs: misinterpreting their
results. It also introduces one of the opportunities for misapplying RCTs in the service of covert rationing. The medical annals
are filled with examples of prominent academics inappropriately
generalizing the results of fastidious trials or inappropriately
applying the results of pragmatic trials to distinctly non-average
individuals.

The belief that randomizing automatically eliminates all statistical bias reinforces this sort of misinterpretation, reinforces
the inappropriate use of therapy, and reinforces the Cult of
Randomization.

4. *Randomized trials are not always ethical.* The insistence on performing RCTs if you want to advance medical knowledge

brushes aside a crucial ethical issue that ought to be raised any
time an RCT is proposed.

The ethical principle that governs all medical research is that
the rights and welfare of the individual research subject take
precedence over the needs of society. This principle was for-
malized after World War II in the Nuremberg Code and was
subsequently adopted by nearly all countries in the Declaration
of Helsinki. The need to formalize the principle of individual
autonomy in medical research arose from reaction to the actions
of those Nazi doctors who, in the name of science, conducted
disfiguring and lethal medical experiments on human subjects
who had no say in their own fate.

The emphasis since World War II on the rights of the individual in medical research does not represent a new pinnacle in
Western thought, as it is often portrayed. Instead, the need to
rely on individual autonomy as a defense against unscrupulous
researchers is an admission of failure. The Nuremberg Tribunal
recognized that in Germany the layers of protection for individual research subjects that ought to have been provided by society
totally broke down. The state did not protect the victims; nor
did their neighbors; nor did the medical establishment; nor did
individual physicians. We are left with the sad truth that only
the individual research subjects can be trusted to hold their own
interests at heart.

The Nuremberg Tribunal judged the failures of the Nazi
physicians with appropriate harshness. It has always been the
obligation of physicians to see that the rights and welfare of the
individual patient are maintained and protected. While the
individual is autonomous, individuals cannot be expected to
make the best decisions for themselves in a technical field like
medicine, especially when they are sick, without the guidance
of an expert. It is the sacred duty of doctors to assist patients in
exercising their free choice. For their failure to do so, the Nazi
doctors paid dearly. The principle of individual primacy in medical research was paid for in blood, on both sides, and it should
not be abandoned lightly.

In this light it is easy to see why RCTs become ethically problematic. Whereas it is the moral duty of a physician to recom-

mend what he or she regards as the best available treatment for the individual patient, by entering a patient into a randomized trial the physician potentially abrogates that responsibility by allowing therapy to be chosen by chance. Randomization, therefore, always presents an ethical challenge, and it must always be specifically justified on ethical grounds before an RCT can be undertaken.

Such ethical justification depends on the physician-investigators being able to defend the proposition that there is no clear indication that Therapy A is substantially better (or worse) than Therapy B, either for the entire population of patients eligible for the study, or for any identifiable subset of those patients. The choice between Therapy A and Therapy B must exist in what is called a state of clinical equipoise, such that medical experts, having honestly and objectively considered all available evidence, are more-or-less evenly divided about which of the two therapies is better.

Clinical equipoise has proven useful to medical researchers over the years as they have attempted to design ethical RCTs. It is deeply disturbing that the Cult of Randomization bastardizes this concept. According to this cult, non-randomized data is always worthless and must be dismissed out of hand; so in any situation in which randomized data is not already available, by definition clinical equipoise always exists. Essentially, then, for Randomization Cultists, RCTs can always be deemed ethical.

The saga of the ICD

So far I have painted in broad strokes some of the ways in which medical science can be abused, and I have claimed that such abuses further the cause of covert rationing. I will now illustrate with examples focusing on the abuse of medical science as it pertains to the use of the implantable cardioverter defibrillator (ICD).

The ICD is a pacemaker-like device that is surgically implanted in patients who have an increased risk of developing a fatal cardiac rhythm disturbance called ventricular fibrillation (VF).* When VF occurs, it causes immediate loss of consciousness (this is called sudden cardiac

* The ICD is the same device for which I became an incidental target of a federal antifraud action, as described in Chapter 5.

arrest), and death invariably ensues within a few minutes (this is called sudden cardiac death) unless the victim is resuscitated. Sudden death due to VF is thought to claim nearly 300,000 Americans lives each year. However, if the victim of VF is lucky enough to have an ICD, the device immediately recognizes the arrhythmia and automatically delivers a shock to the heart to restore the heart rhythm to normal, immediately resuscitating the patient. The ICD successfully terminates VF, preventing sudden death, well over ninety percent of the time.

My reasons for focusing on the ICD in this discussion are twofold. First, I have been involved with this device and the patients who have received it since its inception in the early 1980s, and in my consulting work I continue to be involved with the ICD. I am very familiar with the technology itself, with its clinical application, and also with the difficult and continuing struggles to determine which patients ought to receive these expensive devices.

Second, I have alluded several times to the existence of problematic medical therapies (the ones that improve the outcomes for patients but that greatly increase the cost of care) that render the Axiom of Industry—and many managed care techniques that rely on the axiom, including Pay for Performance—useless in the arena of clinical medicine. The ICD may be the perfect embodiment of such a therapy. The ICD is dramatically effective at what it does but is also extremely expensive. Because it also has the potential of being widely applicable—it could usefully be implanted in hundreds of thousands of individuals each year who are at increased risk for sudden death—if we were to truly follow the science in this case we would do great damage to our healthcare budget. We can't afford to buy ICDs for everyone who might benefit from them. We have to ration—and are rationing—ICDs. Obviously, we are doing so covertly.

Another interesting feature about the ICD is that the medical problem it addresses, while a major public health issue, has no constituency. Breast cancer has a constituency. AIDS has a constituency. Cerebral palsy has a constituency. But nobody ever had a telethon for sudden death. Victims-in-waiting (people who have had or who are at high risk for myocardial infarction and people who have diminished cardiac function) are usually unaware of it. There is no hue and cry on their part for preventive treatment.

Nobody else in the healthcare system (except for cardiac electro-physiologists like me, who get paid for inserting ICDs) really cares about preventing sudden death, either. This is because sudden death is cheap while its prevention is expensive. The ICD is expensive, and when you prevent a sudden death you are keeping a person alive who generally has underlying heart disease and who therefore will continue to consume lots of healthcare resources. This ambivalence toward preventing sudden death extends to many if not most physicians. Doctors who steer their patients toward the electrophysiologists who implant ICDs often do harm to their own cost profiles.

So the ICD is an effective medical device that is expensive, that has wide applicability, that is usually unknown to the individuals who need one, and that third-party payers and many physicians wish would go away.

Looking at how Wonkonians have managed the ICD question, specifically how they have attempted to suppress the use of the ICD in the face of strong evidence supporting its effectiveness, will tell us a lot about how far they are willing to go in corrupting medical science to keep healthcare rationing covert. It will also tell us a lot about how far physicians and medical researchers are willing to go to enable this effort.

Questioning the effectiveness of the ICD

For those of us who have worked with the ICD, its efficacy was beyond question from the earliest days. In my practice alone, within a few years I had scores of patients whose lives were saved, often sensationally, by the ICD—and many were saved several times. Sudden death was virtually unheard of once an ICD was implanted, even in patients at extremely high risk. So I was surprised when, eight or nine years after the first use of the device in humans in 1981, prominent members of the academic community asserted that the efficacy of the ICD had yet to be proven. They acknowledged that the ICD resuscitates patients from VF. But where are the randomized trials proving that it actually makes people live longer? How can we justify spending so much money for a medical therapy whose benefit is completely unknown?

For a while I thought they were joking.

Two guys are hauling a big grandfather clock down the street. Suddenly one of the guys stiffens, turns blue, drops the clock onto the concrete sidewalk, and falls over in a heap. His buddy shakes him, but he's out. The guy looks dead as a doornail. But a few seconds later, pow! The guy jerks, then slowly opens his eyes, sits up and looks around. "Wow!" his buddy says, "that ICD you've got just saved your life!"

"You kidding me!" the guy replies, regarding the ruins of the clock. "When my wife sees this she'll kill me!"

So I suppose that successfully resuscitating people from VF does not necessarily mean their survival will be prolonged all that much. But do we really need to do an RCT to prove its effectiveness? What's going on here?

What was going on was that ICDs were and are expensive. The device costs between $20,000 and $30,000, and when you factor in the cost of the initial medical workup and surgical implantation, the total cost of receiving an ICD can go as high as $50,000. The Tooth Fairy can't afford to buy ICDs for all patients who would benefit from them.

But instead of calling for a way to figure out how to ration ICDs in an equitable fashion, the voices that mattered called for RCTs to prove whether this therapy really did what anyone with eyes in their head could see it was doing. The proposal seemed so preposterous to some of us early adopters of the ICD that we did not think the demand for an RCT would take hold. We reasoned that nobody was insisting on RCTs to prove the benefits of surgery for acute appendicitis—and the efficacy of the ICD was every bit as dramatic and obvious as that. Besides, such a trial would require doctors to randomize half of the enrolled cardiac arrest survivors to some clearly inferior therapy, thus placing them in mortal peril. Doctors just wouldn't do that, would they?

But we were being naïve. By the late 1980s, nearly everyone within the medical establishment, and certainly the Wonkonian and Gekkonian payers,

AVID Anti-arrhythmics versus Implantable Defibrillator study
ICD implantable cardioverter defibrillator
NIH National Institutes of Health
RCT randomized clinical trials
VF ventricular fibrillation

embraced the notion that modern medicine must always be evidence-based, meaning that no new therapy (at least, no expensive new therapy) should ever again see the light of day without a body of evidence, gathered from RCTs, to support it. This was my first direct experience with the Cult of Randomization, and I quickly learned that the absolute imperative to do RCTs trumped any other considerations.

The importance of being AVID

In response to the demand for an RCT, several prominent electrophysiologists got together with scientists from the NIH and designed one. The Antiarrhythmics versus Implantable Defibrillator (AVID) trial had a simple design. Survivors of cardiac arrests would be randomized into two groups. One group would receive the ICD, and the second group would not.* The measured endpoint of the study would be the overall death rate in each group. The purpose of the study was to see whether the ICD really allowed people who were at high risk for sudden death from VF to live longer.

Some of us electrophysiologists initially believed that AVID would fail to garner support, but we underestimated the Cult of Randomization. Doctors from all around the country agreed immediately with the medical thought leaders—a randomized trial was the only way to prove the efficacy of the ICD—and they quickly volunteered to enroll their patients in the AVID trial.

Within a few months, most electrophysiologists who had initially disagreed with the need for AVID were stifled. Anyone who continued to speak out against AVID was dismissed with an exquisite disdain. The AVID trial was on, and you either supported it or shut up.

* Patients randomized to "no ICD" also received antiarrhythmic drugs. However, all scientific evidence available at that time (since confirmed by numerous additional clinical trials) indicated that antiarrhythmic drugs offered no measurable survival benefit to the kind of patients being enrolled in AVID. So in justifying this trial, proponents of AVID were not arguing that antiarrhythmic drugs constituted effective therapy for these patients, merely that the ICD had not been demonstrated in an RCT to be any better.

Some of the original dissenters became investigators themselves. Their argument: Why not? The trial is going forward whether we want it to or not. Besides, we're so sure of the ICD's efficacy that we want to help prove it. AVID is not necessary on scientific grounds, but on political grounds if we don't prove how well the ICD works in a randomized trial, it will always be questioned. So what's the harm in helping to get the study over and done with as quickly as possible?

Was there harm in conducting the AVID trial?

The AVID trial embodied all four of the generic harms to which RCTs are prone.

1. *AVID was expensive and time consuming.* This RCT kept the medical community in limbo for several years, during which time ICDs were withheld from many thousands of patients who could have received them and benefited from them. Some did not receive ICDs because a decision on Medicare reimbursement was delayed until the results of the "definitive" RCT became available. Others did not receive ICDs because the very existence of the AVID trial gave comfort and cover to doctors who were disinclined to offer the device to patients who had survived cardiac arrest. After all, if the ICD were really known to be effective, prominent electrophysiologists and the NIH wouldn't be doing the AVID study, would they?

2. *AVID was unnecessary.* Survivors of cardiac arrest were known to have a risk of recurrent cardiac arrest approaching fifty percent after three or four years, and the ICD was known to be extremely effective in aborting recurrent cardiac arrest. This, plus nearly a decade of clinical experience in which thousands of patients could tell you the dates and times their ICDs had acted to save their lives, logically indicated that an RCT was not necessary to prove that ICDs were useful in such patients.

3. *AVID's design was not statistically valid.* The AVID trial made all cardiac arrest survivors eligible for randomization to ICD or drugs and thus was designed as a pragmatic RCT rather than a fastidious RCT. The trial included all subsets of cardiac arrest survivors, even though clinicians have long been able to identify subsets of cardiac arrest survivors for whom the ICD is known to prolong overall survival.

   Consider what we'll call Subset 1, patients in whom the ICD will prolong overall survival. This subset includes cardiac arrest survivors who have well-preserved cardiac function and no other life-limiting conditions. We expect these people to live for many years, as long as sudden death is prevented.

   On the other hand, consider Subset 2, patients in whom the ICD will not substantially improve overall survival. Subset 2 patients might be cardiac arrest survivors who also have severe underlying cardiac disease. Such patients have only a brief life expectancy whether they die suddenly or not.

In clinical practice before the AVID trial, patients in Subset 1 would almost always receive an ICD; to withhold the device would be malpractice. Patients in Subset 2 would probably not receive one—and if they did, their doctors could not realistically expect to substantially improve their overall survival.

In the AVID trial, however, patients were to be drawn from a heterogeneous population that included all subsets of cardiac arrest survivors. The results were destined to reflect whether sufficient numbers of patients from Subset 1 were enrolled to allow for a statistically prolonged overall survival for the entire group. AVID, being a pragmatic trial, measured only the average benefit of the indiscriminate use of the ICD and nothing more.

For many investigators involved in this trial, the expectation that they were to offer up readily identifiable Subset 1 patients for randomization presented an ethical problem. Many "solved" this problem by not enrolling these patients in AVID, instead giving them ICDs outside of the study. (From my off-the-record conversations with several AVID investigators, I know that this practice of covert pre-selection was widely used.) While withholding such patients from the AVID trial benefited those patients and assuaged the guilt of the investigators, this practice also biased the results of the trial. By preferentially withholding patients whom the ICD is likely to help, and by thus preferentially enrolling patients (Subset 2) who are unlikely to show overall benefit, investigators biased the study against the ICD. Some of us published commentaries at the time speculating that, because of this selection bias, the AVID trial might end up showing little if any overall survival benefit with the ICD.

4. *AVID lacked sufficient ethical justification.* The most disturbing feature of the AVID trial was the dubiousness of the arguments advanced to justify the ethics of the trial. Recall that in order to justify a randomized trial, it must be fairly asserted that Therapy A appears no better (or worse) than Therapy B, either for the entire population of patients eligible for the study, or for any identifiable subset of those patients.

Critics of the study asserted, in print and in public forums, that this necessary condition did not exist for AVID, as we have just seen, and that the study therefore was not ethically justifiable. Proponents of the AVID trial responded to this assertion with several arguments. None adequately addressed the ethical issue.

Ethical Argument 1: Proponents pointed to the existence of prior RCTs that had also been accused initially of being ethically unjustified and that ended up yielding useful and unexpected information. Not only is this argument a non sequitur but it also embraces the ethically bankrupt notion that the end justifies the means. The ethical justification of a trial does not depend on its ability to yield useful information. Instead it depends on whether it is reasonable to ask individual patients to subject themselves to randomization, and thus whether the treatments to which the patients are being randomized have roughly equivalent chances of being effective. The determination that a trial is ethically justified must be made beforehand, not retrospectively with the results in hand.

Ethical Argument 2: Others pointed out that the most respected heart rhythm specialists in the world had carefully considered the ethical issues and deemed the AVID trial to be ethical. This is the Argument of Authority, the major defense of the Nazis at Nuremberg, and it carries no ethical weight. The authorities who deemed the AVID trial ethical disallowed consideration of all non-randomized data (such as the hundreds of witnessed cardiac arrests automatically terminated by ICDs); because no randomized data existed, they concluded that there was no evidence to support efficacy of the ICD. This same expediency would also render many other standard clinical practices eligible for randomized trials—an RCT comparing surgery to observation for gunshot wounds to the chest or an RCT comparing penicillin to placebo for streptococcal pneumonia would be justifiable on these grounds.

Ethical Argument 3: Still others asserted that the question asked by AVID was so important that it would be unethical *not* to do the study. Leaving aside the issue of whether the question being asked by the AVID trial was a valid one in the first place

(I have asserted that it was not), this argument is still specious. It was an abrogation of the requirement that researchers protect the rights and welfare of the individual research subject. It was an explicit call for placing the needs of society above the needs of the individual. If a study is sufficiently important, this argument goes, it is sufficiently ethical.

Ethical Argument 4: Finally, some defenders of the AVID trial asserted that new economic realities call for a "new ethic." This argument explicitly called for abandoning ethical precepts because of pressing economic concerns. That medical researchers are doing so, of course, is my whole point. Those who made this argument were at least honest enough to admit that they weren't able to honor "traditional" medical ethics.

The results and the lasting effects of the AVID trial

The AVID trial ended prematurely, in April, 1997, when the study's safety monitoring committee determined that the patients randomized to the ICD experienced a statistically significant prolongation of survival.

Many of us who had feared the worst were initially delighted that the ICD had prevailed despite the statistical bias against it. We were not surprised to learn that, while the prolongation of survival was statistically significant, the magnitude of that prolongation was almost laughable. In the AVID trial, the average prolongation of survival achieved with the ICD was two and a half months. This is what you would expect in a trial that preferentially enrolls Subset 2 patients (that is, patients in whom sudden death might be prevented, but whose life expectancy even without sudden death is short). You would expect to increase their survival, but only by a little bit.

In the end, AVID did not prevent the ICD from being adopted as the treatment of choice for survivors of cardiac arrest. So it could have been a lot worse than it was.

That this unnecessary RCT could so easily threaten the use of a remarkable treatment like the ICD is a potential tragedy. The AVID trial firmly established at least two harmful precedents for medical science. If the AVID trial was really justifiable and necessary, then:

+ RCTs are necessary to prove efficacy for virtually every form of therapy, even blatantly obvious ones.

+ If society wants to do an RCT badly enough, then it can do so, even if the rights and welfare of individual research subjects need to be tossed aside as the first step; and it can count on support of the medical establishment and individual physicians every step of the way.

Randomized trials after AVID

If you are a payer in the healthcare system, demanding that RCTs be performed in all cases automatically produces a delay of several years in your having to begin paying for new therapies. In the majority of cases, where clinical equipoise actually exists and the new therapy is not yet known to be better than the alternative, it is entirely appropriate to require an RCT and accept the delay it produces. But in cases like that of the ICD, where the new therapy is known to be effective but is expensive, the chief benefit of the RCT is not in the knowledge it produces but in the delay. In theses cases, the RCT itself becomes a mechanism of covert rationing.

The AVID trial, while inappropriate from a scientific and ethical standpoint, nonetheless cleared the way for the routine use of the ICD in patients who survive cardiac arrests. Wonkonians, having placed so much emphasis on the need for a definitive RCT, then fighting their way through the ethical barriers to drive the study to completion, could hardly turn their backs on the results (as close a thing as those results turned out to be) once the study was over.

Cardiac arrest survivors, however, constitute only a tiny minority of the 300,000 people each year who go on to die suddenly from cardiac arrhythmias. For ninety-nine percent of the individuals at high risk for sudden death, the ICD remained unavailable.

But now, proponents of the ICD saw how things worked. If you want to get the ICD approved and paid for, you need to pick a population of high-risk patients and conduct an RCT to prove that they live longer with ICDs. This was an expensive and time-consuming process, but at least it provided a clear path toward expanding the availability of this treatment to patients who needed it.

Several RCTs were launched over the next years to test the use of the ICD in selected high-risk populations. These clinical studies differed from the AVID trial in two important ways. First, they were generally fastidious trials rather than pragmatic trials. That is, they enrolled narrowly defined groups of patients. The fastidious design of these trials limited the odds that investigators would be able to engage in any covert or subconscious pre-selection of patients that might bias the results. Second, asking patients to participate in these studies was ethically justifiable. In AVID, ICDs were systematically withheld, in the process of randomization, from cardiac arrest survivors who could have and should have received these devices had their doctors not enrolled them in the trial. In these later RCTs, enrolled patients were not eligible for ICDs outside of the trial. So, while the clinical equipoise requirement was still not met (because these patients were at high risk for sudden death and predictably would live longer with ICDs), enrolling them in the trial did not violate their individual rights and welfare. Instead, it gave them their only shot at receiving needed medical care. The ethical issue here was not in asking patients to participate in the trials but in requiring the trials to be conducted in the first place.

The results from the first two of these fastidious RCTs (the MADIT and MUSTT trials, both of which were initiated before the results of AVID were reported) were reported in the late 1990s. Both trials showed that the ICD provided a significant survival benefit for the groups of high-risk patients they enrolled. Based on these trials the FDA quickly approved a new indication for use of the ICD, and CMS agreed to pay for them. However, the fastidious selection criteria these studies had used in enrolling patients—criteria, CMS made clear, that had to be met to the letter, when subsequently offering ICDs to eligible patients, to avoid a fraud rap—proved to be so convoluted and difficult to remember, let alone achieve, that this new indication for ICD use did not appreciably increase the number of patients who received ICDs in the real world.

Wonkonians had the world by the tail. They had the ICD proponents off doing tedious and expensive RCTs that, due to their fastidiousness, were hard to apply in clinical practice. And Wonkonians demonstrated their magnanimity by expanding the indications for ICD use based on the results of these RCTs, trumpeted and thereby reinforced the success of the RCT pathway for

AVID   Anti-arrhythmics versus Implantable Defibrillator study
CMS   Centers for Medicare and Medicaid Services (formerly HCFA)
ICD   implantable cardioverter defibrillator
MADIT   Multicenter Automated Defibrillator Implantation Trial
MUSTT   Multicenter Unsustained Tachycardia Trial
RCT   randomized clinical trials

expanding clinical knowledge, and at the same time barely spent any additional money.

But then clinical investigators showed up with the MADIT II trial.

MADIT II and the abuse of statistics

In early 2002, results were published in the *New England Journal of Medicine* from the Second Multicenter Automated Defibrillator Implantation Trial (MADIT II). This RCT sent a new wake-up call to Wonkonians.

The MADIT II trial, which had begun enrolling patients in 1997, was designed with a different cast than other post-AVID randomized trials. While it was still a reasonably fastidious trial, it was not as strictly fastidious as either MADIT or MUSTT. If this trial were to show a survival benefit with the ICD, it would be easy to apply the results to real-world patients, and the population of high-risk patients eligible to receive ICDs would expand dramatically.

The MADIT II trial included patients whose only criteria for enrollment were that they must have had a prior myocardial infarction and their cardiac function needed to be diminished (their left ventricular ejection fractions had to be thirty percent or less). Enrolled patients were randomized into two groups. The first group received ICDs, and the second group did not. Numerous subgroups were defined ahead of time for later analysis, based on such clinical features as age, sex, cardiac function, presence of diabetes, etc., so that any influence of these features on the effect of the ICD could later be estimated.

In 2001 the study was halted when the patients randomized to the ICD group were shown to have a significantly lower risk of dying than patients treated without the ICD. The survival benefit provided by the ICD was present not only for the enrolled patients as a whole but also for every subgroup that had been defined for analysis.

The MADIT II results were widely hailed as simple, straightforward, and compelling. Within a few months, the FDA approved a new indication for implanting the ICD in patients matching the MADIT II criteria. The American Heart Association, the American College of Cardiology, and the North American Society of Pacing and Electrophysiology released updated guidelines for using ICDs that included the new MADIT II indication. Most health plans in the U.S. agreed to pay for ICDs for this new indication. All that remained was for CMS to extend Medicare reimbursement coverage to this new group of patients.

CMS balked, dragging its feet for months. During this time, doctors were faced with a nasty dilemma. They could either use ICDs in MADIT II–like patients, and risk not getting reimbursed or, more ominously, getting hit with a federal fraud rap; or they could withhold ICDs in these patients despite compelling data from an RCT, guidelines from professional organizations saying they should, and an FDA-approved indication. Most doctors opted to expose their patients and not themselves to the risk and withheld the ICD, awaiting the verdict of CMS.

After interminable internal deliberations that failed to produce a decision on whether to expand coverage for ICDs, CMS took the unusual step of convening a special Medicare Coverage Advisory Committee (MCAC) to make a recommendation. This committee, whose members were chosen by CMS and who therefore were not biased in favor of the ICD industry, held a public hearing in February, 2003. I attended this public hearing as an interested party.

The meeting proceeded much like a court trial, with a prosecution, a defense, and a jury. CMS acted as the prosecution, charging, in essence, that the MADIT II study was imperfect and, being imperfect, did not constitute a compelling reason to extend payment for ICDs. The MADIT II investigators, consummate and irreproachable academics, presented the defense. They agreed their RCT had not been perfect, as no RCT could ever be perfect in clinical medicine, but it was as well designed and well conducted a clinical trial as had ever been performed. With a deliberate and painstaking presentation of the scientific data, they made the case that the results of the MADIT II trial were so straightforward and statistically significant as to overwhelm whatever niggling criticisms CMS was able to mount. The feeling in the room was that members of the MCAC (the jury), despite some sense that a few members were sympathetic to the CMS position, were not going to be able to vote with CMS on this issue without embarrassing themselves.

CMS was not finished, however. They produced their own statistician who had massaged the data from the MADIT II trial in, to put it politely, unusual ways and had come up with a theory that sounded to me something like this: If we assume A and presume B, and if the trial had been conducted this way instead of that, then perhaps for one particular theoretical subgroup of the MADIT II population the results might possibly have turned out different.

This sort of what-if-you-had-done-it-this-way argument could be applied to any RCT that has ever been conducted. And the only real answer to such an argument (aside from pointing out that if you have to resort to this, your position must be statistically bankrupt) is to patiently explain as follows: We didn't do the study that way because, well, we were asking a different question than the one you apparently wish we had asked. If you think that's such an interesting question, then by all means have at it with your own RCT, and Godspeed to you. But as for the question we did ask, which the medical profession considers to be the most important question, here are the results. CMS's statistician, hearing a reply along these lines and seeming a bit embarrassed at having had to advance such a line of argument in the first place, sat down.

CMS gamely continued trying to diminish the significance of the MADIT II study, but the battle was lost for them. At the end of the day, the MCAC voted 7–0 in favor of approving the MADIT II indication.

CMS then took this self-initiated recommendation from their own advisory committee and retired again into internal deliberations. To everyone's surprise, in June of 2003 they announced that they would only partially cover the MADIT II indication.

It turned out that CMS, on further deliberation, had devised a novel way of cutting the statistics of the MADIT II trial, one they had not thought up in time for discussion at the MCAC meeting; and using this new methodology they discovered a substantial subset of the MADIT II population which did not deserve the ICD. Nearly everyone in the academic medical community recognized that CMS had engaged in blatant statistical manipulation. Their statistical method was, in fact, fully discredited a short time later. (Their coverage decision stood until 2004, when a second RCT was reported that duplicated the findings of MADIT II.) Faced with evidence that CMS was being creative with statistics in order to withhold life-saving medical therapy from patients, medical thought leaders expressed shock and dismay privately, but few were willing to make public statements criticizing CMS's statistical reasoning. Instead, they said things like "We are pleased CMS has agreed to cover some patients, though disappointed they did not include all of them" and "The coverage decision was good, but not great" and "They're covering about fifty percent of the MADIT II population, so the cup is half full."

The medical director at CMS at the time, Sean Tunis MD, was surprisingly forthcoming on the reasoning behind the MADIT II coverage decision. At the 2003 meetings of the North American Society of Pacing and Electrophysiology, he said repeatedly that it is all about the money. The Medicare budget, he said, has no wiggle room. His message was that when people are trying to get Medicare to buy large amounts of an expensive medical therapy, that therapy may have to be held to some higher standard of proof. (The unusual statistical methods by which they arrived at the MADIT II coverage decision presumably tells us what such a higher standard looks like.)

On one hand CMS did face a dilemma. The MADIT II trial presented them with incontrovertible scientific evidence that ICD usage should be expanded, in an era when Medicare's budget is growing tighter and tighter. On the other hand, it would be a lot easier to accept their decision if they had just come out and admitted they have to ration ICDs, instead of using a spurious statistical analysis and trying to pass if off as science.

Is there a better way to control costs with the ICD?

Can we do better than conducting unnecessary and unethical RCTs and then corrupting the analysis of scientific data if we don't like the results? Sure we can.

An easier, more equitable, more honest, and more scientifically legitimate approach than rationing by RCT would be to declare openly that we must ration the ICD because of its cost and then state how much we're willing to spend to prolong an individual's survival with an ICD. Having made such a declaration, all we would need to do to determine which individuals can receive ICDs and which cannot is to do the appropriate calculations.

The calculations are easy, thanks to the Axiom of ICD Survival, which states:

Over a given period, the ICD will significantly prolong the survival of a population of patients as long as the risk of death from cardiac arrhythmia in that population is sufficiently high, and the risk of death from other causes is sufficiently low.

We encountered the Axiom of ICD Survival, without actually calling it out, when we discussed the AVID trial. We defined two subsets of patients at that time, based on their respective likelihoods of experiencing sudden death versus non-sudden death. The outcome of the AVID trial hinged on which subset of patients would be preferentially enrolled in the trial.

We can devise a spreadsheet, based on the Axiom of ICD Survival, that tells us, given a population of patients, how much money we would need to spend to extend the life of one individual by one year. We would enter into this spreadsheet four variables:

1. The annual predicted risk of sudden death
2. The annual predicted risk of death from all other causes
3. The cost of implanting the ICD you're proposing to use
4. How long that ICD is expected to last.

The first two variables could be estimated from existing epidemiological databases, such as the Framingham study.

The first spreadsheet (Figure 2, on page 184) shows the calculations for a group of patients whose annual risk of sudden death is estimated to be ten percent, whose annual risk of non-sudden death is five percent, and for whom the cost of a five-year ICD is $30,000. The spreadsheet estimates the cost per life-year saved for these patients at about $29,000.

The use of the ICD in a somewhat healthier group of patients is represented in the second spreadsheet (Figure 3, on page 185).

The second spreadsheet shows the calculations for patients with a three percent yearly risk of sudden death and a one percent yearly risk of non-sudden death, using the same ICD. Here, the cost per life-year saved is over $83,000. The cost of saving a life is higher in this second group because fewer of these patients—whose yearly risk of sudden death is only three percent—will suffer an event in which their ICDs are used over five years.

To determine whether an ICD is justified under this open, objective rationing scheme, all we have to do is decide how much we are willing to spend to purchase one additional life-year. Traditionally, a medical therapy is considered cost-effective if it costs less than $50,000 per life-year saved. If we were to stick to this tradition, the patient whose information is calculated in the first example would be offered an ICD; the patient in the second spreadsheet would not. The ICD is still being rationed, as it is today; but in these examples it is being rationed openly, objectively, and fairly; and the rationing decision is accomplished in five seconds instead of five years.

Here is where it gets interesting. Think about how the manufacturers of ICDs would respond to such a methodology. For the first time, the price of ICDs would directly determine which patients could receive a device and which manufacturer's device they could receive. The lower the price and the greater the longevity of an ICD, the greater the number of patients who could receive one and the more devices the manufacturer would sell. Real price competition would take place in the medical device industry for the first time.* Engineers would no longer be called upon by ICD manufacturers to add more bells and whistles to ICDs (which is what electrophysiologists typically ask for) but would be asked to build simpler, longer lasting, more reliable devices, as cheaply as possible. Market forces would be unleashed in a more cost-effective direction.

> * The cost of manufacturing a high-quality ICD is approximately $1,500 per unit. Units currently sell for $15,000–30,000. So there is room to reduce the price in response to competitive pressure without affecting the manufacturing process and thus the quality of the device.

By rationing ICDs openly, guided by the Axiom of ICD Survival, we would ration more fairly and more equitably than we are today, we would be able to quit playing fast and loose with research ethics and research mathematics, we would drive down the cost of ICDs, and we would stimulate innovation in a new direction. We might end up rationing less than we are now under our current system of covert rationing. More, perhaps even most, individuals at increased risk for sudden death would finally gain access to ICDs—a new breed of simple, inexpensive, yet highly reliable ICDs at that.

Covert rationing and medical science—

a summary

Covert rationing of healthcare poses a threat to the integrity of medical science. We have seen the lengths to which Wonkonian bureaucrats are willing to go in abusing clinical trials—experiments conducted in living patients—to get to the answer they want. We have seen how the need to keep costs down has taken one of the most important innovations in the history of medical progress—the randomized clinical

Annual risk of sudden death	10%
Annual risk of non-sudden death	5%
Cost of ICD	$30,000

	Year 1	Year 2	Year 3	Year 4	Year 5
Patients alive at beginning of year	100	95	90.3	85.7	81.5
Projected non-sudden death	5	4.75	4.52	4.29	4.07
Projected sudden death	9.5	9.03	8.57	8.15	7.74
Projected total death without ICD	14.5	13.8	13.1	12.4	11.8
Projected total death with ICD	5	4.75	4.52	4.29	4.07
Patients saved this year	9.5	9.03	8.57	8.15	7.74
Saved patients from last year still alive	0	9.03	17.1	24.4	30.0
Total saved patients still alive	9.5	18.05	25.7	32.6	38.7
Total life-years saved this year	4.75	13.5	21.4	28.5	34.8
Cumulative life-years saved	4.75	18.23	39.7	68.3	103
Patients alive at end of year	95	90.3	85.7	81.5	77.4
Total life-years saved	103				
Average life-years saved per patient	1.03				
Cost of ICD per life-year saved	$29,000				

Figure 2. Cost calculation for ICDs in a high-risk population.

Annual risk of sudden death	3%				
Annual risk of non-sudden death	1%				
Cost of ICD	$30,000				

	Year 1	Year 2	Year 3	Year 4	Year 5
Patients alive at beginning of year	100	99	98	97	96
Projected non-sudden death.................	1	0.99	0.98	0.97	0.96
Projected sudden death.................	2.97	2.94	2.91	2.88	2.85
Projected total death without ICD	3.97	3.93	3.89	3.85	3.81
Projected total death with ICD	1	0.99	0.98	0.97	0.96
Patients saved this year	2.97	2.94	2.91	2.88	2.85
Saved patients from last year still alive	0	2.94	5.82	8.64	11.4
Total saved patients still alive	2.97	5.88	8.73	11.5	14.3
Total life-years saved this year	1.48	4.44	7.28	10.1	12.8
Cumulative life-years saved	1.48	15.89	13.17	23.3	36.1
Patients alive at end of year	99	98	97	96	95
Total life-years saved	36.1				
Average life-years saved per patient	0.361				
Cost of ICD per life-year saved	$83,000				

Figure 3. Cost calculation for ICDs in a low-risk population.

trial—and converted it from a tool based on firm scientific principles to
a cult based on mindless dogma. And we have seen how Wonkonians
are ready to claim the final word in directing scientific endeavors, interpreting their results for practicing physicians, and handing down those
interpretations in the form of centrally mediated medical practice
guidelines.

As bad as these developments may be, they are less disturbing than
the distorted thinking we are beginning to see on the part of medical researchers themselves. When we see the illogical becoming logical
and the unethical becoming ethical on the part of bureaucrats, well, at
least they're just bureaucrats. Bureaucrats do not have an ethical obligation to patients (or to anybody, for that matter). Research physicians,
on the other hand, do. When we see the pressures of covert rationing
beginning to co-opt the thought processes of medical scientists, we can
be sure there's more at stake than misinterpreted or spurious results
from clinical trials. For when we begin undermining the scientific and
ethical integrity of medical research to keep the rationing covert, in
the process we are tossing aside the rights, welfare, and autonomy of
individual human research subjects and, by extension, everyone else.

7

Covert Rationing
and End-of-Life Medicine

IS IT A COINCIDENCE that the first state to approve a program of explicit healthcare rationing is also the first state to approve physician-assisted suicide?

This may seem like an unfair question, especially if you're an Oregonian. Oregon is the only state whose citizens have had the courage to openly address the issue of healthcare rationing,* and it is not surprising that the same people would take up a second highly contentious issue related to healthcare. So Oregon's passage of laws related to both of these issues may indeed be a coincidence of courage.

At the same time, the juxtaposition of the first operational assisted suicide law with the first state-sponsored plan for healthcare rationing illustrates the relationship between end-of-life care decisions and the need to limit spending.

There are three areas of contention related to end-of-life medical care—advance directives, physician-assisted suicide, and medical futility. All three involve ethical dilemmas that have engaged respected ethicists on both sides. The ethical point of contention is the same for all three—individual autonomy versus the needs of society as a whole. All three ask this question: How much control does a patient have over the events surrounding his or her own death?

* In the early 1990s Oregon developed a system for open healthcare rationing, which was intended only for patients on Medicaid. It had significant design flaws and was never implemented, but the citizens of Oregon at least demonstrated that it is possible to address the problem of healthcare rationing openly and civilly.

The autonomy of the individual—a person's right of self-determination—is a vital principle. But individual autonomy is not perfect even in concept; it has inherent limitations. In the pursuit of life, liberty, and happiness, no person has the right to limit or jeopardize the rights of other individuals or the welfare of society. This limitation creates an unavoidable tension between the rights of an individual and the needs of society. The general problem of how to protect individual autonomy without sacrificing the legitimate needs of the collective accounts for many of the internal conflicts in our nation's history.

The issue of autonomy is vital to the end-of-life disputes. Acknowledging that dying patients have the right to make critical healthcare decisions often provides a final measure of control and dignity to their lives. To those in the end-of-life movement, the battle is for affirmation of the individual autonomy of the dying patient and against the technocratic, unfeeling healthcare machine that is too intent on following its own rules and procedures.

There would be no conflict if the individual's end-of-life desires did not place certain demands on society. But when dying patients ask that their own deaths be hastened, a tension arises. Our society protects the physical life of individuals. So when individuals issue demands that healthcare providers stop protecting their physical existence or even act to end it and that the state embrace those demands, a potential conflict is created. And we have to consider whether such demands might begin to erode an essential aspect of our social contract.

This question is hard enough on its own. It becomes unanswerable in the context of covert healthcare rationing.

Central to the end-of-life disputes, though not often openly discussed, is the issue of cost. Pleas for the expansion of end-of-life autonomy talk about how much money is being spent today caring for patients in the last few months of life. Up to thirty-five percent of Medicare expenditures, we often hear, go to the six percent of enrollees in their final year. The implication is that if we honor individual autonomy, as a bonus we also stand to save countless millions of dollars. There is a compelling financial incentive for society to yield on its jealous protection of individual life. Unsurprisingly, those who cut the checks, the health insurers and the government, have expressed sympathy and support for some aspects of the end-of-life movement.

But covert rationing turns the issue of end-of-life autonomy on its head. Under a system of covert rationing, placing the autonomy of the dying person above all other considerations ultimately *devalues* the worth of the individual.

In this chapter I will show how, in all three end-of-life controversies, the ethical issue of individual autonomy is inextricably entwined with the practical issue of cost; and how covert healthcare rationing sweeps away any hope of resolving these issues equitably.

Advance directives

Advance directives allow patients to establish beforehand, usually by means of a written document, what kinds of medical treatment they would want and not want should they fall victim to a serious, life-threatening illness that leaves them unable to express their wishes. Advance directives can be either a statement of very general desires ("I do not want my life prolonged by any artificial mechanical means") or a list of more specific wishes ("I do not want to be attached to a mechanical ventilator"). They are supposed to work by providing guidance to physicians who, in their fiduciary capacity, are charged with acting in their patients' best interests, even if the patient can no longer express a preference.

Advance directives and autonomy

By allowing patients to make such choices ahead of time, advance directives can spare them from being subjected to treatments they would consider demeaning, undignified, painful or otherwise undesirable, should they become incapacitated at a later date. Well-constructed advance directives always operate in the direction of preserving individual autonomy. "Well-constructed" implies that they are clearly and concisely written, that they honor the ethical and legal norms approved by society and thus preserve the general social contract, and that they provide physicians with clear rules for honoring the patient's wishes. There should be little ethical argument against such an advance directive.

Most disputes with advance directives revolve around whether or how well a particular directive meets these criteria. Advance directives that fail to do so can create more confusion and ethical conflict than they prevent. And many times advance directives are indeed less than perfect. The major problems are twofold: Advance directives express imperfect knowledge, and they are imperfectly expressed.

A healthy, robust individual cannot always know how he or she will feel years into the future, when illness strikes and it becomes time to exercise an advance directive. Every doctor who cares for critically ill patients has seen many who, despite advance directives to the contrary, unhesitatingly choose to be attached to a ventilator, for example, when the time comes, rather than face certain imminent death. Experienced doctors know that advance directives do not always indicate what a patient will actually choose when the time of choice is upon them. They also know that, while conscious patients have the opportunity to repeal their advance directives, unconscious or incapacitated patients do not.* In executing an advance directive for an incapacitated patient, the conscientious physician interprets that advance directive in light of many other factors—her personal knowledge of the patient, the opinions of the family as to what the patient would want done, and the chances of long-term recovery if the therapy being considered is used. Then she will negotiate with responsible family members an approach that appears to meet the patient's presumed desires.

* At least *most* physicians know this. I have encountered more than one doctor attempting to discount the patient's clearly expressed present desire to continue with aggressive treatment, because of a previously written advance directive. These doctors reason that either the patient's illness must be affecting their judgment, or a prior written document has more legal weight than the patient's current voiced wishes.

Case study:
An ambiguous advance directive

Bruno, a previously healthy man of 68, suffered a stroke. He became comatose, and two hours later he developed respiratory distress. Dr. Jones, Bruno's neurologist, expected his respiratory condition to improve over time. But right now Bruno needed to be attached to a ventilator or he would die within hours. The problem was that Bruno had signed an advance directive prohibiting ventilators under many circumstances.

Dr. Jones was not sure what to do. How much weight should she give to Bruno's advance directive? If she were to withhold the ventilator, Bruno would die. If she were to put Bruno on the ventilator, chances are he would recover, but with at least some permanent neurological deficit. Which would Bruno choose if he were able to express his choice *now?*

Dr. Jones talked to Bruno's family about the situation. Bruno's daughter said the advance directive speaks for itself and should be honored, but his son expressed doubt as to whether *this* was precisely the kind of circumstance Bruno meant when he indicated he didn't want the ventilator. Bruno's wife was distraught, and while she could not offer advice about the advance directive, she was not ready for Bruno to die.

Then there's the interpretation of the specific language in Bruno's advance directive. This particular advance directive was downloaded from the Internet for Bruno by his daughter, and it is boilerplate. Dr. Jones had seen this language before; she didn't believe that Bruno changed anything in it—apparently he just signed it as it was. Bruno's son said that Bruno had signed it in the first place just so his daughter would stop nagging him about it. In any case, this particular directive is distressingly vague about its prohibitions. Regarding the ventilator, it appears to prohibit its use "unless there is a reasonable expectation of a meaningful recovery."

Dr. Jones tried to evaluate the wishes expressed in Bruno's directive in light of his situation. With aggressive therapy she expected perhaps a sixty percent chance of surviving this hospitalization. Is that a "reasonable expectation?" If Bruno did survive, he might be permanently paralyzed and unable to talk. Is that a "meaningful recovery?" She had seen many patients with devastating strokes eventually achieve a satisfactory, even a reasonably happy, existence. Yet, she knew, few of them would have predicted ahead of time that they'd be willing to live with such a condition. The definition of a "meaningful recovery" depends heavily upon whether one is a robust young man thinking about a stroke in the abstract, or an elderly man actually living it and whose only other option is death.

Bruno's three family members studied Dr. Jones's face, awaiting her recommendation—the wife pleadingly, the son expectantly, and the daughter challengingly.

The easy way out for Dr. Jones was to "honor" Bruno's advance directive and withhold ventilator therapy. That decision would certainly fall within the parameters of the directive, would be acceptable (albeit reluctantly) to Bruno's wife and son, and would be welcomed by Bruno's daughter. It would also be welcomed by her hospital and the HMO that owns it. And Dr. Jones realized that she invited less official scrutiny by *following* an advance directive than by *interpreting* it.

But she took a deep breath and told Bruno's family she thought they should use the ventilator. "I think he has a pretty decent chance of making an acceptable recovery," she said, "although I can't guarantee anything. But the way I read the situation, I think he'd want us to try.

"So how about this?" she continued. "Let's agree to give him forty-eight hours on the ventilator. By the end of that time we'll have a much better idea of how much recovery we can ultimately expect. If he still needs the ventilator and shows no sign of recovery from the stroke, we can always take him off at that point, and we'll all know we gave him every chance."

Bruno's wife and son were relieved that the doctor thought it would be okay to keep trying. Bruno's daughter was angry and muttered something about how Dr. Jones had better hope her father doesn't "end up as a vegetable," but she didn't try to veto the ventilator. As Dr. Jones left Bruno's family, she prayed that Bruno himself would agree with her decision when he recovered—*if* he recovered.

Most people, I suspect, would want a physician like Dr. Jones, who takes her patient's advance directive seriously but does not treat it as a binding legal document. For many reasons, advance directives can never be perfect representations of a patient's future desires under all circumstances. They need to be interpreted according to the situation at hand. They can offer strong clues as to how to honor a patient's autonomy, but they cannot be the sole arbiter.

The appropriate use of advance directives requires the physician to act as a true advocate, to selflessly place the desires expressed in the directive in context with everything else that might affect the patient's wishes, and then make a recommendation that, to the best of his or her ability, honors those wishes. Unfortunately, to the extent that doctors can no longer act primarily as their patient's advocate, advance directives become less an instrument of autonomy and more an instrument of covert rationing.

Advance directives and cost

The federal government, under the Patient Self-Determination Act, requires Medicare-certified hospitals to inform all patients about the availability of advance directives at the time of every hospital admission. All fifty states have passed statutes that further support this effort. HMOs have jumped on the bandwagon, encouraging patients to adopt advance directives and creating incentives for doctors to discuss them with patients.

It's hard to believe that the enthusiasm with which HMOs and state and federal governments have embraced advance directives arises from their fervor for increasing patients' autonomy. Most patients are not that credulous, as the large majority have withstood the onslaught of encouragements to adopt advance directives. Perhaps they feel the big payers protest too much about their lack of end-of-life autonomy. My guess is that patients are displaying a combination of apathy and suspicion toward the advance directive opportunity.

The feds and insurance companies do not come right out and say that their interest in advance directives has to do with reducing expenditures. But if autonomy were their chief concern, would they designate the hospital admissions clerk as the point person for soliciting advance directives? We have seen how critical it is for patients to consider the circumstances under which they would want therapy withheld and to carefully spell out those circumstances. It would be better to not have an advance directive than to have an ambiguous one that misleads doctors about one's wishes for end-of-life care. Asking a patient to sign an advance directive at the time of hospital admission (often by including it in the pile of routine and mind-numbing legalistic documents that he must sign if he wants to receive medical care), likely without appropriate guidance (save possibly a one-sentence summary from the admissions clerk such as, "This tells the doctors you don't want to be kept alive on a machine like a vegetable"), and possibly under duress, tells us whether the motive is to guarantee the patient's autonomy or to cut costs.

Payers have been disappointed by their failure to realize measurable cost savings from advance directives. This failure is due both to the low percentage of patients who have adopted them, and to the insistence of many physicians on "interpreting" advance directives when they do exist (a hopeful sign that the doctor–patient relationship has not breathed its last).

Some HMOs have offered to support patients' autonomy by refusing to reimburse doctors and hospitals that provide care against the wishes expressed in an advance directive. Such a policy saves money for the HMOs, and it lines up with the overall effort to assure that doctors make *all* their medical decisions with legal, regulatory, and financial considerations foremost in their minds. It also has the effect of making the advance directive the final arbiter of a patient's wishes—wise patients in an era of covert rationing will know their doctors and their insurance companies well before adopting one.

Physician-assisted suicide

Aside from abortion, there is no controversy in medicine more contentious or polarizing today than the one surrounding physician-assisted suicide. Proponents of assisted suicide usually invoke a prototypical scenario to illustrate their position: Consider the patient riddled with widely metastatic cancer, facing an all too slow but inevitable death and suffering from severe, uncontrollable pain. Does not such a patient have a right to ask their physician for the means to end their suffering? And does the physician not have the right to respond without committing a crime?

It is a compelling question. This is the kind of scenario used in polls showing that the majority of Americans are in favor of physician-assisted suicide. Few would argue that this terminal, pain-racked patient should not expect his physician to relieve the suffering. Few would expect that physician to deny the desperate pleas of the patient. Most would believe it unethical for a doctor to deny those pleas.

With good, compassionate medical care, this difficult clinical problem ought to be rare; pain should be manageable in most cases without having to resort to assisted suicide. In the majority of patients with terminal pain, symptoms can be controlled with pain medication, even though the medication may need to be given in high doses or by novel routes of administration, and even though doing so may risk hastening the patient's death. This aggressive use of pain control measures in terminal patients is usually quite effective and is consistent with professional standards of behavior. It honors the autonomy of the individual patient and does so without impinging on the rights of society. Sometimes even heroic pain management fails and leaves the patient asking for death. But with adequate, creative, and aggressive pain control efforts, such instances are uncommon.

Unfortunately, some doctors don't understand pain management techniques or are too afraid to use them and, as a result, too many patients suffer needlessly as their lives draw to a close.* However, it somehow does not seem appropriate to just go ahead and kill the patient as the first option in redressing this medical shortcoming. A better approach, one might think, would be to insist on improved physician education and clear professional standards for pain control.

While the argument for assisted suicide centers on relieving the suffering of terminally ill patients with intractable pain, in actual practice these are often not the individuals who seek this remedy. By and large these were not the patients who sought out Jack Kevorkian, the famous assistant of the suicidal. Most who requested his assistance wanted to end their lives for other reasons, commonly because they suffered from disease-related depression, a debilitating sense of losing control over their own destiny, or fear of becoming a burden to their families. Some did not even have terminal illnesses. This is a pattern that holds in Holland, where assisted suicide and euthanasia are acceptable as a matter of public policy. Intractable pain is the motivator in a minority of Dutch patients who ask for assisted suicide.

Whatever the real-life usage of this "therapeutic option," however, there is a vigorous and often passionate movement in the U.S. in support of physician-assisted suicide. Some of the people in this movement undoubtedly believe that individual autonomy needs to be rescued from the clutches of the unrelenting, unfeeling, smothering bio-techno-medical machine. Others may be suffering from some underlying psy-

* Doctors had reason to fear federal prosecution for providing adequate pain medication after the U.S. Attorney General, in November, 2001, issued a directive empowering the Drug Enforcement Agency to investigate physicians who gave "too much" narcotic medication to dying patients. (See Quill TE and Meier DE, The Big Chill—Inserting the DEA into end-of-life care. *The New England Journal of Medicine*, 354:1–3, January 5, 2006.) On January 17, 2006, however, the U.S. Supreme Court overruled this directive, saying that the federal government did not have the power to overrule the states in defining "legitimate medical practice," specifically, medical practices sanctioned by the states relating to physicians' use of narcotics in terminal patients. This ruling was consistent with another Supreme Court decision from 1997, which (while unanimously striking down a constitutional *right* to assisted suicide), stipulated specifically that physicians are encouraged to use aggressive pain control measures in terminal patients when necessary, even if those measures have a chance of hastening death.

chological disorder. In still others the movement may be a vehicle for a political voice. And there are more than a few supporters of assisted suicide who have gone through the trauma of witnessing a loved one experience nightmarish end-of-life medical care at the hands of poorly trained physicians.

More than for the other two end-of-life controversies we are discussing in this chapter, the debate over assisted suicide is a debate over medical ethics. Most medical ethicists have come down strongly in favor of this practice, because the right to assisted suicide is so clearly implied by the principle of individual autonomy.

But while I have stressed the importance of individual autonomy throughout this book (one of my major themes is that individual autonomy needs to be saved from the ravages of covert rationing), close examination of the ethical question in this case suggests that, at least under our present paradigm of covert rationing, the endorsement of end-of-life autonomy threatens to lead us where we don't want to go—the coercion and devaluing of the individual.

The ethics of physician-assisted suicide

The arguments advanced by professional ethicists regarding end-of-life medicine can be difficult to follow. This is too bad, because couching ethical opinions in jargon and arcane twists of logic places the rest of us in the position of having to accept the ethical bottom line without really understanding how that bottom line was reached. It reduces ethics to received wisdom and elevates professional ethicists to a priesthood. Advancing unintelligible ethical reasoning is, well, unethical.

Once you cut through the argot, here is how most medical ethicists regard end-of-life autonomy in general and physician-assisted suicide (and its close cousin, euthanasia), in particular:

Point 1   We as a society have already decided that the individual patient's autonomy is the crucial factor in choosing to end life. We made this decision when we formally asserted the individual's right to refuse medical treatment, even life-sustaining treatments, and even if the disease for which treatment is being refused is curable. This was the critical ethical choice for us, and we have made it. Thus, we have already decided that pas-

sive euthanasia—letting nature take its course—is ethical if the
patient desires it.

Point 2   There is no ethical difference between passive and active
euthanasia. That is, there is no difference between letting nature
take its course and helping nature along a bit. In one case, the
doctor acts to remove or withhold life-sustaining therapy, thus
hastening death. In the other case, the doctor acts to administer the means of hastening death. In either case, the doctor has
taken an action that hastens death—the two acts are ethically
equivalent.

Point 3   Once active euthanasia has been determined to be ethical, there are no remaining ethical grounds for objecting to the
lesser question of physician-assisted suicide. If it is ethical for a
doctor himself to act to hasten death, there can be no objection
to his handing the patient the switch that triggers the suicide
machine.

Conclusion   As we have already asserted the right of the patient to
refuse life-sustaining therapies, ethical consistency requires us
to allow both physician-assisted suicide and active euthanasia.

Most ethicists believe the Supreme Court was wrong in 1997* when
it denied a constitutional right to assisted suicide.
Many ethicists were scandalized that the Court made
a clear ethical distinction between letting nature take
its course and hastening death, especially because it
did so in the face of nearly unanimous agreement in
the ethics community to the contrary.

The bottom line is that the same ethical principle
of individual autonomy that makes it acceptable for
patients to refuse life-sustaining therapy also renders
physician-assisted suicide and active euthanasia ethical.
There is no generally accepted ethical barrier to either.

And here is the problem I have with the analy-
sis medical ethicists have advanced on this issue. By admitting that
patients have the right to refuse medical therapy (and how could we do
otherwise?), we have embraced the principle of individual autonomy
apparently to the exclusion of all else, triggering an elaborate chain of
logic that requires us—in order to be ethically consistent—to sanc-

* In that year, the U.S. Supreme
Court overturned rulings from
lower courts that had declared
unconstitutional two state laws
criminalizing physician-assisted
suicide (thus declaring the laws
legal). On the other hand, in its
ruling the Court also implied that
there is no constitutional ban to
keep states from enacting laws that
allow assisted suicide. So there is
neither a constitutional right to nor
a constitutional ban from assisted
suicide.

tion not only assisted suicide but also active euthanasia and who knows what else. There's got to be another side to the story.

The other side to the story is that the right to individual autonomy cannot be absolute, any more than any other ethical principle can be absolute. Ethical principles often conflict with one another, in what we call an *ethical dilemma*; and an ethicist ought to help us think about ways of resolving such a dilemma. This is best done not by completely abrogating one of the conflicting principles (since both principles are, by definition, important) but by attempting to achieve a reasonable balance between the two, aimed at optimizing the overall results. When a medical ethicist says, "Individual autonomy is all there is to it, and we have no choice but to follow that principle wherever it may lead us," as I see it he is derelict in his duties. Such an ethicist can be dangerous.

In any culture the rights of the individual will be in conflict with the rights of society at large. Which rights ought to predominate will vary from society to society and even from time to time. In socialist countries the rights of the collective have primacy over those of the individual. In the United States, the rights of the individual ought to predominate—but being predominant is not the same as being unchecked.

The question of physician-assisted suicide presents an ethical dilemma.; insisting on absolute individual autonomy in this case will significantly affect society. Before we endorse assisted suicide—opinions of medical ethicists to the contrary notwithstanding—we must assess its impact on the rights of society. And we cannot estimate the cost to society without considering that, in the U.S., covert rationing of healthcare is a fact of life.

The impact of physician-assisted suicide on society

The cost-saving aspects of physician-assisted suicide, and where it will lead

As in the case of advance directives, the cost-saving aspects of physician-assisted suicide are rarely discussed openly. Yet these aspects reside just beneath the surface of many passionate arguments for legalization of assisted suicide. It's purely an issue of autonomy, these arguments go, but hey, as it turns out it's also a win-win for both sides. The individual gets his autonomy, and society saves a little money to boot.

In contrast to the case of advanced directives, when it comes to assisted suicide the payers have stayed pretty much on the sidelines. It would be unseemly for either Wonkonians or Gekkonians to become big boosters of assisted suicide, and so far medical ethicists are doing a good job of carrying the ball.

But don't expect such reticence to persist after assisted suicide becomes widely available. Once our society decides that assisted suicide is a legitimate means of expressing one's autonomy, wouldn't it be the duty of government and insurers to establish smooth processes by which such autonomy could be expressed?

The enthusiasm for potential savings occasionally bubbles to the surface. Writing in *The American Journal of Economics and Sociology*, K.K. Fung, a professor of economics, argues that tremendous cost savings could be realized by using financial incentives to *induce* patients with terminal illnesses to end their lives.* His plan, blandly called "physician-assisted death with benefit conversion," would pay such patients—more probably their estates—a very nice sum, based on a percentage of what otherwise would be spent on their healthcare, to instead opt for a voluntary, painless, and dignified death at the hands of their doctors and at a time of their choosing. Thus, not only should voluntary physician-assisted suicide be made legal; but we should also take steps to encourage this choice as a means of reducing the cost of healthcare.

* Fung KK, Dying for money: overcoming moral hazard in terminal illnesses through compensated physician-assisted death. The American Journal of Economics and Sociology 1993;52:275.

While such a proposal might look outlandish to many of us, it places a logical Gekkonian spin on what is more typically a Wonkonian issue. The only reason such a scheme seems over the top to us, Gekkonians might say, is that our thinking has not yet evolved sufficiently. We just need a little time to get used to the idea.

This example points out the corrupting influence that covert rationing will have on what otherwise might be an ethical issue. Physician-assisted suicide as an occasional and extraordinary solution to a rare, intractable clinical dilemma is one thing; institutionalized and encouraged as one of several healthcare options, however, it will become quite another.

We can easily visualize the promotion of assisted suicide as an attractive choice, as a new individual freedom, hard-won from the paternalistic healthcare system. Magazine ads and pamphlets (included with your hospital admission packet) will tell how you have the power to save yourself from the grasp of the medical automatons, to be rescued from their needles, biopsies, and scans, to take control of your destiny and remove yourself to a place where, free from pain and enveloped by peace, you can be eased into the next life. You no longer have to suffer. You no longer have to worry about being a burden to your family. It's in your power to do one last thing for yourself and for the ones you love. It's your choice, you are told lovingly—and expectantly.

Even if you choose not to listen to this stuff, your children and grandchildren will. And even if they don't say it, sooner or later they'll be thinking, *Well, it's sort of getting to be about that time, isn't it?*

And before you know it, the choice for assisted suicide will become the duty for assisted suicide.

Devaluing end-of-life care

In our healthcare system today, we pay a lot of attention to those who are dying. The hospice movement is strong, and medical research in the past decades has helped immensely with caring for the physical and emotional needs of the dying. Resolution of many personal, emotional, and family issues is facilitated in the last days of life, thanks to the recognition that these things are important not only to the patient but also to those the patient will leave behind. Yet such efforts are expensive and emotionally taxing, even for those who have developed expertise in end-of-life care.

If an easier (and cheaper) way were available, careful and compassionate end-of-life care would be de-emphasized. We don't need it any more, HMOs would say. People are choosing suicide in celebration of their autonomy. And by making good end-of-life care harder to come by, they would render assisted suicide a more attractive choice.

Making society callous to suffering

While nobody likes to talk about it, suffering people can be insufferable. In their emotional and physical pain, they can be demanding, self-absorbed, and abusive. They often need constant, difficult, unpleasant care. No matter how compassionate we caretakers may be—healthcare workers and family alike—there is always some element of wishing the sufferer would be gone.

Insightful healthcare workers recognize this dark-side impulse as a natural one; and this recognition helps them to work through their own ambivalence about the suffering patient. It also helps them to counsel family members, who often feel guilty because of the same kinds of ambivalent feelings. The prohibition against euthanasia and assisted suicide makes the bedside a safe place to work through these issues—we can recognize and deal with our darker impulses, knowing that, no matter what, we don't have the option of acting on them.

And working through such impulses is healthy. By doing so, we learn to understand and live with the suffering of others; we learn compassion for the human condition; ultimately, we learn to be more accepting when it is our own turn to suffer.

But if there were an alternative, if we didn't have to deal with watching our loved ones suffer or with the feelings of frustration, anger, and guilt their suffering causes within us, then wouldn't it be easy to take advantage of that alternative? Over time, it would become hard to understand why anybody would tolerate suffering (and why they would be so unfeeling as to expose the rest of us to the discomfort of having to watch them suffer and to having to care for them while they selfishly did so) when there was such an obvious, painless, and commonly used alternative. After a while we would learn to apply this solution to more and more forms of suffering, and our tolerance for any form of suffering, real or perceived, would erode. Suffering individuals would no longer teach us compassion for the human condition; they would merely provoke disgust.

This is not just a prediction. It has, you'll remember, happened before.

Inviting lawyers to the bedside

There's no way we'll ever tolerate physician-assisted suicide without safeguards. Legal safeguards are the main reason assisted suicide will never be abused, according to its proponents. Consider what such laws will do, however. They will directly insert lawyers, for the first time on a routine basis, into end-of-life care. And when we remind ourselves that the only other model we have for legal killing in our society (outside of warfare) is capital punishment, we get a flavor of what such legal wrangling might mean.

Coming to terms with death is hard enough on everybody as it is. Do we really want to add lawyers to the mix of family, friends, medical personnel, and clergy at the bedside? Do we really want to turn the process of dying into another difficult legal process?

The slippery slope

The slippery slope argument is dismissed out of hand by most in the end-of-life movement. It doesn't hold water, they say. It is illogical to argue that something as affirming of individual autonomy as assisted suicide can ever lead to the abuses of individuals by society. And if, in reply, one tries to describe to them how it already has happened in recent memory, they tend to become indignant and shut off all conversation: If we can't discuss this without you calling me a Nazi, then we have nothing to talk about.

People in the end-of-life movement are not Nazis. The vast majority are good, compassionate, well-meaning people who have the best interests of dying patients at heart. But if you examine the facts coldly and logically, and if you factor in the depth of our increasing economic crisis in healthcare, the slippery slope argument becomes compelling.

Let's deal first with the Nazis. The Nazis were obsessed with the purity of race, with removing all "imperfect" humans from the breeding pool. That was their ideology, and we don't have that ideology.

Yet the evolution of the arguments advanced by the Nazis to justify their actions sounds eerily familiar. Long before the Nazis came to power, German scholars were calling for legal euthanasia as a means of promoting mercy and personal choice in the face of intractable suffering, using language identical to the language we are hearing today. This movement steadily gained steam, and during the economic crisis of post–World War I Germany it came to be advanced as a way of controlling spending on individuals who were seen as burdens to society. The so-called science of eugenics added the imprimatur of the scientific community to the humanitarian and economic arguments made by proponents of euthanasia. By the time the Nazis came to power, the groundwork had been laid for their handiwork. It had been laid not by

fiends but by well-intentioned scientists, doctors, lawyers, and economists. To dismiss those events as irrelevant to our culture is foolish.

Also relevant to the slippery slope argument is the Dutch experience with euthanasia. The Dutch decriminalized euthanasia in the
early 1990s and legalized it in 2001. Doctors practicing euthanasia in
the Netherlands are expected to follow certain guidelines, to be sure.
These guidelines require intolerable suffering on the part of the patient
that causes them to persistently request to be allowed to die; the patient
must have a good understanding of what he or she is requesting; no
other reasonable solutions can be apparent; and at least two physicians
must concur that euthanasia is the only good choice.

Recent reports on the Dutch experience have been mixed. American
proponents of assisted suicide see a shining example of the societal
benefits of permitting end-of-life autonomy of choice. Opponents see
a series of terrible abuses (noting, specifically, an utter disregard of the
prescribed guidelines). To me, the most striking feature of the Dutch
experience and the most relevant to the slippery slope argument is
that hundreds of cases of "active involuntary euthanasia" are apparently occurring each year.* In other words, patients are being killed at
the hands of their doctors and without their explicit * Van der Wal, G, Dillman,
permission. All, it is said, are leading insufferable exis- RJM. Euthanasia in the
tences, and all are being euthanized solely for humane Netherlands. *British Medical*
reasons.   *Journal* 1994;308:1346.

What do medical ethicists say about such a thing? Not all agree, of
course, but it turns out that it is fairly easy to derive an ethical argument in support of involuntary active euthanasia from the premise
of upholding individual autonomy. It goes like this: The principle of
autonomy demands that patients be allowed to refuse therapy; refusal
of therapy is the ethical equivalent of voluntary euthanasia (as we have
seen); as voluntary euthanasia is a right of individuals with intractable
suffering, it follows that it would be unethical to withhold euthanasia from suffering individuals just because they are incapacitated and
unable to give their permission. Hence, involuntary euthanasia is ethical for suffering patients who are unable to give their permission.

This leaves us at a place where others can decide for an individual
what constitutes intractable suffering and when that individual is
incompetent to make such a determination for him or herself. Where

these "others" end up drawing the line on whether a person's existence is of value or whether a person is competent can be influenced by all sorts of external factors.

In Nazi Germany, those external factors included a belief in the purity of the Aryan race, and that belief led to horrible excesses. Again, we don't have that belief here.

What we do have is an imperative to ration healthcare, which means that potentially beneficial care is going to have to be withheld from somebody, somewhere. Can we be sure that, once we start down the road of allowing patients to choose death, we will be able to withstand *our* external influences and stay our hands from ending the suffering of some who might not be so sure of their choices or who are incapable of making a choice—especially when, by so doing, we will make more healthcare available to others who could actually benefit from it?

I believe the slippery slope argument is valid in this case.

Erosion of the doctor–patient relationship

I don't need to say too much more about this. A vignette will suffice.

Why is that doctor smiling?

Imagine yourself at age seventy-five in a hospital bed, with a serious illness but one that is potentially treatable with a lot of effort. Your doctor walks in, smiling.

If physician-assisted suicide and euthanasia are not available, you can be reasonably sure he's smiling with confidence. He thinks he can cure you, and his smile tells you so. You relax. You feel better already.

But what if assisted suicide and euthanasia *are* legal? What would his smile mean then? He still might be smiling with confidence, of course. But maybe he's smiling for another reason. Maybe it's that sheepish, somewhat sympathetic, ain't-life-a-pisser smile that can herald bad news. Maybe he's about to pull up a chair, slowly let his smile fade, and say, "Well, you know, things don't look so good this time, Charlie." He'll pause, then let the smile return, "But the good news is, we can make it all pretty easy on you."

Or worse, he might not say anything. He might offer some vague opinions, like "Well, Charlie, we're sitting on some pretty nasty blockages here. But I've seen worse." That smile again. "I'm real certain things are going to work out just fine. And all that pain and windedness? Well, that's going away. Promise." Then he leaves. And he leaves you guessing. Just how hard *is* he going to work to make you well, before he decides the other way is better?

You've even heard—well, you've heard they don't always tell you beforehand.

It's hard to imagine anything more destructive to the trust between a doctor and a patient than knowing that your doctor, at some point, may shift from trying to cure you to trying to usher you into the next life as cheaply and painlessly as possible (by encouraging suicide, by offering euthanasia, or by just doing the euthanasia because you're so incompetent you can't see it's the only thing to do).

If people want to commit suicide, and if the ethicists agree that assisted suicide is okay, then let the ethicists do the assisting. I have little to say against ethicist-assisted suicide. But leave the doctors out of it.

So what should we do about physician-assisted suicide?

We should not legalize physician-assisted suicide and euthanasia, and certainly not while we're covertly rationing healthcare. The potential for abuse is too high. Institutionalizing and popularizing these procedures will carry too high a price for our society. And the ultimate price we would pay, supposedly in the pursuit of individual autonomy, ironically, is a *devaluing* of the worth of the individual. This is a particularly precious example of the corruptive nature of covert rationing.

Does foregoing assisted suicide mean we'll need to abandon our suffering patients? No, we need to redouble our search for ways to relieve the physical and emotional suffering of patients approaching the end of their lives. We've already made a lot of progress in this area.

But what about those cases where terminal patients have intractable pain despite all usual attempts to ameliorate it and are begging for relief? Here, it is the duty of physicians to relieve the suffering, even if it requires the administration of enough narcotic medication to produce coma or even risk hastening death. Many physicians, not unreasonably,

fear prosecution for using pain control measures that risk the hastening of death. But the relief of suffering is an ancient primary directive
of the medical profession. Aggressive pain control, not aimed at inducing death but risking it, is a principled action that doctors ought to
take, even at their own personal risk, on behalf of and in concert with
their patient, to whom they owe a duty to relieve suffering if a cure is
impossible.

This sort of action depends on a trusting relationship between the
doctor and the patient. But covert rationing, which is clearly one of the
forces behind the push to legalize assisted suicide, is destroying the
relationship between doctors and patients that makes such intimate,
trust-based actions possible.

Medical futility

On this last end-of-life issue I'll be brief, as I merely wish to reinforce
my main point.

Those who still believe that the rise of the end-of-life movement is
solely due to the quest for increased patient autonomy, and that it has
nothing to do with cost, need look no further than the issue of medical
futility. From the standpoint of autonomy, medical futility is the flip
side of advance directives and physician-assisted suicide. For medical
futility is the issue of what to do about the patient who is demanding care that the medical establishment has deemed futile (that is,
extremely unlikely to be beneficial).

In these cases the patient requesting futile care is in the throes of
an inexorable—but often expensive and prolonged—process of dying,
generally in an acute care hospital and often in an intensive care unit.
There is no hope of substantially prolonging their survival, but there's
plenty of opportunity, before death actually occurs, to spend lots
of money on care that objective medical science agrees is extremely
unlikely to be of any use. And it is just such care that the patient or
the family is demanding. Patients in these cases generally feel just as
strongly about not giving up as the patients requesting assisted suicide
feel about hastening death. Accordingly, in medical futility cases the
patient asserts her autonomy by insisting that "everything" be done.

If autonomy were really the issue to those in the end-of-life movement, then the people who stand foursquare behind the autonomy of

the patient when urging her to establish an advance directive or when she seeks physician-assisted suicide would also strongly support her when she wants to express her autonomy by asking for *more* care. But that's not what is happening. Many supporters of the end-of-life movement are strangely silent on the issue of medical futility.

The cost considerations of end-of-life futility are not subtle. Every struggling hospital has the facts and figures to show that a substantial proportion of their financial losses come from taking care of patients who are critically ill and who have little chance of a full recovery. So doctors, hospitals, insurers and the government are all anxious to limit their spending on futile end-of-life care. This is not unreasonable. We *shouldn't* spend billions on futile healthcare (as long as we can figure out prospectively which care is really futile).

Ideally, these disputes ought to be resolved through the vehicle of the classic doctor–patient relationship. A true physician-advocate always tells the patient the truth. And if the truth is that there's nothing useful to be done, the patient eventually accepts that truth, because the doctor is trustworthy under the classic doctor–patient relationship, and the patient accordingly moves on to addressing any remaining life-issues that ought to be resolved at such a time. In a healthy doctor–patient relationship, futile care is not offered, nor is it requested.

The weakening of the doctor–patient relationship makes this ideal resolution very difficult. Furthermore, as rationing by omission is a chief mechanism of covert rationing, patients are (quite reasonably) more likely to demand that no stone be unturned. After all, when they're covertly rationing, the only way you can be sure that everything reasonable is being done for you is by demanding that everything possible be done. The growing demand for futile end-of-life care may be yet another hidden cost of covert rationing.

The hospitals that are left holding the bag are not about to take this lying down. They have invented ways of dealing with patients and families who are demanding inappropriate care. Generally, the process begins with a series of sympathetic but intense discussions between hospital personnel and the family (and the patient, if feasible). The team of hospital personnel recruited to this effort most often includes concerned doctors, medical ethicists, social workers, and clergy—all of whom have done this before. Faced with an onslaught of caring individuals such as these, the patient and family usually see the light. If they still insist on receiving the futile care, their case is submitted for formal review by a hospital bioethics committee which, after hearing from all interested parties, including the same team of experts who met with the family, issues a binding judgment on the disputed medical care. Said binding judgment is often (remarkably enough) in favor of withholding the therapy in question. If the patient and family still want to fight, they can try to find another hospital willing to spend money on a therapy that already has been deemed futile in a formal hearing, or they can initiate a lawsuit. But in practice few courts are willing to second guess the well-developed, expert-rich internal procedures that hospitals have developed for the purpose of resolving ethically challenging issues like medical futility. So, for the most part, hospitals have learned to deal effectively with end-of-life futility issues.

I am not knocking this process. In general, it is a humane and reasonably fair way to gain resolution of a very difficult problem. I describe it here simply to point out that this process makes no pretense of awarding absolute priority to the patient's individual autonomy. Instead, the patient's autonomous wishes are weighed against the wishes of society, as represented by a hospital committee. This process attempts to honor the patients' autonomy but does not defer to it. And clearly, when it comes to futile medical care society's proxy has the final say.

It is notable that the activists who insist individual autonomy must remain sacrosanct when resolving other end-of-life issues have nothing to say when that same autonomy is set aside during questions of end-of-life futility. When autonomy and cost both support the same side of an issue, it's easy for everybody to say they're acting to uphold autonomy. It's only when autonomy and cost are on opposite sides of an issue that we can see what's really the principal motivator.

The end-of-life controversies—conclusion

The issues surrounding end-of-life medical care are of vital importance both to individuals and to society. Perhaps more than any of the other issues raised in this book, the way we handle end-of-life care will determine what kind of a people we become in the twenty-first century.

End-of-life activists like to remind us that they are fighting to preserve the autonomy of individuals at the end of their lives. But insisting on autonomy in end-of-life decisions creates a paradox. For what is death if not a reminder that the right of self-determination is at best a temporary gift?

Gift may not even be the right word here. Perhaps a better word would be *necessity*. For individual autonomy, while a basic American principle, is not the highest possible good. Our reliance on individual autonomy is not some pinnacle of ethical thought but is merely a palliative, a partial and inadequate (though necessary) compensation for having to live in an imperfect world. As we face our exit from this imperfect world, the ideal of individual autonomy necessarily loses much of its significance.

Giving the dying patient a sense of control over their last days is a humane thing to do, and we ought always to do it, to the extent we can do so without harming society. But to throw all other considerations to the wind, to make the dying patient's autonomy the overriding concern that trumps all others, ignores reality, ignores other things the dying patient needs more than his autonomy, is harmful to society and calls into question our real motives.

While giving the dying patient some sense of control is important, it is not the most important thing at that time of life. Instead of encouraging a hasty exit there are things we should be doing that really need to be done. We should offer relief from physical and emotional pain, offer help in resolving remaining issues of family or personal conflict, and offer spiritual support. We should let the dying person know that he won't be abandoned, that we are embracing him, not culling him from the herd. It is by such an affirmation of that person's continuing importance that we honor his value as an individual.

Covert rationing precludes trust-based end-of-life care. It destroys the trust between doctors and patients and even between patients and loved ones. Covert rationing corrupts everything it touches.

Part III

An American Solution to the Healthcare Crisis

8

Modeling an American
Healthcare System

BY NOW YOU CAN see that Quadrant III healthcare, based on covert rationing, is a lousy way to run a healthcare system. Not only is Quadrant III healthcare harming millions of Americans—on both ends of the stethoscope—but it is also eroding the principle of individual autonomy. It is doing all this without solving, or even slowing in any substantial way, the fiscal crisis that makes the rationing necessary in the first place. There has got to be a better way.

This third and final part of the book explores what such a better way might look like and how we might achieve it. This chapter begins to imagine a healthcare system that is fair, effective, and fiscally sound. Because open rationing will be an important feature of any real solution to our healthcare problems, the next chapter looks at how we might establish a methodology for open rationing that supports American values. The last chapter considers how individual Americans, by acting independently and in their own self-interest, might catalyze such a reformation of the American healthcare system.

Toward an upper-quadrant healthcare system

In the first chapter we considered the essential characteristics of each of the four quadrants of the healthcare universe as defined by the GUTH. We have seen that neither of the lower quadrants supports an equitable or sustainable healthcare system. This suggests that we ought to aspire to an upper-quadrant healthcare system, where high quality and transparency reign. Unfortunately, as soon as we begin to consider what a pure Quadrant II or Quadrant I healthcare system might look like and what it would take to get there, neither of those options appears to be feasible either.

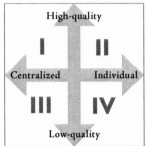

A pure Quadrant II system is easy to dispense with right away. In Quadrant II, patients would pay for all of their own healthcare themselves, thereby regaining control over their own medical destiny. But such a scheme has been priced out of the realm of possibility. There aren't enough people who can fund their own healthcare, at least not when they become sick and actually have to use medical services.

On the other hand, a pure Quadrant I system, with a completely equitable, centralized system of open rationing, is equally difficult to visualize in the U.S. Other Western nations ration healthcare much more openly than we do, but the methods they use would be next to impossible to sell to Americans. The rationing is often "by queue": If you need an expensive procedure, such as a cardiac bypass or hip replacement surgery, you're placed on a waiting list, and if you survive long enough to make it to the top of the list then you can have your surgery. (That many do *not* survive long enough to receive needed care seems to be regarded as an unfortunate but, considering the resultant savings, not deeply lamented fact of life.) Certain expensive (though effective) medical products or services are not made available to anyone, no matter how long they're willing to wait in line. In other cases rationing is done by age, so you might be eligible for a particular medical service only until you're, say, sixty (about when the likelihood increases that you will need it).

The bureaucrats directing rationing in these other countries have a significant advantage over bureaucrats in the United States. In many Western societies, individual citizens seem far more amenable toward open healthcare rationing than Americans would be, for at least three reasons:

- Outside the United States, expectations of what the healthcare system can or ought to provide are often low—the culture of no limits is principally American.
- People in many Western countries, especially in Europe, seem more willing than Americans to subordinate their individual

needs to the greater good. Such subordination may reflect a rational trade-off—the government provides many of their individual needs, and in return the citizens tolerate the delays that occur from time to time in meeting those needs. Call it passivity, call it an innate propensity toward socialism, or just call it civic equanimity—whatever you want to call it, Americans don't have it.

+ Especially in countries that traditionally have honored strict differences among the social classes, patients may be less likely to question the opinions of authority figures, such as physicians. This latter characteristic might explain why, even in countries where systems of open healthcare rationing are deeply embedded, a lot of the rationing actually remains covert.*

We just don't have this kind of substrate for open rationing in the United States.

Given these constraints, let us define the problem. We want to design an American healthcare system that operates in the upper quadrants. That an entirely self-pay, Quadrant II system is out of the question pushes us toward Quadrant I and thus toward open rationing. But as we look around the world for a model of open healthcare rationing we could apply in the U.S., we find none compatible with the American character.

We're going to have to devise a healthcare system that incorporates open rationing but that is suitable for Americans. In trying to envision such a thing, I am going to suggest straddling Quadrant I and Quadrant II, with one foot in each quadrant. We can conceive of a healthcare system that preserves the best parts of Quadrant I and Quadrant II, while limiting the negative aspects of each, and that honors the worth of every individual.

* I once asked a British physician how he goes about informing patients over the age of 60 who have renal failure that they're not eligible for dialysis under Great Britain's National Health Service and therefore will soon die. He looked at me with a surprised expression and said that they actually don't tell their patients that. They just tell them that they are very sick, that nothing can be done, and that they ought to go home and put their affairs in order.

What features are needed in an American healthcare system?

A healthcare system that includes a component of open rationing and that is equitable, just, and palatable to Americans has to embody two characteristics omitted from most healthcare systems around the world. These are: ensuring the autonomy of individuals; and guaranteeing continued medical progress.

Individual autonomy and empowerment

Healthcare rationing, by withholding useful medical care from one person in favor of another, asks individuals to suppress their pursuit of life and happiness for the good of the whole. Under the best of circumstances rationing will present a challenge to Americans. However, rationing does not have to violate the autonomy of the individual.

Rationing that is done openly and honestly, with full disclosure of all the rules that determine how the rationing is conducted (rules that are developed in an open process), and that employs fair and transparent procedures that apply to all individuals can be compatible with a culture of individual autonomy. Covert rationing, on the other hand, with its incomplete disclosure of the facts, its obfuscation, deception, and lies, cannot. A healthcare system that employs rationing and supports basic principles of American culture will have to ration openly and transparently.

Such a system will have to find ways of empowering individuals within that system, too. "Empowerment" here means two things:

+ Patients must be empowered to pursue every option available to them within the system of rules that determine how their healthcare is rationed. This implies that patients will have access to true advocates, to professionals who understand medicine in general and the patients' medical needs in particular and who, placing the patients' individual needs ahead of every other consideration, can work within the system of rules to assure that they get all the necessary medical care that is coming to them. In other words, this form of empowerment requires a full restoration of the doctor–patient relationship. I will have a lot to say about how such a restoration might be accomplished in Chapter 10.
+ The second form of empowerment applies to the patients themselves. We need to develop tools and systems that enable interested patients to take a direct hand in guiding their own medical care and making appropriate medical decisions. This second form of empowerment flies in the face of traditional thinking on

the proper role of patients. Most societies have taken a paternalistic view that the doctor knows best. The patient's role is to go to the doctor, then do what the doctor recommends. Despite recent lip service to patient empowerment, the paternalistic view of the patient's role is deeply embedded, nurtured, and, in fact, necessary in our own system of covert rationing.

Some would argue that the paternalistic view is defensible: Medicine is complex and nuanced. In the U.S., doctors attend four years of college, then four years of medical school, then three years of residency; most add another two or three (or more) years of subspecialty training before they're turned loose to practice medicine. And even then some of them don't really know what they're talking about. To expect patients to become sophisticated enough to do much more than accept the recommendations of their highly trained doctors is inherently problematic.

According to proponents of the paternalistic view, it is laughable to suppose that your average patient can spend a few hours on the Internet and thereby learn enough to even understand, let alone help manage in any meaningful way, their own medical care. More likely, they'll pick up a bunch of tangential and confounding notions or out-and-out misinformation that will confuse, delay, and derail any fruitful interactions they might have with their doctor. It is absurd to think that your average patient can do anything more than screw things up by butting in to the doctor's business. The doctor will tell them what they really need to know, and if the doctor wants them to learn more, he'll tell them where to go for the information. The whole idea, often tossed around by navel-gazing commentators, that patients should or could become sufficiently empowered to manage their own healthcare is nothing more than a cruel hoax. Let the pros make the medical decisions. That's what they're paid for.

While there's more truth to this paternalistic view than I like to admit, it is a view we're going to have to leave behind in our new American healthcare system. If our system is to succeed, patients will have to be regarded as autonomous individuals, full partners—if not the senior partners—in the doctor–patient relationship, and active participants in the medical decisions that pertain to them, even to the point of calling most of the shots whenever possible. To fulfill this role properly, patients will have to empower themselves by acquiring as much focused knowledge as they can regarding their own medical conditions. Patients don't have to become doctors themselves, but they do need to become knowledgeable enough to hold their own in a conversation with one, to understand what the doctor is talking about, to ask questions that are focused and pertinent, and (perhaps most importantly in a system that relies on doctors to ration healthcare at the bedside), to recognize when the doctor is leaving important options out of the discussion altogether.

Achieving a sufficient state of empowerment will not be easy. Even for patients of strong intellectual capacity, the tools for this sort of self-empowerment are generally inadequate today. It takes a special patient to become empowered through knowledge and to use this empowerment effectively. Many of those who disparage patient empowerment as a strategy have nothing against it in principle; their objection is a practical one; it's just not possible, they'll say, for most patients to become empowered.

Making the autonomous, empowered patient the centerpiece of our proposed American healthcare system is going to be even more problematic than making the system universal. Why, then, must we insist on it? There is no other way to assure patients that their rights and welfare will be sufficiently safeguarded.

The era of covert rationing has shown that neither the insurance carriers nor the government nor even the patient's own physician can be relied upon, when the going gets tough, to do their best for the individual patient. The pressures to do otherwise are too great. Empowering individuals within the healthcare system is not so much an attempt to reach some new pinnacle of medical ethics as it is an admission of failure, a recognition that nobody can be relied on to care what happens to the patient except the patient himself.

As difficult as it will be and despite all the good arguments about its impracticality, assuring the autonomy of the individual patient and putting systems in place that enable him to oversee his own medical care will have to be part of our new American healthcare system. Fortunately, once a demand is recognized for products and services that enable and facilitate patient empowerment, our free enterprise system will respond. Chapter 10 explores some of the tools available today, and some that are likely to be developed, to advance this kind of empowerment.

Ensuring continued medical progress

While our traditional Quadrant IV Tooth Fairy healthcare system was fiscally doomed from the beginning, its effects were not all bad. It was the if-you-build-it-and-it-works-it-will-get-paid-for paradigm of the Quadrant IV system that stimulated the amazing progress in healthcare and medical technology we have all enjoyed since the end of World War II.

During the last five or six decades, most important medical advances either originated in the United States or were stimulated by the knowledge that the American healthcare system would provide a ready market for inventions and products originating elsewhere.

In developing our new American healthcare system we're going to have to back off from the no limits mentality that obligated us to push ahead to find cures for every disease, up to and including death itself. But medical progress over the past sixty years has prolonged the lives of our loved ones, has relieved suffering, has mitigated or prevented disability, and has provided a powerful stimulus not only to the American economy but also to our native American optimism and can-do spirit.

It would be a crime against humanity to abandon the vast and mature infrastructure that has produced this kind of progress, to stop advancing healthcare progress, and to agree to settle forever for the level of medical care that we have today (or perhaps even a lower level). To continue finding new ways to prolong lives and relieve suffering and disability, to stave off our own societal enervation and fatalism, and to nurture our national spirit, our new American healthcare system must assure that incentives remain in place to guarantee continued innovation and progress in medical care.

Six principles
for an American healthcare system

Given these considerations, we can now discuss the six principles necessary for designing a fair, equitable, and uniquely American healthcare system.

Principle 1
We must define clearly the purpose of healthcare services

Until now, our culture of no limits has made it unnecessary—or impossible—to agree on the purpose of healthcare services. But as soon as we admit that there *are* limits to what we can spend, we have to specify that purpose. We have to keep this definition in mind as we decide on the scope of activities that our limited healthcare dollar will cover.

I approach this problem by defining the purpose of healthcare services as I see it, then considering the implications of this definition as it relates to rationing.

The purpose of healthcare services is to maintain or restore the individual's health when possible or to optimize functional capacity, control symptoms, and compensate for restrictions when a disease or disability cannot be cured or prevented.

What this definition does

This definition implies that the overriding goals of the healthcare system are to prevent and treat disease and to provide individuals who cannot be rendered disease-free or disability-free with their best opportunity to enjoy the rewards of life. It charges the healthcare system with a public health task (searching for ways to prevent and treat diseases that afflict humans) and with an individual health task (to optimize the health and functional status of individuals, whether or not they have diseases that can be "cured").

What this definition does not do

Many people would consider this statement subversive, for it removes from the province of healthcare services activities they would want to include: It does not require doctors to prolong life as long as possible, whatever the cost in dollars or in suffering; it does not require altering the normal progression of life (for example, halting the aging process); it does not charge the healthcare system with seeking out or administering treatments that enhance the lives of people in the absence of disease or disability (for example, face-lift surgery or hair transplants). This definition acknowledges limits to what the healthcare system can do and to what it should be expected to do.

Many would like to see a broader definition. For instance, some would require the healthcare system to provide individuals with physical, mental, and social wellbeing.

Such an inclusive definition encourages the medicalization of society, whereby various conditions not traditionally considered diseases are redefined as such. Medicalization presents a real difficulty for us in the context of open rationing. Some people classify shyness as an illness that reduces a person's capacity for social wellbeing, for example. But do we really want people with cancer to have to compete with the shy for healthcare resources? Under a system of open rationing, we ought to limit the scope of healthcare services to real, honest-to-goodness diseases and disabilities and rescind the list of boutique illnesses our society has created in recent years.

You may or may not agree with the specifics of my proposed definition, and that's fine. But before we can begin to devise an equitable system of open rationing, we have to define the scope of healthcare services.

Principle 2
There must be open competition for resources between healthcare services and all the other services society provides

Having defined the purpose of healthcare services, we need to prioritize that purpose in relation to all the other services society is expected to provide. These include national defense, the interstate highway system, education, the criminal justice system, garbage collection, and others. Those who think in terms of the no limits paradigm for healthcare can have trouble with the idea that healthcare has to compete with the stealth bomber for our limited public resources. But to the extent that healthcare will be publicly funded under our new system, that is the way it is; and a fair system of open rationing forces us to recognize this.

We should prioritize services through an open budgetary process, considering dollars allotted to healthcare in relation to all other necessary expenditures. We can increase healthcare benefits by allotting more dollars to healthcare, but only by reducing some other benefit—increasing the class sizes in elementary schools, for example. Having to consciously make such trade-offs may cause us to reevaluate all our priorities.

Principle 3
As much as possible, rationing decisions should be left to the patients affected by those decisions

Rationing decisions will be fairer and more acceptable if they are made by patients themselves instead of imposed (through coercion of physicians) by a distant bureaucracy.

Not long ago, individual patients and doctors made spending decisions. Quadrant IV healthcare insulated both doctors and patients from the cost of their healthcare decisions. There was no incentive for patients to forego the most expensive testing or the newest therapy available, whatever the cost and no matter how small the expected marginal benefit.

A system of open rationing should remedy this disconnect by establishing incentives for patients to take the cost of medical services into account when making decisions about their own healthcare. The more cost-efficient the decisions patients make on their own behalf, the less rationing will have to be forced by a third party.

One way to provide such incentives is to integrate a modified form of Health Savings Accounts (HSAs) into our rationing system. HSAs provide a strong incentive for individuals to reduce nonessential healthcare spending and thus have the potential to reduce the overall level of imposed rationing that will be necessary. Later in this chapter I show how these modified HSAs would work for all Americans in a proposed new model for healthcare.

Principle 4
Healthcare coverage must be universal

Every American should be fully covered by our new healthcare system. Universal coverage is required not just because everyone needs healthcare or because we Americans ought to be generous to one another or because it's the humane thing to do. Universal coverage is required because *justice* requires it.

Actually, justice requires universal coverage today, even before we design a new healthcare system. This is because, under our present system, everyone in the United States (not just citizens, and not just taxpayers) shares in the cost of everybody else's healthcare and so is owed the benefits of healthcare. The shared costs include:

+ Mandatory payroll deductions to pay for Medicare and Medicaid
+ The higher income taxes individuals must pay to offset tax-deductible health insurance premiums purchased by businesses for their employees
+ The higher prices paid for goods and services that companies charge to cover the costs of those premiums
+ The massive societal burden we are creating when we allow our healthcare spending to be passed off to future generations by way of the national debt

These costs are borne by everyone residing in the United States, so every individual has a just claim to healthcare.

Our new healthcare system will reside partly in Quadrant I, and to the extent that it does, it will require public funding, possibly to a greater extent than our current Quadrant III system does. Furthermore, under a system of open rationing, healthcare services will be competing for funding with the other services our society must provide. So every individual who either pays into or lives under the public funding system—that is, every participant in the American social contract—will have a stake in how healthcare decisions are made. Justice requires universal coverage.

This justification for universal coverage is *not* the same as an entitlement. An entitlement is granted on the basis of some quality of the individual (such as being an American citizen, or over sixty-five, or a human being). An entitlement is bestowed on individuals not as part of a contract but instead as an arbitrary grant, awarded by the government, just because of who they are. In theory, an entitlement can be arbitrarily withdrawn as well. But in practice, once they grant an entitlement politicians are loath to take it away or even to limit it. A new entitlement is soon seen by its recipients—and by the bureaucracy that administers and regulates it—as something that is owed forever, no matter what else society must sacrifice in order to provide it.

In contrast, the universal coverage I'm talking about is owed to individuals not because of who they are but solely as a result of their being party to a social contract, under which healthcare is a consideration given in return for certain services the individual provides society.* Because society will have effected a contract that extracts a price from individuals to provide a public benefit, justice dictates that all individuals who pay the price should have an equal right to partake of the public benefit.

* Typically, the services envisioned in such a social contract include the payment of taxes, availability to perform jury duty, serving in the military if drafted, assisting law enforcement officers when requested, and other such societal obligations. In our new healthcare system, one such obligation would be to subject oneself to rationing decisions.

The universal coverage I'm talking about will look a lot like an entitlement to most observers, and I may be talking about a distinction without a difference. Still, there are important reasons to distinguish the two.

We can set boundaries for universal coverage defined in this way. There would be no obligation to provide individuals with every manner of available healthcare under all circumstances; the only obligation would be to provide every individual the level of healthcare provided as a public benefit to all other individuals, under the terms of the social contract. An entitlement to healthcare, on the other hand, is an open-ended promise in which "healthcare" comprises anything and everything one might think of that has any possibility of restoring a bit of health.

To summarize, unless we move toward a self-pay model for healthcare (which is not even remotely possible), universal coverage needs to be an intrinsic part of an American healthcare system as a matter of justice. By declaring the principle of justice to be the sole reason for providing universal coverage, however, we will move healthcare (as subtle as this movement might seem) out of the realm of entitlement; thus we will retain the right to set boundaries for what we mean by universal healthcare coverage. These boundaries are necessary for any system of open rationing. The hard work lies ahead, but at least we have established a principle for setting reasonable limits on the healthcare our system is obligated to provide.

When I say coverage should be universal, I do not mean to say only that it should be offered to everybody. I also mean that participation in the new American healthcare system is a *requirement*. Everybody must play. I especially mean to include here the rich, the influential, and—get ready—even members of Congress. Only by mandating the participation of the movers and shakers can we ensure that the design of our new healthcare system—especially the rationing component—will get the care and consideration it deserves.

Principle 5
Clear rules of rationing must be decided in an open forum

Rules for the open rationing of healthcare should be decided from the perspective of patients (that is, of the public), not of economic, medical, policy, or ethics experts. Experts will introduce conflicts of interest. Healthcare economists will favor sacrificing fairness in favor of maximizing total societal good (more on this later). Medical experts will want to include whatever services and procedures they get paid to perform. Policy makers will want to include only services they can easily regulate. And who knows what the medical ethicists will want to do!

Only the public has the right to make these determinations. They are the ones paying for the services (because the services are not being given to them as an entitlement); and they are the ones who will have to live with the results.

Thus, whatever rationing methodologies are to be used, they must be open, widely discussed, and based on a broad consensus.

Principle 6
Healthcare services must be prioritized according to clear ethical standards

Open rationing of healthcare must be grounded in ethics. If we were not concerned with maintaining our ethical principles, we might as well let covert rationing persist. So we have to articulate the ethical precepts we will abide by as we do the actual rationing—that is, as we prioritize healthcare services to determine what will be covered and not covered.

The ethics of rationing are not straightforward, however, because the ethical precepts we would wish to follow, instead of giving us clear guidance as to how to go about prioritizing healthcare services, contradict each other. Specifically, no rationing system can both maximize the fairness and maximize the good that is achieved with the dollars spent. We are going to have to make some sort of a choice between optimizing fairness and optimizing overall good. Such ethical decisions will be the

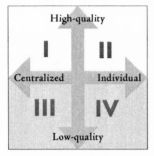

most difficult step we'll have to take in devising a system for rationing and will be the strongest determinant of our success or failure. Furthermore, the choices we make will go a long way toward determining what kind of society we will become during the twenty-first century—and thus we should not leave these choices up to professional ethicists. They are going to have to be decided through a broad public consensus. We should therefore consider the ethical precepts that will guide our rationing in some detail, and Chapter 9 does just that.

What might an upper-quadrant healthcare system look like?

I am about to describe a model for a new American healthcare system that straddles Quadrant II and Quadrant I, and that incorporates the six principles I have just discussed. This model healthcare system (see Figure 4) comprises three tiers. One major tier incorporating open healthcare rationing (the middle tier) is sandwiched between two smaller tiers of self-funded healthcare. A broad outline of this model follows in this chapter. I discuss aspects of the model in greater detail in the following chapters.

Tier 1 consists of a modified HSA plan. Under this plan, each individual has his or her own HSA, into which they deposit money each year. This money can be spent only on healthcare.* The first $2,000 per year of each adult's healthcare expenses ($1,000 for each child under 18) comes out of the HSA. Once the yearly threshold is spent, any additional healthcare needed is subject to Tier 2 coverage.

* In this example, I am arbitrarily allowing $2,000 per year in Tier 1 expenditures for each adult and $1,000 per year for each child under 18. These values seem reasonable to me as an initial estimate (with the additional safeguards and caveats mentioned in the text), but careful fiscal analysis will be required to settle on the true optimal values.

For households whose annual income is above a certain upper threshold, the money that is required to be deposited each year into each individual's HSA ($2,000 for each adult, $1,000 for each child) is non-taxable, similar to an Individual Retirement Account (IRA). For households whose income falls below a certain lower threshold, these funds would be directly deposited into individual HSAs by the federal government. For households whose

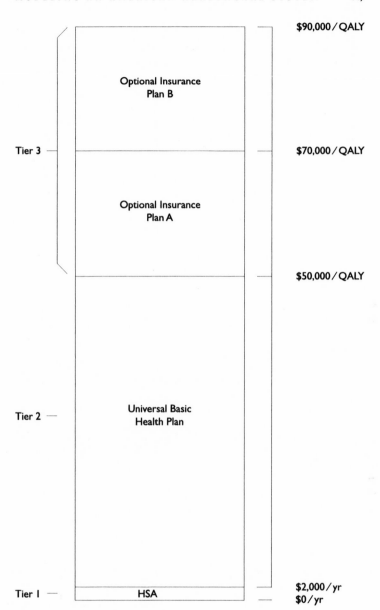

Figure 4. A model healthcare system.

income falls between the lower and upper income thresholds, a slid-
ing scale could be used to determine how much tax-deductible money
they must contribute, and how much the federal government will contribute annually toward the individual HSAs. In this manner, every
person will have a fully-funded HSA regardless of income.

Any money in the HSA that is not spent on healthcare during
course of the year remains in the HSA and earns tax-free interest. The
money that accumulates in this fund is the property of the individual
owner—the government has no claim on it and cannot tax it. Funds
that accumulate over the years, which could become quite sizeable, can
be treated in two ways. They can be either rolled over into an IRA
when an individual reaches seventy or they can be used at any time to
buy Tier 3 healthcare.

Tier 2 is a Universal Basic Health Plan (UBHP) that covers everybody in the U.S. who has a Social Security number. It kicks in after
the $2,000 deductible ($1,000 for children), paid out of the HSA (Tier
1), is used up for the year. The UBHP provides healthcare coverage
under a system of open rationing. (The next chapter considers what
that system of open rationing might look like and how we might go
about designing it.) In broad outline, all medical services that achieve
a target level of cost-effectiveness are covered. In the example used in
Figure 4, the UBHP covers all healthcare services that can be provided
for up to $50,000 per quality-adjusted life-year (QALY).* Services that
consume more than $50,000 per QALY are not covered.

* Using QALY as a cost-
effectiveness measure is fraught
with problems and is extremely
controversial. The standard methods of calculating QALY is not
adequate for the rationing scheme
we are proposing here. The next
chapter discusses QALY in some
depth and illustrates how the
ethical precepts on which we base
our rationing decisions guide our
calculation and subsequent use
of QALY.

This arrangement gives the biomedical industry
more than one approach to developing medical products and services to be covered under the UBHP.
Namely, they can work to improve the effectiveness of
their products or to reduce the cost of providing their
products or, preferably, to do both. This system of
rationing gives them a clear cost-effectiveness target. If
they meet it, their reward is predictable.

Both Tier 1 and Tier 2 are universal plans. Everyone
will participate in these two tiers.

Tier 3 is optional. Individuals may choose to pur-
chase for themselves any health services that fall outside the cost-effectiveness range covered by the UBHP. Also, individuals may choose
from an array of insurance plans to cover healthcare services that are

not sufficiently cost-effective to be included in the UBHP. In Figure 4, two optional plans are shown. One covers medical services that can be provided for $50,000–$70,000 per QALY, and the other covers medical services up to $90,000 per QALY. Tier 3 healthcare can be purchased either out of pocket or from excess funds in one's HSA.

Justifying the model

Scores of objections to this model have no doubt popped into your mind already. I do not take offense. I am certain that any proposal for a new healthcare system will generate objections. Besides, my intent is not to present a finished healthcare plan in its entirety, like Moses producing a complete system of laws from the mountaintop. Rather, my intent is merely to demonstrate that it is possible to imagine a system that resides in the upper quadrants of the healthcare landscape and that meets the six principles required for an acceptable American healthcare system. I am certain there are many variations on my proposal and even entirely different models that might be far better than this one. So instead of addressing criticisms aimed at specific features of this model, I will address criticisms aimed at its more general features.

> HSA   Health Savings Account
> IRA   Individual Retirement Account
> QALY   quality-adjusted life-year
> UBHP   Universal Basic Health Plan

The keystone of this model is the second tier, the UBHP, which uses a system of open rationing to distribute most healthcare—most of the more expensive healthcare, at least—provided under this system. Tier 2 is straightforward Quadrant I healthcare. I understand how passionately negative most people are about rationing healthcare. Even if you agree that open rationing is necessary, we all know that it will be easy to do it badly. The way in which Tier 2 is conceived, sold to the public, and implemented will finally determine its acceptability. In the next chapter, I attempt to explain how we can devise an equitable system of open rationing, and I am not saying more about it here, except this: Remember that we're not choosing whether to ration or not. That decision has already been made and it's out of our hands. All we're choosing is how to ration and how to incorporate that rationing into an overall healthcare system that is fair, just, and acceptable to the American public.

Tier 1 accomplishes several things. It places everyday, routine, maintenance healthcare under the individual's control. People are spending their own money, so they are much more judicious about how it is spent than if it were the Tooth Fairy's money. Because people are spending their own money and because people need to be able to compare costs and services, healthcare providers that want to stay in business have to, for the first time, figure out how to make this information available and useful to patients. Patients, not health plans, are the customers, so providers have to learn to meet the needs of these new customers, which is something they've forgotten over the last several decades.

This is particularly true for family doctors and internists, the primary care physicians, the doctors most likely to be paid from Tier 1 funds. They are paid, for the first time since their granddads were practicing medicine, by the patients themselves. Patients are their customers. That one revolutionary fact goes a long, long way toward restoring the classic doctor–patient relationship. Patients, not the government or the HMOs, determine doctors' viability as practitioners.

Because costs are a consideration for patients in Tier 1, a good bit of the wasteful spending for routine care is eliminated. Self-directed rationing in Tier 1 reduces the amount of imposed rationing that has to occur in Tier 2.

To people who object to HSAs because they provide an incentive for individuals to avoid needed healthcare so as not to spend their own money, I reply as follows: First, this entire system is predicated on the idea that mechanisms are in place to facilitate the self-empowerment of individual patients. That is, tools and services will need to exist to enable patients to make intelligent choices about when to spend money, and what to spend it on. Second, as we design our Tier 2 UBHP, based on open rationing, we can give patients incentives to take advantage of appropriate preventive and screening opportunities with their HSA funds. That is, we may choose to incentivize healthful Tier 1 behaviors by arranging to give appropriate weight to subsequent rationing scores. Third, it's not as if HSA money can otherwise be spent on Xboxes or cigarettes. Money in HSA accounts can only be spent on healthcare. There is little incentive to hoard it by avoiding needed routine care. Fourth, a major problem with today's healthcare system is that forty-six million Americans have no health insurance at all and have little or no opportunity to receive routine healthcare. It seems to me that it is a good bargain to trade that system for one where, if routine care is still being avoided, it is as a matter of personal choice and not of lack of choice. Finally, we may have to recognize that autonomous individuals have the right to make bad personal choices. We have to assure ourselves that whenever such bad choices are made, they are not made because of a lack of opportunity, lack of information, lack of rightful funding, or for any other systemic reason.

The third tier is likely to generate the most controversy. Tier 3 offers healthcare not available in the UBHP to individuals able and willing to pay for it outside of the UBHP. The potential inequity inherent in such a system is mitigated by several factors.

One factor is feasibility. Any healthcare system we devise—especially in America—will fail if we artificially restrain people of means from exercising their fiscal freedom. Restraining this freedom does not work in Canada (whose efforts to keep individuals from going outside of the system has created a powerful flow of wealthier Canadian patients and their dollars to healthcare facilities located in American border states), nor Great Britain (which has given up altogether trying to restrain people from seeking care outside of the National Health Service and has allowed a shadow self-pay healthcare system to develop for the rich). It will certainly not work in America. By acknowledging this fact, we can take steps to control, for the sake of societal equity, the inevitable exercise of individuals' fiscal freedom.

By mandating that everyone receive any medical services covered by the universal healthcare system only through that system, we have already mitigated the problem. Everyone must participate exclusively in the UBHP for the services that are offered by the UBHP. The only medical services available outside the universal healthcare system are those not covered by the UBHP. Almost by definition, these are medical services that society has deemed non-essential.

Second, we would be entirely within our rights to charge rich people a stiff "Tier 3 tax" whenever they choose to go outside the universal system for additional, big-ticket medical care. (Note that we do not want to charge people such a tax for small-ticket items not covered by the universal health plan. Read on to see why.) The dollars collected through such a tax can be added to the healthcare budget and used to expand the services available for everyone. This tax provides a strong disincentive for, say, the rich and well connected to go outside of the system to buy extra care (so while they are not forbidden, they also are not particularly anxious to do so). Such a disincentive should keep everyone, including the rich and influential, interested in assuring that truly essential healthcare services are covered under the universal program. There are many challenges associated with such a Tier 3 tax, so before implementing one we had better consider all the ramifications carefully. My point here is that there are steps we can take to mitigate any unfairness this system presents.

Third, by allowing non-covered medical products and services to be marketed and sold outside of the universal healthcare system, we create a path for continued medical innovation. This is especially true for the development of a robust market for inexpensive medical products sold directly to consumers. Many relatively cheap products that large numbers of people might want to purchase will not be cost-effective

---

Principle 1

> We must define clearly the purpose of healthcare services.

Principle 2

> There must be open competition for resources between healthcare services and all the other services society provides.

Principle 3

> As much as possible, rationing decisions should be left to the patients affected by those decisions.

Principle 4

> Healthcare coverage must be universal.

Principle 5

> Clear rules of rationing must be decided in an open forum.

Principle 6

> Healthcare services must be prioritized according to clear ethical standards.

enough to be covered by the universal plan. Home monitoring devices for your elderly grandparents, for instance, while individually inexpensive, may not be cost-effective to society (say, $500,000 per life-year saved) but still may be useful and affordable for individuals. We want to encourage, not discourage, this sort of self-funded healthcare and this sort of economic activity.

Fourth, companies developing expensive medical products whose cost-effectiveness is not sufficient to warrant coverage or is not yet known have in Tier 3 the opportunity to sell those products outside the universal system until adequate cost-effectiveness data can be compiled to bring them into Tier 2. Thus, individuals rich enough to purchase these unproven medical products offer themselves up as test cases for products and services that, through their investment, may some day prove cost-effective enough to become universally available. Tier 3 thus becomes yet another aspect of the social contract; a consideration is received for services rendered.

In summary, while there are no doubt many flaws to the model I am proposing, I believe I have demonstrated that it is possible to create a fair and just healthcare system that adheres to the six principles outlined in this chapter.

The elephant in the room, however, is that this model requires us to agree to ration healthcare openly and then to figure out how to do it. I address this challenge in the next chapter.

9

How to Ration Healthcare

THROUGHOUT THIS BOOK I HAVE argued that healthcare rationing is unavoidable, that the question, Should we ration? is answered, and that it's time to move on to the question, How should we ration?

Rationing by itself, whether of the Quadrant III or Quadrant I variety, will not be sufficient to solve the American healthcare crisis. What we need is a system that, while it employs rationing (rationing being unavoidable), requires rationing to be conducted openly and equitably, limits that rationing as much as possible, and still allows individuals to retain significant autonomy over their own healthcare. While a methodology for openly rationing healthcare is not by itself the solution to our dysfunctional healthcare system, it is a necessary component of a solution.

The open rationing of healthcare—specifically, adopting an official public policy stipulating the rationing of healthcare and adopting a transparent methodology for conducting that rationing—is a scary prospect. It certainly scares the starch out of the public officials who ought to be discussing it with us. It may not be long, however, before some smart politician figures out that the roiling discontent with our healthcare system is caused by the covert rationing that's already occurring and that an increasingly angry public may be ready to listen to a straight and logical explanation of what's really going on.

When people come to understand that rationing is already occurring and will continue to occur no matter what, they may listen to a proposal for reforming our healthcare system that includes open rationing. Gaining public support for such a thing will take more than appeals to reason, more than convincing the public that our current system of covert rationing is bad, more than listing the advantages that might accrue from a healthcare system that includes open rationing.

To sell open rationing to the public, we have to paint an accurate picture of what our system of open rationing will look like. We're going to have to show them exactly how we propose to do it. That is the aim of this chapter.

Establishing an ethical basis for rationing

In the last chapter I outlined the six principles that ought to guide our creation of a new American healthcare system. The last of these principles is that we need to base our open rationing (a necessary component of that larger system), on ethical precepts. Let's consider what those ethical precepts should be.

Fundamental ethical precepts for rationing

One of the main themes of this book is the conflict between the needs of the individual and the needs of society. Any stable society requires a system of ethical norms for resolving these individual versus society conflicts. In socialist societies, such ethical norms are pretty straight-forward, because individuals are expected to subsume their own needs to the greater good (a requirement that helps explain why these societies tend to fail).

But in the United States, a society founded on the principle of individual autonomy, the ethical norms governing conflicts between the individual and society tend to be more complicated. Especially in an arena like healthcare, where individual needs and societal needs cannot both be fully served, ethical norms must be in place to balance competing interests.

To visualize the problem, think of the ethics of healthcare as being organized into two concentric spheres (see Figure 5 on page 238). The outer sphere holds the ethical precepts adopted by *society* to guide the behavior of the healthcare system for the benefit of the entire population of patients it serves. These outer-sphere precepts help ensure that the needs of society as a whole are addressed in an ethical manner by the healthcare system.

Contained within (and thus subject to) that outer sphere of ethical precepts is an inner sphere, which defines the ethical norms that govern the behavior of the healthcare system for the benefit of individuals. Inner-sphere precepts help ensure that individual needs within the healthcare system are addressed in an ethical manner—yet in a manner consistent with the outer-sphere (societal) precepts. So, while the physician's primary concern must be for the welfare of the individual patient, and while physicians must operate according to ethical principles that reflect this duty to individuals (the inner-sphere precepts), their behavior must also conform to the ethical constraints imposed by society on the entire population (the outer-sphere precepts).

Because individuals operating within the inner sphere must honor the outer-sphere ethical precepts, you might surmise that the needs of society always take precedence over the needs of the individual. And to some degree, this is the case. But it is more useful to think of the inner-sphere precepts as immutable ethical beliefs that serve the autonomy of the individual and the outer sphere as a coating, fashioned by society and therefore changeable, designed to protect (and not usurp) that inner core.

The inner sphere—ethical precepts for individuals

The inner sphere of ethical precepts—the core—tells the physician to place the interests of the individual patient above all else, within the bounds imposed by society. Classically, this inner sphere consists of two ethical precepts: individual beneficence and individual autonomy.

>*Individual beneficence* requires that doctors always strive to assure that their activities benefit their individual patients.

>*Individual autonomy* requires doctors to enable their patients to exercise their right to self-determination regarding their own medical care. That is, the patient has a right to know, and the doctor is obligated to inform them, of any information that might help them make decisions about their healthcare. (Covert rationing requires the medical profession to abandon this core obligation.)

But while individual autonomy is critical, it has its limits. When a patient or the patient's proxy demands that everything be done, they are exceeding the bounds of autonomy if doing "everything" means that

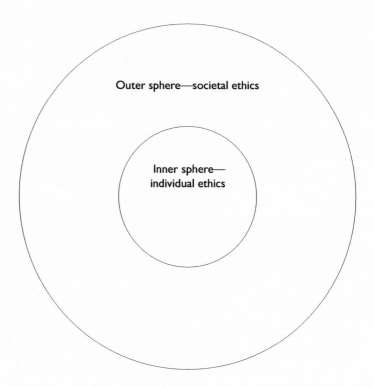

Figure 5. Organization of ethical precepts into concentric spheres. The inner precepts of individual beneficence and individual autonomy are subject to the societal precepts of social beneficence and distributive justice.

some other individuals would be deprived of what otherwise would be rightfully theirs. These *bounds of autonomy* are defined by the outer sphere.

The outer sphere—ethical precepts for society

Under any equitable system of rationing we are going to have to carefully define our outer sphere of ethical norms, because those are the standards that bound and govern the inner-sphere behaviors of individual physicians and patients. The outer sphere, like the inner, consists classically of two ethical precepts, in this case societal beneficence and distributive justice.

> *Societal beneficence* requires the healthcare system to maximize the overall public good realized from whatever resources society expends on healthcare. Societal beneficence is not the same as individual beneficence, because what is optimal for an individual patient may reduce the overall benefit to society, and vice versa.

> *Distributive justice* requires the benefits of the healthcare system to be distributed fairly, that is, in a way that does not discriminate against individuals or groups based on who they are. In the context of rationing healthcare, the precept of distributive justice presents challenges. For example, are the aged, the disabled, the genetically disadvantaged, or any other definable groups to have more, fewer, or the same healthcare opportunities as everyone else?

Healthcare rationing and the spheres

Now we can see why the American healthcare system is inequitable and unethical. A hallmark of both our recent Quadrant IV Tooth Fairy healthcare system and our current Quadrant III healthcare system is the lack—thanks to our culture of no limits—of effective outer-sphere, societal norms that would bound the appropriate behavior of individual doctors and patients. This lack makes it possible for some patients to soak up a disproportionate share of healthcare resources, while others are left with next to nothing. Inequity, sanctioned and sustained by formal Wonkonian or Gekkonian policies and procedures, abounds.

Reestablishing equity should have nothing to do with adjusting the precepts of the inner sphere. Individuals (to paraphrase the

Declaration of Independence) have self-evident rights to their individual autonomy. Inner-sphere precepts are granted us by natural law, or by the Creator, or by the Magna Carta (depending on your personal views). As Americans, we should avoid modifying inner-sphere precepts except under extreme duress.* Outer-sphere precepts—the mechanism by which we can *legitimately* limit the scope of inner-sphere behaviors—are negotiated by society and are therefore subject to change. To develop an equitable system for openly rationing healthcare, it is the outer sphere that we must address.

* Chapter 4 shows, though, that prestigious medical organizations have already violated the inner sphere. Rather than demanding that society get its own outer-sphere precepts in order so as to distribute limited resources equitably, these authorities have opted to move the principle of distributive justice down into the inner sphere, where it becomes the responsibility of individual physicians. You can't actually do that, of course, because distributive justice is inherently an outer-sphere norm. Nonetheless, these august bodies have declared it so, formally placing doctors in the position of having to serve the best interests of their individual patients (autonomy, beneficence) while at the same time rationing healthcare covertly, at the bedside (distributive justice). Such a "solution" is illogical, nonsensical, and indeed impossible. But it is no more incompatible with reality than many of the other behaviors we have required of our Quadrant III system of covert rationing.

Establishing outer-sphere ethical precepts

The two precepts in the outer sphere, under any system of healthcare rationing, present us with an ethical dilemma. You cannot have both perfect societal beneficence and perfect distributive justice simultaneously. You've got to pick which one takes precedence.

Assuring fairness versus maximizing good

If we have to ration healthcare, we want the rationing process to do two things. We want it to be fair (that is, we want to adhere to the precept of distributive justice), and we want it to yield the maximum amount of healthcare benefit for the dollar (that is, we want to adhere to the precept of societal beneficence). Unfortunately, we cannot maximize both of these goals at the same time.

Consider the following illustration: Two men, both fifty, are diagnosed with the same rare form of cancer. A treatment exists to cure this type of cancer, but the healthcare system can only afford to treat one of these men. The first man is otherwise healthy and if cured can be expected to recover fully. The second happens to be bedridden with severe multiple sclerosis (MS); if he is cured of cancer, he will remain severely disabled and will probably have a reduced life expectancy due to that disability. To which man should society offer treatment?

Some would say that, obviously, society should treat the man who is otherwise healthy, as we would be buying him a high-quality life of substantial duration. If we treated the other man, we would be saving a relatively low-quality life, and for a shorter duration. Treating the otherwise healthy man would therefore clearly maximize the good (societal beneficence) society achieves with its money.

But others would point out that the second man (the one with MS) wants to live just as much as the first, that his life has the same intrinsic value as the other man's, and that withholding therapy from him just because of his MS would be unfair. Discriminating against people with MS—or any other disability—is a flagrant violation of the principle of distributive justice. Fairness dictates that all individuals should have an equal claim to the benefits of therapy.

It should be obvious that we cannot have it both ways. How we decide to distribute society's resources in this case (and in every case) depends on how we prioritize the two conflicting ethical principles. We might decide that maximizing fairness should predominate over maximizing good. The only way to absolutely maximize fairness, in fact, would be to withhold therapy from both men (this would be the only option that would equalize the results). But then both would die, and our adherence to strict fairness would reduce the amount of good we've achieved to zero. On the other hand, if we decide we want to maximize beneficence (the total amount of good we can buy with society's money), we would have to treat the otherwise healthy man. But by choosing to do this, we would be removing the patient with MS from consideration altogether, reducing fairness to zero.

Whatever we do, we cannot both maximize good and maximize fairness. So, if we're going to devise a scheme for the open rationing of healthcare, we have to choose explicitly between these two ethical precepts or decide specifically how to distribute our priorities between them.

The basic ethical dilemma inherent in devising a rationing scheme is of more than just theoretical importance. The way we balance fairness and good determines whether open rationing ends up being a significant improvement over what we have now or ends up as bad as many fear it might.

An argument for giving primacy to fairness

While we ought to get as much bang from society's healthcare buck as possible, that is, optimize societal beneficence, we should not do so by subordinating the principle of distributive justice. In rationing health-care, we should avoid discrimination against individuals or groups by virtue of their race, sex, nationality, genetic makeup, or diseases and disabilities.

Why should assuring fairness predominate over maximizing good? Because if we agree to limit societal beneficence in the name of distribu-tive justice, we will strive to expand covered medical services for every-one and thus to expand the overall good we're achieving. Our tendency will be to find new ways of biasing the total goodness upward (while maintaining fairness), by collecting better cost-effectiveness data, find-ing new efficiencies, discovering new treatments and technologies, or choosing to divert more funding into the healthcare system.

On the other hand, if we hold maximum good to be the dominant standard and treat fairness as a secondary consideration, we will always be tempted to bias fairness downward, that is, to expand the categories of patients whose lives are judged relatively valueless based on disease or disability, as this would be the simplest path to achieving more total good per healthcare dollar spent. Once we set a precedent of maximiz-ing good at the expense of fairness it will be difficult to turn back but easy to advance. We should not assume that we will be significantly more resistant to such behavior than other cultures have proven to be.

Most of us, I think, would rather live in a society that takes the former path rather than one that takes the latter.

A proposed ethical standard for rationing

I propose an Equal Opportunity Standard (EOS) for balancing the two ethical precepts in the outer sphere:

All individuals should have an equal opportunity to enjoy the fruits of life, within the constraints imposed on them by nature.

This EOS is a reformulation of the principle of distributive justice, suitably bounded for the purposes of rationing. It says that, while we ought to let fairness (that is, distributive justice) predominate, we also ought to constrain it to allow society to accrue a reasonably optimal amount of good.

The EOS gives primacy to fairness by recognizing that all individu-als are of equal intrinsic worth, that is, *all* individuals should have an *equal* opportunity to enjoy the fruits of life. However, the EOS prevents the excesses of unfettered fairness in two ways.

First, the EOS does not insist that the principle of distributive justice requires equivalent outcomes among individuals. It strives only to gain for individuals an *equal opportunity* for those good outcomes. Not all opportunities, even equal opportunities, yield equivalent results. Given equal opportunities for a favorable result, some individuals will have good outcomes and others poor outcomes. The EOS accepts this.*

Second, the EOS recognizes that not even equal opportunity is possible in all cases. Sometimes the vagaries of nature limit opportunities. A person's illness or disability may reduce their odds of responding favorably to a therapy. Under the EOS, society does not have to spend unlimited amounts to provide a therapy that is unlikely to yield a good outcome.†

In rationing healthcare under the EOS, the distribution of resources would not be based on either attempting to maximize the overall good that accrues to society or attempting to equalize outcomes among all individuals. The EOS does not make the problem of maximizing fairness versus maximizing good go away, but it changes the question. Instead of asking, Saving which of these two individuals will maximize overall good? or How can we guarantee equivalent outcomes for these two individuals to maximize fairness? we will be asking, Given these two equally worthy individuals, how can we optimize the opportunity for good outcomes for both?

* I understand that this notion of striving for equal opportunities, rather than equal outcomes, will be unacceptable to some. This distinction, in fact, defines a fundamental and never-ending debate within and among civilized societies. Philosophically, American culture has been based on a striving for equal opportunities (that is, on the right to *pursue* happiness) and not for equal results (which could only be achieved by removing an individual's rights in favor of a powerful central authority). The EOS embraces this foundational American idea

† We will need to address what we mean by a constraint that is "imposed by nature." For instance, should we treat patients differently if we suspect their illness might be at least partially due to lifestyle choices? This is an issue we must explicitly address before using the EOS for actual rationing decisions.

The EOS—a statement of math as well as ethics

The EOS is a compromise between a strict beneficence standard and a strict justice standard. It reinforces distributive justice while helping optimize total societal good; and it offers sufficient flexibility for tackling difficult rationing problems.

The EOS, in addition to being a statement of principles, is a statement of mathematics. As we develop our scheme for the open rationing of healthcare, one way or another we're going to have to rank medical services by some numeric value. And the EOS shows us how to do the math.

The following section of this chapter shows how the EOS can guide the computations for making decisions within any system of open rationing. I am including this section not because I particularly enjoy math or because I assume you will enjoy it. I am including it instead because, having asserted that a well thought out ethical standard offers sufficient guidance to us as we devise a methodology for open rationing, I am obliged to demonstrate how.

Before I get to the math, let me describe how the EOS enables the mathematics of rationing. In particular, the EOS helps us with four ethical questions that must be resolved before we can conduct the business of openly rationing healthcare.

Four critical questions for rationing

Question 1   *Is it ever appropriate to ask about an individual's intrinsic worth?*

Under the EOS, all individuals should have an equal opportunity to enjoy life. So all individuals are of equal intrinsic worth. The answer to Question 1 is No.

Question 2   *Is it appropriate to account for underlying medical conditions that objectively reduce an individual's chance of responding to a medical therapy?*

For example, the presence of severe chronic lung disease significantly reduces the chance that a patient will realize a good outcome with coronary artery bypass surgery. Should this reduced probability of a good outcome be a factor in determining whether the individual ought to be offered the surgery? The EOS recognizes that constraints of nature will sometimes limit an individual's opportunity to enjoy life. The answer to Question 2 is Yes.

Question 3   *Should a person's age be taken into account?*

Whether to use age as a factor in rationing healthcare is a contentious issue among medical ethicists. Most who argue for it base their arguments on the principle of societal beneficence—maximizing public good. The total good derived from a life-saving procedure, they would say, is greater in a younger patient than in an older patient (because saving the life of a ninety-year-old might buy only two years of additional life, whereas saving the life of a ten-year-old might buy seventy years of life at the same cost). This reasoning sacrifices fairness (that is, the equivalence of two human lives) in favor of overall public good. Like all procedures that maximize good by assigning different values to various classes of humans, it leads to the slippery slope argument. That is, if you can devalue the elderly in the name of maximizing public good, then you can also devalue individuals on the basis of disability, illness, intelligence, sex, left-handedness, or race in the name of maximizing public good.

On its face, the EOS would seem to support those who insist on *not* taking age into account when rationing: If all individuals are of equal intrinsic worth, then ninety-year-olds ought to receive the same rationing priority as ten-year-olds. However, a closer look at the EOS can lead us to the opposite conclusion.

Under the EOS, saving the life of a ten-year-old might take precedence over saving the life of a ninety-year-old, but not because it would maximize overall good. Instead, the younger person has had relatively little opportunity to enjoy life—an opportunity we should strive to make equitable. By giving priority to the younger person, we come closer to achieving an equal opportunity between these two individuals—over the course of each of their lifetimes—than if we had given priority to the elder.

The slippery slope argument does not hold here because we are not setting a precedent by discriminating on the basis of some inherent difference between two individuals. Instead, we are saying that *every* individual should have a fair chance to enjoy life, and the ninety-year-old has already had eighty more years of opportunity than the ten-year-old. So under the EOS, rationing by age does not assign different values to individuals at all. What it does do is attempt to equalize opportunities between equally worthy individuals *over the course of their lives*. Thus, each individual will enjoy both the priority of the young and, later (if they are lucky enough to become elderly) the reduced priority of the old. Unless early death ensues, every individual over the long term will share the same distribution of age-related risk within the system of rationing.

Prioritizing by age under the EOS constitutes a special case, because equalizing the lifetime opportunity to enjoy life actually *requires* factoring age into the rationing decision, and doing so sets no precedent for rationing based on any other inherent differences among individuals.

While, admittedly, the EOS could be used to argue either point of view on the age issue, I personally believe it more correctly supports taking age into account, and I also believe this to be the more equitable position. For at least the purposes of this chapter, the answer to Question 3 is Yes.

Question 4   *Should diseases or disabilities produced by the actions or choices of the patients themselves be taken into account?*

In other words, should patients whose medical disorders are at least partly related to lifestyle choices (for example, smoking, obesity, riding motorcycles without a helmet) receive a lower priority in a rationing scheme?

The argument for assigning lower rationing priority to individuals whose medical conditions that are partially self-induced is one of equity. By making poor lifestyle choices, the reasoning goes, these individuals are choosing to soak up some of the healthcare resources that might otherwise accrue to people who themselves have chosen healthy lifestyles. A lower rationing score for those who make poor lifestyle choices would tend to equalize the playing field.

While there is nothing in the EOS that would preclude our adjusting the rationing priorities of those who make poor lifestyle choices, doing so would be problematic. Judging which medical conditions are due to lifestyle choices and which are not (was this man's heart attack caused by his chronic failure to exercise ninety minutes per day?) and deciding which self-induced conditions (obesity? alcoholism? drug addiction?) are due to individual choice and which are mediated by genetically determined tendencies would create significant, ongoing, systematic tensions that would tend to disrupt and undermine the entire rationing system.

*   Another reason is to avoid encouraging those obsessed with maintaining perfect health to the point of excluding from their lives much of what you and I might consider normal human joys. These individuals already view the rest of us with disdain and wish to control our behavior. I don't want to egg these people on, or legitimize *their* distinctive and ultimately disabling pathologies.

For these and other practical reasons*, a rationing system under the EOS should not specifically account for conditions that we think are self-induced or partially self-induced. We should treat all underlying diseases or disabilities, whether mediated by lifestyle choices or not, as constraints imposed by nature.

This does not mean that individuals who habitually make bad personal choices will necessarily soak up more than their rightful share of healthcare resources. Many self-induced illnesses (alcoholic cirrhosis, for example) objectively reduce an individual's odds of responding favorably to many therapies. In these cases, the therapy might be withheld anyway, because offering it would not improve their opportunity to enjoy life (see Question 2). In any case, for the purposes of this chapter, the answer to Question 4 is No.

Now let's take a look at how to do the math.

A methodology for open rationing—doing the math

The QALY

Any equitable system of healthcare rationing requires an objective measure for ranking healthcare services. The measure proposed most often by economists and ethicists for comparing the intrinsic worth of various medical services is the quality-adjusted life-year (QALY).

The QALY is a unit of time that relates calendar years to quality of life. One QALY represents one year in normal health. But two years at 50 percent of normal health also amount to one QALY. The general question is how much time a given therapy can be expected to add to a patient's life in terms of these normalized years (QALY). If a therapy adds quality but not time to one's life—for example raising a patient from 50 percent of normal health to 75 percent of normal health but not otherwise slowing the progress of a terminal disease—that improvement can also be expressed in QALY.

The benefit of a therapy for a patient (B), expressed as a number of QALY, is the product of three factors: the probability, p, that a therapy will be effective (the odds that it will provide a benefit), the expected duration, d, of that benefit (in years), and some index, q, for the patient's expected quality of life (QOL) after the therapy is applied. The formula for calculating B is:

$$B = p \times d \times q$$

The probability, p, is a number between 0 and 1. (For example, the probability that a treatment will be beneficial might be 50 percent, which is expressed as the number 0.5.) And the QOL index, q, is also expressed as a number between 0 and 1, representing a percentage.* (For example, if an index tells us that life in a wheelchair is only half as worthwhile as life without a wheelchair, then life in a wheelchair would be assigned a QOL index of 0.5.) B is the number of years, adjusted for quality, that we can expect to be added to the life of a patient if we use the therapy in question, hence, quality-adjusted life-years.

Consider a treatment guaranteed to prolong the life of a person by one year. If the individual receiving that treatment is expected to have a normal QOL during that extra year (that is, a life with a value of 100 percent), then B for that treatment would be

* The QOL index results from one of several methods that attempt to answer the question, "If you had to live with health condition X, you would consider your quality of life to be what percentage of normal?" The answer would be in the form, "The quality of life with health condition X is Y percent as good as being in normal health." Y / 100 is the QOL index, q.

$$B = p \times d \times q$$

$$B = 1.0 \times 1.0 \text{ yr} \times 1.0$$

$$B = 1.0 \text{ QALY}$$

On the other hand, if this treatment, while still prolonging life, also caused the patient to live that extra year of life in a wheelchair, and if the QOL index we were using indicated that living in a wheelchair is only half as worthwhile as living without a wheelchair, the therapy would provide only 0.5 QALY.

$$B = 1.0 \times 1.0 \text{ yr} \times 0.5$$

$$B = 0.5 \text{ QALY}$$

This calculation can be applied to therapies that do not affect the length of life at all. Consider a treatment that did not affect longevity but allowed a patient previously confined to a wheelchair to begin walking normally. For every year of predicted survival after that therapy, there would be an increase in B from 0.5 to 1.0, for a net gain of 0.5 QALY.

The QALY gives us a way to measure the total benefit produced by a therapy, so that the values of very different treatments for very different diseases can be compared to one another and ranked numerically. In this way QALY is a tool for ranking all kinds of medical services for the purpose of rationing, that is, deciding how best to spend our healthcare dollars.

When rationing healthcare, the cost (C) of a therapy is what concerns us, specifically the cost of a therapy per unit of benefit—or the cost-effectiveness (E). Our benefit is B and our unit of benefit is QALY, so

$$E = C/B$$

and the unit is dollars per QALY.

The ethics of QALY

Calculation of B is not ethically neutral. The method we use to calculate B expresses our decision on which outer-sphere ethical precept—distributive justice or societal beneficence—should predominate.

Consider the case of a 70-year-old wheelchair-bound man with cancer. A treatment for his cancer is available that has a 10 percent chance of producing a cure. What would B (expressed in QALY) be for using this therapy in this patient? Well, it depends on how you calculate it.

One way of calculating B takes into account that the individual for whom this therapy is being considered is a 70-year-old, who probably has a 10-year life expectancy, if the cancer can be cured, and who is wheelchair-bound. For this individual, the *probability* of a cure is 10 percent, the expected survival if the therapy is effective is 10 years, and the expected QOL index during that 10 years is 0.5 (given our hypothetical index that said patients in a wheelchair have a quality of life only 50 percent of normal).

B benefit of therapy
C cost of therapy
d duration of benefit
E cost-effectiveness of therapy
EOS Equal Opportunity Standard (All individuals should have an equal opportunity to enjoy the fruits of life, within the constraints imposed on them by nature.)
p probability of beneficial therapy (number between 0 and 1)
q QOL index (number between 0 and 1)
QALY quality-adjusted life-year (unit)
QOL quality of life

B for this therapy then would be

$$B = 0.1 \times 10 \text{ yr} \times 0.5$$

$$B = 0.5 \text{ QALY}$$

If the cancer treatment costs $30,000, then the cost-effectiveness (E) of using this therapy in this man would be

$$E = C/B = \$30,000/0.5 \text{ QALY} = \$60,000/\text{QALY}$$

On the other hand, for a 40-year-old man who has the same cancer and who is not wheelchair-bound, the calculation would look quite different:

$$B = 0.1 \times 40 \text{ yr} \times 1.0$$

$$B = 4.0 \text{ QALY}$$

The cost-effectiveness in treating this man would be

$$E = C/B = \$30,000/4.0 \text{ QALY} = \$7,500/\text{QALY}$$

From these calculations, it looks like it is eight times more cost-effective ($7,500 per QALY versus $60,000 per QALY) to treat the second man as the first. If we were living under a rationing system that was willing to pay $50,000 per QALY, the second man would be allowed to receive the treatment, but the first man would not. By buying the therapy only for patients like the second man, society would be receiving 4 QALY (instead of only 0.5 QALY) for every $30,000 spent purchasing the cancer treatment.

The computation we have just done—adjusting the factors to the individual under consideration—allows us to steer our spending to those individuals whose treatment is most likely to buy our society the most QALY for the money. In other words, it allows society to maximize its bang for the buck. This is the kind of calculation we should do if we decide that societal beneficence is the dominant ethical precept.

By giving societal beneficence priority over distributive justice, we systematically discriminate against anyone with any sort of condition that reduces their underlying QOL. When we calculate

B so as to maximize societal good, in essence we are assigning a numeric value to an individual's inherent worth. We are comparing two human lives numerically so we can direct our spending to the worthier individuals. This method systematically discriminates against anyone who is disabled or disadvantaged in any way. So, while societal good is maximized, societal fairness and equity is minimized (if not brutalized).

If we reject this result and choose instead to give priority to distributive justice, we have to come up with an alternative method of calculating B. To optimize fairness in our rationing process, we must consider all individuals to be of equal worth; therefore everyone should have an equal chance to receive the benefits offered by the healthcare system.

To calculate B in a way that maximizes distributive justice we need to use some sort of normalized value for both the QOL and duration factors in the formula for B. In the example we have been using, all individuals might be assigned a QOL index of 1.0. Similarly, some standard duration of benefit could be chosen for all patients being considered for this cancer therapy, regardless of their age, say 20 years. With these adjustments, our 70-year-old wheelchair-bound patient's score would now become

$$B = 0.1 \times 20 \text{ yr} \times 1.0$$

$$B = 2.0 \text{ QALY}$$

The cost-effectiveness calculation would become

$$E = C/B = \$30,000/2.0 \text{ QALY} = \$15,000/\text{QALY}$$

By altering our ethical priorities and changing our calculation accordingly, this patient's B score (and the cost-effectiveness of treating him) would be improved significantly. The second man, the 40-year-old who does not need a wheelchair, would now receive the same score as the first man (because all individuals are treated the same).

So by maximizing distributive justice, we would no longer be rationing by the individual, but instead *by the medical service*. Under such a rationing system, a list of medical services would be devised, and cost-effectiveness values could be computed for each one. Medical services would then be ranked according to these scores, and society would draw a line somewhere on this list. Medical services above the line would be covered, while those below the line would not, no matter who the patient is.

This same list would apply to all individuals; that is, the individual characteristics of the people who might be receiving these services would not be taken into account. So, a society that had agreed to pay up to $50,000 per QALY would end up buying cancer therapy for both the 70-year-old man in the wheelchair, and the 40-year-old man who is otherwise healthy. This result is eminently fair. However, under this scenario, society would receive only 2 QALY for each $30,000 spent on the cancer treatment (instead of 4 QALY for $30,000, as under the societal beneficence scenario). While overall fairness will have been optimized by shifting to a distributive justice paradigm, the total amount of societal good achieved per dollar spent will be significantly reduced.

There are additional reasons that total societal good would be diminished under a strict distributive justice paradigm. As all individuals are given equal weight under this model, B, and therefore cost-effectiveness, cannot be adjusted for patients who are extremely elderly, or who are in the terminal stages of a fatal illness, or whose underlying medical conditions greatly reduce the probability that the proposed therapy would be effective for them. All of these individuals would receive the same priority as would otherwise healthy individuals, and society would find itself spending its healthcare dollars on people who are unlikely to benefit from treatment.

Given these problems, many commentators have thrown up their hands in dismay and declared comparing treatments using QALY to be a non-starter. However, there are two reasons we should not abandon QALY in our quest to devise a system for open rationing. First, nobody has described another feasible method of comparing and ranking dissimilar medical services, a task that is essential to open rationing. Writing off QALY would be tantamount to writing off open rationing and would pretty much doom us to continue covert rationing of the Quadrant III variety. And second, as it turns out we do not have to choose between a strict societal beneficence method and a strict distributive justice method of calculating B. We have another choice—the EOS method.

EOS to the rescue

The EOS can guide our calculation of B to optimize societal beneficence without discriminating against individual patients on the
basis of their diseases or disabilities.

B is the product of three factors—a probability factor, a duration factor, and a QOL index factor. Choosing values for these
factors is a function of our ethical precepts.

The EOS attempts to achieve a balance between distributive
justice and societal beneficence. How does this balance translate
to the calculations? The EOS guides us in selecting values for each
of the three factors that go into the calculation of the benefit, B,
and cost-effectiveness, E, of a treatment.

The EOS and the QOL index factor

The QOL index, q, is an estimate of what the patient's expected
quality of life will be after the proposed therapy is applied. In most
cases, this QOL index represents the patient's baseline state.
That is, assuming the proposed therapy is effective, the patient's
life will return to some underlying, baseline state of quality. If that
baseline state involves living in a wheelchair (or any other chronic
disease state or disability), the patient's QOL index will accordingly be reduced.

Under a societal beneficence ethical standard, as we have seen,
an adjustment is mandated in the QOL index for underlying diseases and disabilities, to maximize the overall benefit to society
when healthcare resources are distributed. In contrast, under a
distributive justice ethical standard, no such adjustment is allowed.
What should we do under the EOS?

We have already resolved this question (Question 1, page 244).
Under the EOS, it is *never* appropriate to take into account any
measure of an individual's intrinsic worth. For the purposes of our
QALY calculation, we can restate this as a rule.

Rule 1   *In calculating cost-effectiveness, do not adjust the QOL index
for an individual's baseline disabilities or medical disorders.*

The EOS and the probability factor

The probability factor is the likelihood that the proposed therapy
will be effective. In most cases, some general probability value will

be used (for example, a particular treatment for cancer may be known to produce a cure 10 percent of the time). But sometimes an individual's underlying medical conditions affect the chance of responding to the proposed treatment. When calculating cost-effectiveness, should we take such individual variances in the probability factor into account?

We have already resolved this question as well (Question 2, page 244). The EOS explicitly recognizes that constraints of nature sometimes limit the opportunity for a good outcome. Such constraints of nature ought to be accounted for. This can be stated as another rule.

Rule 2   *In calculating cost-effectiveness, adjust the probability factor whenever an individual's underlying disability or medical disorder objectively limits the chance that the proposed treatment will be effective.*

The EOS and the duration factor

Duration is the most important of the three factors used in the calculation. When we assign a projected duration of benefit, d, to a therapy, we are in effect establishing the maximum possible value of B that therapy can attain. The probability and QOL index factors, p and q, because they are always less than or equal to 1, can only reduce the number of years provided by the duration factor. So the duration factor is the major determinant of the ultimate benefit, B, and to a large extent determines how the rationing of medical services will proceed.

Deciding on the most appropriate value for d is especially important for therapies that have the potential of preventing death or that can effect a lifelong improvement in a patient's health. This is because, in these cases, the duration of benefit is equal to the predicted life expectancy of the patient receiving that therapy. For such therapies we need to consider potential adjustments to the duration of benefit for three conditions that affect life expectancy: the patient's age, the patient's underlying medical conditions, and the patient's lifestyle choices.

Age-related adjustments to the duration of benefit

We have already discussed and resolved the question of whether age-related adjustments should be made in rationing healthcare under the EOS (see Question 3, page 244). At least for the purposes of this chapter, we have decided to do so. This can also be restated as a rule.

Rule 3   *In calculating cost-effectiveness, adjust the duration factor to take into account the individual's age-based life-expectancy.*

Underlying medical conditions affecting duration of benefit

Some individuals have underlying diseases or disabilities that significantly reduce their life expectancies whether or not they receive the therapy being considered. How should we adjust the duration factor to account for these underlying medical conditions?

The limitation in expected duration of benefit produced by an underlying medical condition is similar *in every way but one* to the limitation in duration of benefit produced by age. That one difference, though, is critical. Underlying medical conditions that reduce life expectancy are *not*—in contrast to age—equally distributed among all individuals over the course of their lives but instead are distributed randomly, inequitably, and often tragically. Therefore, to allow an adjustment to the duration factor for these underlying conditions would not increase distributive justice but would severely reduce it, by systematically discriminating against individuals who are disabled or ill. It is another way of assigning an intrinsic worth to individuals and ranking them accordingly, and would violate the EOS (see Question 1, page 244).

Therefore, the EOS dictates that an adjustment to the duration factor should *not* be made on the basis of underlying medical conditions that reduce life expectancy. This analysis suggests a fourth rule.

Rule 4   *In calculating cost-effectiveness, do not adjust the duration factor for an individual's underlying disabilities or medical disorders.*

Rule 4 applies even for patients who are terminally ill, that is, who have untreatable illnesses that will certainly produce death in a relatively short time. This rule, some might complain, gives an unreasonable advantage to patients who are terminally ill and for whom expensive therapies are being considered. (Ignore for the moment the absurd notion that terminally ill patients could ever be considered advantaged.)

However, by definition *terminally ill* means that no therapy significantly prolongs life. Therefore, for any therapy aimed at prolonging life, the probability factor calculation—and thus the value of B—will always be low. Rule 4, therefore, can still be applied in these patients.

Without Rule 4, these patients would become seriously disadvantaged when it comes to the use of comfort therapies whose potential duration of benefit is substantially longer than the patient's life expectancy. Even with Rule 4, there is no guarantee that aggressive comfort measures would rank high enough to guarantee availability for terminally ill patients. To assure that comfort measures are always offered to these patients, we could remove patients from the rationing system altogether once they are deemed terminally ill, then giving them whatever comfort measures they require, at whatever the cost. If this measure were implemented, it could be done the same way it is done today. Patients today often declare their terminal status by volunteering to enter hospice care. So we could decide to fund hospice care outside the normal healthcare system and make it immune from rationing.

Lifestyle-based adjustments to the duration of benefits

We have already discussed and resolved (at least for the purposes of this chapter) the issue of whether self-induced diseases should be taken into special account under a rationing system (see Question 4, page 246). They should not. Accordingly, we can state a fifth rule.

Rule 5   *In calculating cost-effectiveness, do not adjust the duration factor for medical conditions that are known or suspected to be self-induced.*

Calculating cost-effectiveness under the EOS

Having established some rules for calculating cost-effectiveness under the EOS, let us reconsider our two patients with cancer. Recall that one of our patients is a 70-year-old wheelchair-bound man for whom a $30,000 treatment exists that has a 10 percent chance of producing a cure. A pure societal beneficence standard rules out this disabled patient's getting the therapy, whereas a pure distributive justice standard eliminates such discrimination but also limits the overall good that society will achieve with its healthcare dollars. The EOS tells us (Rule 1) that we are not to take this patient's wheelchair-bound status into account. Thus, his QOL index is taken as 1.0 (in other words, his being in a wheelchair represents 100 percent of his baseline quality of life). Furthermore, the fact that he is in a wheelchair does not affect the probability that he will respond to the therapy, so the probability that the treatment will be effective remains at 10 percent (Rule 2).

The calculation for this patient (assuming that a 70-year-old man has a 10-year life expectancy) would look like this:

$$B = 0.1 \times 10 \text{ yr} \times 1.0$$

$$B = 1.0 \text{ QALY}$$

The cost-effectiveness calculation is

$$E = C/B = \$30,000 / 1.0 \text{ QALY} = \$30,000/\text{QALY}$$

This compares with 0.5 QALY and a cost-effectiveness of $60,000 per QALY using the societal beneficence standard, and with 2.0 QALY and a cost-effectiveness of $15,000 per QALY using the distributive justice standard. The EOS, as intended, represents a balance between these two extremes.

Why there's still a Q in QALY

An astute reader might ask, "Rule 1 says that when you calculate B (in quality-adjusted life-years) under the EOS, you're not allowed to adjust for a person's underlying quality of life, because doing so would systematically discriminate against the disabled and the sick. But if you're not allowed to adjust for quality of life, then where does the 'quality-adjusted' part come in? What you're describing isn't even a 'quality-adjusted life-year' any more, is it?"

This is a good question. It turns out that under the EOS, we do have to make QOL adjustments. But those adjustments are not made to the patient's baseline QOL index (because doing so would systematically discriminate against patients with a reduced baseline QOL). Instead, the QOL adjustments are made to reflect how the proposed therapy itself might result in a *change* to the patient's QOL.* A therapy might improve a patient's QOL or make it worse, and it might do so transiently or permanently. Assessing any change in the QOL index, q, resulting from a therapy does not discriminate against the individual (because the baseline q is always assumed to be 1.0) but instead discriminates among therapies. For many therapies, it turns out that such adjustments for post-therapy q are important to the overall calculation of B and are therefore important in determining the usefulness of that therapy. Thus, a sixth rule for applying the EOS to the calculation becomes apparent.

* In the example calculations so far, the treatments we considered did not change QOL but only offered to prolong life without changing QOL. In reality, most medical therapies have the potential of altering QOL—either positively or negatively.

Rule 6   *In calculating cost-effectiveness, adjust for post-therapy QOL if the therapy itself can either improve or diminish QOL.*

We have now established the complete set of rules needed to calculate cost-effectiveness under the EOS. Let's look at some specific examples of how we might apply them.

Calculating cost-effectiveness for non-life-saving therapies

In the calculations so far, the therapies under consideration have all had the potential to prolong life. For therapies that generally do not prolong survival, the calculation becomes a bit more complicated. When a therapy does not add time to a person's life, we must create a surrogate for time. And in fact, the chief benefit of the QALY is that it provides such a surrogate. If a therapy does not prolong life, then any potential benefit provided by that therapy must derive from a change in QOL. Using QALY gives us a method of converting such changes in QOL to a time equivalent.

Treating symptomatic illnesses

To illustrate how this is done, let's consider the calculation for a therapy that treats a symptomatic illness, potentially ameliorating the symptoms. Consider a man with peptic ulcer disease. We can offer this patient a two-week course of medical therapy that has a 95 percent chance of healing the ulcer and getting rid of his symptoms, at a cost of $1,000. Without medical therapy, the natural history of peptic ulcer disease is highly variable, but most poorly treated or self-treated patients can expect to have significant symptoms for at least 6 months. Furthermore, with active peptic ulcer disease, (we learn from our hypothetical QOL scale) a person's QOL is only 75 percent of normal.

From this information, we can construct the following table representing the data we need to calculate B:

p^*	d	q_{base}	q_{pre}	$q_{base} - q_{pre}$
0.95	0.5	1.0	0.75	0.25

$*p$ = probability of effectiveness
d = duration of effect, in years
q_{base} = baseline quality-of-life (QOL) index
q_{pre} = pretreatment QOL index

The probability that the therapy will work is 95 percent, or 0.95. The duration of effect is taken as 6 months, or 0.5 years, because this is how long people with ulcer disease often have symptoms with inadequate treatment. In other words, if the therapy works it should spare the patient an average of 6 months of suffering. The baseline QOL index is 100 percent (or 1.0), because, from Rule 1, the baseline QOL index is *always* 100 percent. However, the patient we're dealing with is not in his baseline state; instead, he has peptic ulcer disease, which transiently reduces his QOL to 75 percent (or 0.75). If the treatment is successful, it will return him to his baseline state, in which his QOL is 100 percent. The post-treatment QOL difference produced by the therapy is therefore the baseline QOL minus the pretreatment QOL: $q_{base} - q_{pre}$ = 1.0 − 0.75 = 0.25. Whenever we calculate B for a therapy that can change the post-therapy QOL, it is this QOL difference that is used in the calculation. (And this is where the *adjusted* part of "quality-adjusted life-year" comes in.)

This quality adjustment means that during the time the therapy is providing a benefit (by eliminating ulcer symptoms and thereby improving QOL), the patient's QOL index will be improved by an absolute value of 25 percent. In other words, for every year a patient is free of ulcer symptoms as a result of this therapy, we gain 0.25 quality-adjusted years. It is as if we extended a patient's actual life by 3 months. What the calculation lets us do is convert a change in *symptoms* produced by the treatment to a *time equiva-*

Rule 1

> *In calculating cost-effectiveness, do not adjust the QOL index for an individual's baseline disabilities or medical disorders.*

Rule 2

> *In calculating cost-effectiveness, adjust the probability factor whenever an individual's underlying disability or medical disorder objectively limits the chance that the proposed treatment will be effective.*

Rule 3

> *In calculating cost-effectiveness, adjust the duration factor to take into account the individual's age-based life-expectancy.*

Rule 4

> *In calculating cost-effectiveness, do not adjust the duration factor for an individual's underlying disabilities or medical disorders.*

Rule 5

> *In calculating cost-effectiveness, do not adjust the duration factor for medical conditions that are known or suspected to be self-induced.*

Rule 6

> *In calculating cost-effectiveness, adjust for post-therapy QOL if the therapy itself can either improve or diminish QOL.*

lent. This trick lets us compare, in the currency of QALY, the relative values of very different kinds of therapies.

For this therapy, our calculation becomes

$$B = p \times d \times (q_{base} - q_{pre})$$

$$B = 0.95 \times 0.5 \text{ yr} \times 0.25$$

$$B = 0.12 \text{ QALY}$$

On average, we will gain 0.12 QALY, or about 6 weeks, for each patient treated. Finally, since the therapy costs $1,000, its cost-effectiveness is computed as

$$E = C/B = \$1,000/0.12 \text{ QALY} = \$8,333/\text{QALY}$$

With some medical disorders, symptoms may persist without treatment for a patient's entire lifetime, rather than the 6 months in the above example. In those cases, the duration of benefit, d, of the proposed therapy—as with life-prolonging therapy—is related to the patient's age. Assigning a numeric value to d in these cases, therefore, requires the same consideration as for life-saving therapy.

To illustrate, let's recall our 70-year-old wheelchair-bound patient. This time, he does not have cancer; in fact, he's in his usual baseline state of health. But now we have found a treatment that has a 50 percent chance of getting him out of that wheelchair. Unfortunately, the treatment costs $100,000. What would be the cost-effectiveness of offering it to him?

Under the EOS, we must award the patient a baseline QOL index of 1.0 (Rule 1) even though he has a condition (living in a wheelchair) that causes his actual QOL index to be only 0.5. We wish to offer him a therapy that can increase his QOL index substantially (from 0.5 to a post-treatment value of 1.0). But how can we do this, if we've already given him a baseline score of 1.0? We can do it by treating the condition of living in a wheelchair not as his baseline condition but as his pretreatment condition. We can do this because we have a therapy that has a reasonable chance of turning his confinement to a wheelchair into a pretreatment condition.

p	d	q_{base}	q_{pre}	$q_{base} - q_{pre}$
0.55	10	1.0	0.5	0.5

There is a 50 percent chance (0.5) that the therapy will improve his quality of life for the rest of his life (a predicted 10 years, based on his age). The improvement in q (that is, the QOL difference, q_{diff}) if this therapy is effective would be

$$q_{diff} = q_{base} - q_{pre} = 1.0 - 0.5 = 0.5$$

The calculation thus becomes

$$B = 0.5 \times 10 \text{ yr} \times 0.5 = 2.5$$

The cost-effectiveness of this therapy is therefore

$$E = C/B = \$100,000/2.5 \text{ QALY} = \$40,000/\text{QALY}$$

Prophylactic treatments

QOL adjustments also come into play when we calculate cost-effectiveness for a prophylactic treatment—one that does not treat a medical condition but instead may prevent it.

Consider a flu vaccine that is partially effective against a particularly nasty form of influenza. Assume that an individual living in an area where the flu epidemic is present has approximately a 20 percent chance of contracting influenza, but for those who receive the vaccine, the probability is reduced to 5 percent. Therefore, the probability that an individual receiving the vaccine will get the flu is reduced by an absolute value of 15 percent. The duration of illness with this form of flu is approximately 3 weeks (or 0.06 years). Patients contracting the flu get pretty sick—they will have a QOL during that time that is only 20 percent of normal. So, if the flu is prevented, the improvement in QOL in patients who would otherwise have contracted the illness would be

$$q_{diff} = q_{base} - q_{ill} = 1.0 - 0.2 = 0.8$$

The following table gives the data needed to calculate the cost-effectiveness.

p_{imp}*	d_{ill}	q_{base}	q_{ill}	$q_{base} - q_{ill}$
0.15	0.06	1.0	0.2	0.8

* p_{imp} = improvement in probability of avoiding illness
d_{ill} = duration of illness, in years
q_{base} = baseline QOL index
q_{ill} = illness QOL index

Based on this data,

$$B = 0.15 \times 0.06 \text{ yr} \times 0.8$$

$$B = 0.01 \text{ QALY}$$

On average, we would gain 0.01 QALY per flu shot, or about 3 quality-adjusted life-days. If a flu shot costs \$25, the cost-effectiveness calculation would be

$$E = C/B = \$25/0.01 \text{ QALY}$$

$$= \$2,500/\text{QALY (approximately)}$$

When a vaccine or some other form of prophylactic therapy is particularly expensive or is in particularly short supply, we may want to limit its use to individuals who need it the most. These would be the people whose probability of contracting the illness is highest (so that the vaccine might provide a larger improvement in the probability factor in the calculation of benefit) or who could be expected to develop particularly dangerous forms of the disease (so that the QOL difference would be greater) or who might develop prolonged illnesses or even death (thus increasing the duration of illness factor, possibly all the way up to the patient's age-related life expectancy). In these instances, the calculation could be individualized to account for these considerations and to make sure the vaccine is going to those who would benefit the most (those in whom the use of the vaccine yields the highest value for B).

Managing side effects

Finally, quality adjustments are necessary if a therapy can *reduce* the resultant quality of life, that is, if it can cause significant side effects. (Until now, we have been pretending that our therapies do not involve the potential for side effects.)

Consider a 60-year-old man with cancer. A treatment is being considered for this man that has a 35 percent chance of curing the cancer, but that at the same time also has a 30 percent chance of causing severe nausea for up to 6 months and a 5 percent chance of causing permanent heart failure. We will assume that our

60-year-old patient would have a life expectancy of 18 years if the cancer were to be cured but that his life expectancy would be reduced to 5 years if he were to develop severe, permanent heart failure from the therapy, even if his cancer were cured.

To calculate the cost-effectiveness for this therapy in this patient, we must compute the separate contributions to the overall value of B for two aspects of the therapy:

- The drug's predicted effectiveness in curing cancer
- The drug's potential side effects

Effectiveness of cure

Effect	p	d	q
Curing cancer ...	0.35	18	1.0

The chemotherapy we're considering for this patient has a 35 percent chance of curing his cancer, and if the therapy does cure the cancer he will probably live another 18 years. The baseline QOL index (Rule 1) is always 100 percent. Assuming that the cancer itself is not yet causing major symptoms, curing the cancer will not improve the patient's quality of life. So, the contribution to the overall value of B from the predicted effectiveness of the drug in curing cancer is as follows:

$$B_{cure} = 0.35 \times 18\,yr \times 1.0$$

$$B_{cure} = 6.3\ QALY$$

Potential side effects

Side Effect	p	d	q_{base}	q_{side} *	$q_{base} - q_{side}$
Severe nausea ...	0.3	0.5	1.0	0.55	0.45
Heart failure	0.05	5	1.0	0.6	0.4

* q_{side} = side effect QOL index

There are two potential side effects from this chemotherapy—severe nausea and heart failure—that could appreciably alter the patient's post-therapy QOL, q_{side}. The probability that severe nausea will occur is judged to be 30 percent (0.3), and if it occurs it can last up to 6 months (0.5 years). Furthermore, according to our reference tables, the medical condition of severe nausea is judged to yield a quality of life that is only 55 percent of normal.

$$q_{diff} = q_{base} - q_{side} = 1.0 - 0.55 = 0.45$$

So

$$B_{nausea} = 0.3 \times 0.5 \text{ yr} \times 0.45$$

$$B_{nausea} = 0.07 \text{ QALY (approximately)}$$

Similarly, there is a 5 percent likelihood that the chemotherapy will produce heart failure; the QOL if this should happen will drop to only 60 percent of normal (for a QOL difference of 0.4); and the duration of this side effect is estimated to be 5 years (not because the heart failure goes away at that time, but because the heart failure can be expected to result in death within 5 years).

In calculating the contribution to B from heart failure, $B_{heart \, failure}$, we need to consider that not only does the heart failure reduce the QOL while the patient remains alive but it also reduces the duration of life. Thus, a two-part calculation is required to assess the effect of heart failure on B. We need to calculate a QOL component and a duration component.

The QOL component from the possibility of heart failure, $B_{heart \, failure \, q}$, is calculated using logic similar to that used for nausea. There is a 5 percent chance the proposed therapy will cause heart failure, which can be expected to persist for 5 years and which will reduce the patient's QOL to 60 percent of normal.

$$B_{heart \, failure \, q} = 0.05 \times 5 \text{ yr} \times 0.4$$

$$= 0.1 \text{ QALY (approximately)}$$

We need to calculate a duration component, $B_{heart \, failure \, d}$. If a patient develops heart failure as a side effect of the chemotherapy, and if that patient would otherwise have been cured of his cancer, then the heart failure will produce a *reduction* in survival of 13 years. In other words, the heart failure will reduce the 18 years our patient could have expected to live with a cancer cure to 5 years (during which he will suffer from heart failure).

$$B_{heart \, failure \, d} = p_{cure} \times p_{heart \, failure} \times d_{diff}$$

where p_{cure} is the probability that the cancer will be cured, $p_{heart\ failure}$ is the probability that heart failure will develop, and d_{diff} is the reduction in survival (in years) caused by the heart failure. So

$$B_{heart\ failure\ d} = 0.35 \times 0.05 \times 13 \text{ yr}$$

$$= 0.23 \text{ QALY (approximately)}$$

The total contribution to B resulting from the propensity of our therapy to cause heart failure is the QOL component plus the duration component:

$$B_{heart\ failure} = B_{heart\ failure\ q} + B_{heart\ failure\ d}$$

$$= 0.1 + 0.23 = 0.33 \text{ QALY}$$

(We are assuming here that if the cancer is not cured, then the production of heart failure will not significantly reduce the quality of the patient's brief remaining life. This may or may not be a good assumption; if not, additional math would be needed.)

Now we can calculate overall benefit for the proposed chemotherapy as follows:

$$B_{chemo} = B_{cure} - B_{nausea} - B_{heart\ failure}$$

(Because nausea and heart failure detract from rather than add to the benefit produced by the chemotherapy, they are *subtracted* rather than added.) Thus, if we were to use this chemotherapy,

$$B_{chemo} = 6.3 - 0.1 - 0.33 = 5.87 \text{ QALY}$$

Finally, we are ready to calculate the cost-effectiveness of this chemotherapy. If the cost of the chemotherapy is $50,000, then its cost-effectiveness would be

$$E = C / B = \$50,000 / 5.87 \text{ QALY} = \$8,518 / \text{QALY}$$

These examples illustrate how QOL adjustments affect cost-effectiveness calculations under the EOS, despite the fact that Rule 1 prevents us from adjusting the patient's baseline QOL index. As most therapies may have an effect (either beneficial or detrimental) on a patient's post-therapy QOL, we are obligated to factor such effects into a therapy's overall cost-effectiveness.

A general scheme for rationing

There are many ways to implement open rationing based on the EOS. My aim here is not to dictate what such a scheme must look like but is to demonstrate that such a thing is at least imaginable. This discussion assumes we are creating a healthcare system (perhaps similar to the system described at the end of Chapter 8) that incorporates some component of open healthcare rationing.

To implement a methodology for open rationing under the EOS, we need a scheme for systematizing the calculation of benefit and cost-effectiveness values (B and E) for *individuals* who are being considered for specific medical services. Presumably, an open budgetary process will be in place that determines a specific cutoff value for cost-effectiveness. Medical therapies whose cost-effectiveness for a given patient is below that cutoff value (for example, $50,000 per QALY) may be used. If the cost-effectiveness score is above the cutoff, that individual cannot receive the therapy within the rationing system.*

> *B*   benefit of therapy
> *E*   cost-effectiveness of therapy
> EOS   Equal Opportunity Standard (All individuals should have an equal opportunity to enjoy the fruits of life, within the constraints imposed on them by nature.)
> QALY   quality-adjusted life-year (unit)
> QOL   quality of life

1   *Establish a health standards commission*

The rationing plan will have to be coordinated through some publicly accountable body, which I'll call a health standards commission. This commission should include doctors,† nurses, and representative patients, with an advisory role for healthcare economists, statisticians, and (if we're careful) ethicists. The main job of the commission will be to establish a system for determining the appropriate values to use in the calculation of cost-effectiveness.

Two major tasks will fall out of the need to fill in the values needed for such calculations: devising at least one equitable QOL scale; and setting up and evaluating a comprehensive list of condition–treatment pairs.

---

*   Under the system proposed in the last chapter, this individual may still be able to obtain the service through a Tier 3 plan

†   The doctors on this commission should be mainly generalists rather than specialists, as generalists are more likely to have a global view of healthcare, whereas specialists are more likely to have conflicts of interest.

2 Establish a quality of life scale for a range of health states

Mathematical adjustments for a patient's underlying QOL are not permitted in the calculation of cost-effectiveness under the EOS. Nonetheless, some equitable scale for assessing QOL will be necessary in our rationing scheme, because *changes* in quality of life may result from a proposed medical therapy. This information will be important in determining both a therapy's effectiveness and the importance of any major side effects the treatment may produce.

What we need is a scale that assigns a QOL index—expressed as a fraction of a normal quality of life—to various health states. So, as we have postulated, the health state of living in a wheelchair might be assigned a QOL index of 0.5; that is, the quality of life when living in a wheelchair may be judged to be only 50 percent of the quality of life when living with normal health.

Several methodologies have been proposed for determining QOL scales, and none of them is perfect. The main problem with all of them is that they are subjective measures and are prone to methodological variances and measurement bias. The inability to come up with a reproducible, objective measure of QOL has been one prominent argument against using QALY as a unit at all.

While deciding on the fairest QOL methodology is still important, under the EOS the QOL scale is not as critical as it would be under QALY-based methods typically proposed. This is because, when we measure the effectiveness of any therapy under the EOS, we assume the baseline QOL index to be 1.0 for every individual. The QOL scale will be applied only when calculating any *change* in baseline QOL produced by a treatment and the importance of any side effects of the proposed therapy. Any inaccuracies introduced by this application of the QOL index would attach to a particular therapy and not to an individual. So any potential inequities created by an imperfect QOL scale will be spread across the population—and thus blunted—by the use of the EOS.

An additional mitigation for the imperfect nature of QOL scales is possible under the EOS. The commission may decide to measure QOL scales by two or three different methods, then publish the results as, say, QOL Scale 1, QOL Scale 2, and QOL Scale 3. Individual patients could then examine all three scales and pick the one that they wish to have applied to their own cases.

3   Establish a list of condition–treatment pairs

The largest part of the commission's job may be to establish and evaluate an exhaustive list of condition–treatment pairs.

The condition–treatment pair (for example, "penicillin for streptococcal pneumonia") determines the values to be used in a cost-effectiveness calculation. The commission needs to determine eleven elements for every condition–treatment pair:

- The probability that the treatment will achieve the desired effect on the condition being treated
- A list of important underlying medical conditions that affect the probability of benefit
- The degree to which the probability of benefit is affected by each of these underlying conditions
- The predicted duration of benefit
- The extent to which the treatment (if effective) is predicted to improve the pretreatment QOL
- A list of important side effects of the treatment
- The probability that each of the side effects will occur
- The extent to which a side effect (if it were to occur) worsens the post-treatment QOL
- The expected duration of each side effect if it were to occur
- The predicted impact (if any) of each side effect on the overall duration of benefit of the treatment
- The cost of the treatment

4   Calculate benefit and cost-effectiveness

With this information, the commission can set up automatic calculation of the benefit of therapy, B, for a specific condition–treatment pair, as shown in Figure 6 on page 270.

Once the eleven elements are determined for a condition–treatment pair, many of the cells take on known values. That is, values will

	p	d	q_{base}*	q_{post}
Effectiveness				
Benefit of therapy . . .	Patient-specific OR Known	Patient-specific OR Known	1.0	Known
Side-effect Quality Adjustments				
Side effect 1 . . .	Patient-specific OR Known	Patient-specific OR Known	1.0	Known
Side effect 2 . . .	Patient-specific OR Known	Patient-specific OR Known	1.0	Known
⋮				
Side effect n . . .	Patient-specific OR Known	Patient-specific OR Known	1.0	Known

* The baseline QOL index for the effectiveness component is always 1.0 (Rule 1).

Figure 6. Sample worksheet for calculating benefit and cost-effectiveness for one condition–treatment pair.

be assigned to these cells for each specific condition–treatment pair. The treating physician can then fill in the patient-specific values.

The probability of effect may be known or may depend on whether the patient has any underlying conditions from the list (determined for each condition–treatment pair) that affect the probability that the treatment will work, or that a side effect may occur.

The duration of effect may be determined by the age of the patient (for condition–treatment pairs where the effect is likely to persist for a patient's lifetime), in which case the duration of effect is patient specific. On the other hand, for other condition–treatment pairs the duration of effect may be some known period (for example, for treatments which alleviate symptoms temporarily or which alleviate temporary symptoms).

In this manner, when a specific patient is matched to a specific condition–treatment pair, the calculation will be automatic. When the cost of treatment is divided by the resulting benefit, B, the final patient-specific cost-effectiveness of the proposed treatment, E, will be determined.

The commission's main job, then, would be to direct the completion of a table like this one for every condition–treatment pair it establishes. Those data tables can be stored in a computerized database. They can be edited over time as new therapies are developed and as new information is made available on existing therapies.

Once this work is accessible to doctors and their patients, determining cost-effectiveness will consist of identifying the condition–treatment pair being considered for a specific patient. The data table that gives the values for the calculation of B, the resultant calculation itself, and the subsequent cost-effectiveness value, E, would all be transparent and available for both patients and their doctors to see.

Caveats

I have made this process sound easier than it would be. There are many pitfalls in what I have just described, and establishing the processes to do this the right way will require a monumental effort.

One obvious problem is that this system depends on a specific, granular database of condition–treatment pairs. It is not enough to say, "coronary artery stenting for coronary artery disease," as stenting can be performed electively (to relieve angina) or emergently (to halt the progression of an acute myocardial infarction), and cardiologists can use either bare-metal or drug-eluting stents, each of which has its own profile of effectiveness and side effects. Condition–treatment pairs should be developed—and subsequently ranked—for all of these contingencies. Defining an adequate breadth of condition–treatment pairs is daunting.

As the commission evaluates for each condition–treatment pair the probability of benefit, the effect of underlying conditions on that probability, the effect of the therapy on the quality of life, and all the data related to possible side effects, it should use the most rigorous scientific standards possible. In operational terms, the weakest link in any rationing system is the lack of information needed to perform rigorous cost-effectiveness analyses. Therefore, an extensive data gathering system will be needed.

Finally, if we follow a strictly science-and-math-based system for ranking rationing priorities, such as the one I have outlined, we will discover anomalies, wherein services that prove eligible for coverage, when compared to services not eligible for coverage, may seem counterintuitive or even absurd. When the state of Oregon tried to institute a scientific scheme for rationing in the early 1990s (a scheme that was quite different from the one described here and a more problematic one both from an ethical and procedural point of view), they found that they had awarded "dental caps" a priority higher than "surgery for ectopic pregnancy" (a condition which is usually fatal without surgery, but from which patients generally recover completely if surgery is performed).* Any system we develop will produce similar absurdities, and we will need to have a way to deal with these.

* Rationing was never instituted in Oregon, but Oregonians still deserve credit for instituting a public process for rationing and for proving that healthcare rationing can be openly discussed—and even planned for—in a civil fashion by American citizens.

For example, we might want to place condition–treatment pairs into a number of specific categories, such as "therapies that address acute, potentially fatal illnesses and restore normal health," and "therapies that prevent illness in children." We could then rank these categories according to importance, and factor in a bump score for condition–treatment pairs in the more important categories or perhaps establish higher cost-effectiveness thresholds for the high-priority categories. Whatever system we use for adjusting out logical absurdities, the ranking system we end up with must pass the smell test with the general public.

How will industry respond?

How will companies that make products they expect to sell into the healthcare system respond to this kind of open rationing? This proposed methodology would disrupt their present business models. The prices they charge now for their products are determined, somewhat mysteriously, by tradition, by how much they think the system will pay for a particular type of product, by the cost of making the product plus some fudge factor that takes into account how much profit the shareholders expect, or by some other method that does not reflect open-market economics. These pricing structures result from of our Quadrant IV, and now Quadrant III, healthcare systems, where logic, transparency, and principled economic behaviors were early casualties. Disrupting this way of doing business might not be such a bad thing— either for the general public or for the companies themselves.

Companies faced with having to sell medical products under an EOS-based rationing system would have to change their approach to the development, evaluation, and pricing of those products. Consider how the executives of such a company might respond if they find the cost-effectiveness scores of their products too high to be covered by the healthcare system. They can work to increase the effectiveness of their product, so that the probability that it will produce benefit becomes higher. They can work to reduce or mitigate the side effects of their product. Or, they can work to reduce the cost of their product. Whichever method they choose, their efforts will ultimately benefit both patients and the healthcare system. The benefit of such a rationing system to biomedical companies is predictability. Politics and lobbying will become much less important in assuring that medical products can be marketed. And the biotech industry will begin to function in a more normal economic environment, where price points are determined by market factors, not by magic or caprice. Finally, research and development activities will be stimulated, instead of stifled, by this kind of rationing. A predictable path to profits always stimulates research and development.

Today, new drugs and medical devices are often developed specifically for the purpose of keeping prices high, and it often appears as if product development is dictated by the marketing department rather than by actual healthcare needs. "If we can make a new drug that does *this*, we can gain three points of market share." By convincing doctors that *this* new angle on some drug or medical device is suddenly significant, prescribing behaviors can be changed and prices can be kept high (whether or not the new angle has any actual clinical value). The success of such marketing-induced product development, once a product is released, is hit or miss. Success in the marketplace often depends more on expert marketing strategies than on usefulness of the new product.

Under an EOS rationing system, marketing prowess will have much less influence on the success of a medical product. Instead, success will depend on the measurable effectiveness of the product, on its side effects, and on whether its use reduces or increases the cost of healthcare. These are the factors that will determine sales, predictably so—and research and development efforts will be directed accordingly. Marketing hype, on the other hand, will fall on the deaf ears of the QALY calculation.

Summary

This chapter has considered how we might implement the open rationing of healthcare, a feat that will be necessary in our proposed new American healthcare system. We have considered the choices we will have to make as we reflect on the ethical precepts that must guide our rationing procedures.

It is possible to imagine a healthcare system based on open rationing that still safeguards American ideals. We have looked at one way to implement such a system. Now what can we do to change attitudes so we can begin putting such a thing in place? The final chapter examines how patients, doctors, and entrepreneurs, acting in their own enlightened self-interests, can catalyze such a reformation of American healthcare.

How to ration

1   *Establish a health standards commission*

2   *Establish a quality of life scale for a range of health states*

3   *Establish a list of condition–treatment pairs*

4   *Calculate benefit and cost-effectiveness*

10

Catalyzing a Reformation in Healthcare

AN EQUITABLE AND EFFECTIVE healthcare system, one that supports basic American principles by straddling the upper quadrants of the healthcare landscape, is at least imaginable. Achieving such a system requires acknowledging limits to what our healthcare system can provide and then ensuring that those limits are distributed justly. By allowing the American spirit of individualism and innovation to guide our efforts, we can make this new system—even with the open rationing it will require—energizing instead of enervating to our society.

But how can we begin to make it real? Let's first look at the likely outcome if we do nothing.

Wonkonians ascendant

In the battle between Wonkonians and Gekkonians over whether our Quadrant III healthcare system will be controlled by the government or by business-like enterprises, the Wonkonians are on the ascent. Since the 1994 collapse of the Clintons' universal healthcare plan, Gekkonians have had their chance to show what they can do. They have had more than a decade to wield their mega-HMOs in an effort to control costs. But despite the inconveniences and dangers they have foisted on American patients, despite the intensity of their coercive efforts to force covert rationing, and despite the opportunities they have created for greater efficiency by promulgating massive consolidations of healthcare institutions, Gekkonians have proven failures at controlling the accelerating cost of healthcare. What's more, they have discharged their only weapons and they seem bereft of new ideas.* In truth, Gekkonians really had only one idea. They have had many years to try it. It hasn't worked.

* The only recent innovation sponsored by Gekkonians, the Medicare drug plan, while dressed up in a Gekkonian shell (i.e., it is being administered, with flamboyant confusion, by a host of private companies), is fundamentally a Wonkonian idea.

Wonkonians, on the other hand, remain energized by their one big idea, the establishment of a fully centralized, government-controlled, top-down system of healthcare. The model they invoke most often is the Canadian healthcare system. Wonkonians, in addition to not being Gekkonians, are further advantaged by being single-minded about their plans for healthcare; they are politically savvy, well organized, and generally favored by the mass media. Their basic message—that their healthcare system will be fair—is attractive, especially in view of what we have today. And they have absolutely no trouble showcasing satisfied Canadian citizens (presumably from among the ninety percent who have not been seriously ill recently) who are happy to offer testimonials confirming Wonkonians' claims about this style of healthcare. Wonkonians have never stopped lobbying and working for their big idea, and it is likely that if the healthcare debate of 1994 were taken up again today, they would enjoy the support of a substantial proportion of the American public. Although I would find such a system extremely undesirable, I will stipulate that with some care it could be made more equitable— and ethically more acceptable—than the system we have now. (But then, it is difficult to imagine a healthcare system that would be more unfair and destructive than the one we have now.)

Politically, however, Wonkonians were damaged so badly by their prior ill-timed attempt at a government-controlled healthcare system that they seem reluctant to push too hard or too soon this time. The disadvantages of a Canadian-style healthcare system remain all too visible—the long queues, the lack of real medical innovation (except via osmosis from the United States), and the dissatisfaction voiced by increasing numbers of Canadian citizens and doctors. These factors are keeping Wonkonians relatively cautious. But they can see that Gekkonians are failing badly; they can afford to wait.

Biding their time is a wise strategy. A centralized healthcare system that subjects Americans to centrally dictated, population-based, government-controlled decision trees would rub Americans the wrong way. That kind of system relies on a compliant, passive, fatalistic populace resigned to a much lower level of self-determination than Americans have traditionally enjoyed. Today, as in 1994, a majority of Americans would not fit this description.

But several more years of being subjected to Quadrant III healthcare may get us there. This is almost certainly what Wonkonians are relying on. Each day we remain under our present system of inefficiency and inequity, more Americans become completely fed up and resign themselves to the idea of a single-payer, government-controlled healthcare system. It seems to be the least bad of several very bad choices. All Wonkonians have to do is continue advancing the perfidies of our present system and wait. The people will come around.

It is a good strategy, and there is an excellent chance that it will work. Short of riding out our current piecemeal, largely Gekkonian system of covert rationing to the end, that is, until the fiscal time-bomb it is creating actually goes off and wrecks our society, most Americans would find it hard to imagine an alternative to the Wonkonian "solution."

Only one thing can steer us away from the Wonkonian solution—empowering patients to act on their own behalf. Patients with sufficient knowledge and the systems to apply that knowledge will not only wreck covert rationing (which relies on patients being complaisant) but will also make the Wonkonian healthcare solution of centralized governmental control completely unworkable. We will have to discover an alternative to both Gekkonians and Wonkonians; and patient empowerment will reveal to us what that alternative should look like.

Patient empowerment

Covert rationing depends on a credulous public, and on well-behaved patients. Maintaining Quadrant III healthcare requires the general public to ignore the necessity and the reality of rationing, and to believe that any apparent limits on healthcare result from corruption, waste, and inefficiency, which, thanks to the efforts of Wonkonians and Gekkonians, are being rooted out bit by bit. More important, when members of the general public become patients themselves, covert rationing requires them to rely on their doctors and their health plans to determine what's right for them.

This requirement is the Achilles' heel of covert rationing. For once you become a patient, behaving as you're supposed to produces an immediate threat to your own life and limb. In other words, continued covert rationing requires that patients continue to act in a manner that is against their own interests.

Patients who understand this—who understand that it is not in their interest to rely on the advice of their doctors and health plans—can take immediate steps to protect themselves. Instead of passively accepting the diagnoses and recommendations for treatment that are presented to them, these patients will check things out for themselves and seek independent confirmation that nothing is being overlooked or "forgotten." They can make it hard for the healthcare system to practice covert rationing against *them*.

If enough patients do this, the covert rationing of healthcare will no longer be possible. Covert rationing will collapse under its own weight, from within, because of the actions of tens of thousands of individuals acting independently in their own interest. Covert rationing simply will not work any more.

The collapse of our Quadrant III healthcare system will be painful. When it occurs, our healthcare system is likely to become even more chaotic for a time than it is today. Yet it is at this point that we will be forced to face the real limitations to what our healthcare system can provide. Americans will at last be ready to hear the truth. Some brave leader can show us what our real choices are, without being stoned, banished, or ignored. And finally we can begin constructing a new, rational, and equitable healthcare system.

At this moment, when Gekkonian covert rationing collapses under the weight of patients behaving badly (that is, autonomously), Wonkonians will immediately step forward with their solution—a centrally controlled Canadian-style healthcare system. But they will find that Americans are even less ready for such a system than they were in 1994.

Here's why: Covert rationing will not have failed because it wore everybody down to the point where anything seemed better. Instead, it will have failed because of a new multitude of self-empowered Americans. The American populace will fit even less than it does today the profile necessary to establish a paternalistic, top-down, government-run healthcare system. Whatever system we establish at that point to replace covert rationing, whether or not it resembles the system we discussed in the last chapters, it will have to honor the self-actualized, self-empowered, autonomous American patient.

The catalyst to a uniquely American solution to the problem of healthcare rationing, then, is the empowered patient. Americans—not all Americans, not necessarily a majority of Americans, but a critical mass of Americans—are going to have to begin taking their healthcare into their own hands. For this to become possible, a sufficient number of doctors have to recognize that empowered patients are their best hope for salvaging their profession, and they have to support those patients. And the American biomedical industry has to understand that their own survival depends on helping individual patients become self-empowered.

What patients need to do

When you interact with the healthcare system as a patient, your first concern is not reforming the system. Your concern should be getting what you need from a healthcare system that systematically subjects you to covert rationing. This means taking charge of your own healthcare and, by so doing, immunizing yourself against covert rationing.

This is not a trivial task. Having to resolve your own medical problems is frustrating. No matter how much time you spend searching the Internet, listening to the accumulated wisdom of your Great Aunt Hilda, or playing Twenty Questions with taciturn medical personnel, you can never be sure you have the right answer. The system today is not geared toward helping you; for it to work, you have to remain at least partially in the dark. That's what covert rationing is all about.

Still, there's a lot you can do to protect yourself within the healthcare system. You can empower yourself with knowledge. You can manage your relationship with your doctor so that, when it is time to covertly ration care, perhaps *you* will be the patient for whom he occasionally goes the extra mile. You can demonstrate a desire for—and show your willingness to pay for—the tools of empowerment. And when your ability and even your right to empower yourself are challenged, you can firmly stand your ground.

Becoming empowered through knowledge

When you or a loved one faces a medical problem, saturate yourself with as much information as you can about that problem. The point is not to become a doctor yourself but instead to become an informed partner in the physician–patient encounter. The more you know, the more productive your time with the doctor is likely to be and the more likely your doctor is to be thorough in his or her investigations and explanations.

If you have been given a specific medical diagnosis, you should try to learn all you can about it. What causes it? Can it be prevented? Which factors help determine the outcome? What symptoms should you watch for? How is it diagnosed, and how is its progress monitored? What are the potential treatment options, and what are the pros and cons of each? And once you have this information you should always ask yourself: Now that I know more about this condition, does the diagnosis seem to fit, or are there features of my medical condition that don't add up? Does the treatment advice my doctor has given me make sense? Should I talk to my doctor about the discrepancies I have found? Should I get a second opinion?

It may be that you have not yet received a specific diagnosis. You may have unexplained symptoms, or you may only suspect that you have a particular medical problem. Here, independent study will likely not be quite as productive, because it will be more difficult for you to focus on a specific condition. Still, some investigation while you wait to see your doctor can be helpful. You can read about the symptoms* that concern you and try to get an idea of what sorts of medical problems they may indicate. When you see your doctor, you can focus your questions and concerns more productively—and you may find yourself better able to gauge the appropriateness of the response.

Resources for self-empowerment

One way to get your feet wet is the old-fashioned way—with books. Consumer-oriented health encyclopedias are available at almost all public libraries and bookstores, as are books written about scores of specific medical conditions. But today a chief resource for patients who want to learn about medical problems is the Internet.†

The Internet has countless resources for any health condition you can name, but once you branch away

---

* A useful online resource for learning about the potential significance of various symptoms is the Symptom Checker at http://symptomchecker.about.com, a free site provided by Harvard Medical School through About.com.

† The Internet can be a useful resource even for those who want to get their information from books. Sites like Amazon.com and BarnesandNoble.com allow you to better judge the usefulness of a book before you buy it, with reviews, excerpts, and links to similar books.

from known and trusted sources, you're entering the Wild West. A lot of the stuff you'll find there is simply bizarre and wrong; for this reason many experts have urged patients to avoid the Internet altogether, arguing that they're more likely to become confused, misled, or disturbed than enlightened. There is definitely a risk-to-benefit ratio that needs to be taken into account when you use the Internet to get medical information; but if you're careful, a lot of the crazy stuff is easy to recognize.*

And so is a lot of the good stuff. Three websites that are useful as general resources are those of the Mayo Clinic (http://www.mayoclinic.com), the National Institutes of Health (http://health.nih.gov), and the American Academy of Family Physicians (http://familydoctor.org). All of these sites offer good, basic information about most common medical conditions.

There are three other sites you should consider:

+ **WebMD**

  (http://www.webmd.com)

  While WebMD has not fulfilled the original intent its founders envisioned in the 1990s (see Chapter 2), it is a valuable resource for individuals seeking information on diagnosis, prevention, and treatment of medical conditions. Just be aware that it is supported by healthcare companies, and much of the information comes from sponsors.

+ **Revolution Health**

  (http://revolutionhealth.com)

  This intriguing site, which opened for business in early 2007, was founded by Steve Case, the guy who started AOL. Case's mission (born, apparently, from Case's personal experience trying to navigate a dysfunctional healthcare system) is to provide online tools for patients to empower themselves. Among these is a personal, online healthcare record. Health information comes from several prestigious medical centers. The most interesting feature is an affordable, subscription-based concierge service, through which members can get live, personal attention with issues related to their health. At this

---

* The most common sign of quackery is the combination of (a) a claim that the government-medical-industrial complex is withholding valuable information from you; (b) a claim that the writer knows the real cure; and (c) the offer by said writer to sell you said cure (or a book about it). This form of quackery, I'll admit, smacks at least a little of what I've been saying myself—that doctors have been coerced into withholding from patients information that is material to their medical care. But there's an important difference. The information that doctors are actually withholding under our system of covert rationing would, if divulged, lead to some form of expensive therapy that the healthcare system itself would have to pay for. In contrast, the shills want you to buy things you can only get from them.

stage, Revolution Health appears to be independent of corporate
and insurance influences and thus has the potential of becoming
a true consumer-oriented enterprise. It is worth checking out.

◆ **About.com Health**
(http://about.com/health)

About.com is a collection of over six hundred websites on
almost any topic you can think of. More than fifty of these sites
are related to health and healthy lifestyles. Each site is run by a
guide. The guides are individuals who are experts in their health-
related subject matter. Interestingly, not all of the About.com
health guides are medical professionals; many of them are highly
intelligent patients, or relatives of patients, who have become
experts in their topic, often out of necessity. The guides, all of
whom have interesting stories to tell, are available for online
exchanges of ideas. Consequently, About.com offers a more personal sort of experience than you can generally find with other
online health sites.

Finally, independent disease-specific websites run by patients can
sometimes be quite helpful—if you are cautious. Unfortunately, many
of these sites are agenda-driven and peopled by conspiracy theorists;
and while they can help get you riled up, they tend to offer little in
the way of useful information. But some are indeed worthwhile and
can provide practical advice on diagnosing, treating, and coping with
specific medical problems; and they may help with finding doctors
who are adept at treating patients with these disorders. Frequently,
such sites also provide online discussion groups where patients can
exchange information. Examples of useful patient-run, disease-specific sites include the Sudden Cardiac Arrest Association (http://www
.suddencardiacarrest.org), and the National Dysautonomia Research
Foundation (http://www.ndrf.org). The individuals who run both
of these sites (whom I have met and with whom I have had long discussions) are interested only in helping their fellow patients find the
resources they need. So, if you are cautious, patient-operated, disease-
specific sites can be helpful. Just keep in mind that you're looking for
useful medical information, not activism.

Once again, the reason for learning as much as you can is not to
become a doctor yourself, but to become a confident and comfortable
consumer who can discuss your medical condition with a doctor. And

the questions that come to mind as you talk with your doctor will be more focused and pertinent the more you know. (If you have a basic understanding of your medical condition and you still can't understand what your doctor is saying, that ought to be a clue that either he doesn't understand this stuff himself or the two of you are just having a hard time communicating.)

Most important, you'll begin to notice if your doctor is just leaving things out. If you think he is, you can ask him: "Doc, what about that cardiac resynchronization therapy? I've read where it's supposed to really help a lot of people with heart failure." This serves two purposes. It forces your doctor to discuss cardiac resynchronization therapy with you. And it serves notice that when *you* are the one sitting across the desk from him, he's dealing with someone who understands the situation. He's going to have to be sure he discusses *all* the options with this one. Becoming empowered by knowledge is not an easy thing to do, but the payoff is tremendous.

Managing your relationship with your doctor

Before you invest a lot of time nurturing a relationship with your doctor, you want to know that the doctor you have is worth the effort. Two important factors must be in place before you declare yourself satisfied with your doctor. The first is that she must be a good communicator; no matter what other fine features your doctor may have, if you can't communicate with her you're in trouble.

Is your doctor really listening to what you are saying? Does she demonstrate that she understands your concerns by responding meaningfully to them? When she explains medical issues to you, does she make them understandable? Can she think on her feet, to find new ways to help you grasp particularly difficult concepts? Is she patient with you, waiting for you to get what she's saying, or does she try to embarrass you into *saying* you understand, with shakes of her head or the rolling of her eyes? Do you like her, and does she seem to like you? (This is important when it's time for her to go to bat for you.) The inability to communicate effectively with your doctor is sufficient reason to move on to someone else.

The second factor that must be in place is that your doctor should be intelligent and well educated. Sometimes it's hard to know for sure how knowledgeable your doctor is. But at a minimum you should check to see if he is board-certified in his specialty. Two sources can help. The *Directory of Physicians in the United States* and the *Official American Board of Medical Specialties Directory of Board Certified Medical Specialists* list doctors who are board certified. These books are available in most public libraries, and your doctor should show up in them.

Does your doctor *seem* smart to you? When you ask a question about a health problem, are the answers thoughtful, logical, and cogent? Do the answers match what you believe to be true and, if not can the doctor explain the discrepancy to your satisfaction? (Here again, being knowledgeable yourself comes in handy.) Does he give his answers confidently, or is he dissembling? It's fine for a doctor to answer, "I don't know," as long as he promises to find out the answer and then follows through on that promise. And pay attention to whether your doctor only has book smarts or has academic knowledge tempered by experience and common sense.

A doctor who seems knowledgeable and who communicates well with you is probably worthy of the time and effort you're going to have to expend to nurture a fruitful relationship.

Why your doctor–patient relationship needs nurturing

In becoming an effective, empowered patient, you have to take the generally (and intentionally) weakened state of the doctor–patient relationship into account. Assuming that your doctor is always going to be acting in your best interests—no matter how good a doctor he is, or how ethical—is potentially a big mistake.

Your doctor (if you've chosen wisely) deeply *wants* to honor the traditional doctor–patient relationship; doing so is his first duty as a professional. Despite all the coercive pressure to the contrary, your doctor *will* occasionally go up against an HMO for the benefit of a patient. He needs to do this as a matter of professional pride—just to be able to live with himself. (The HMOs understand this, too. Letting the doctor win one now and then—after they put up a stiff resistance—costs them some money; but in the long run it helps keep the doctor mollified. It's just a cost of doing business.) But a doctor cannot go to the wall for every patient or for every issue that comes up for a given patient. The process would be grindingly difficult and fatal to his career. The doctor must choose his battles carefully.

The effective patient understands all this, and you should nurture your relationship with your doctor accordingly. Tailor the relationship in such a way that, when the chips are down, *you* are likely to be one of those for whom your doctor will go to the wall. To be such an effective patient, consider following these five general strategies:

Strategy 1—Be empathetic Doctors need a little empathy too, and will often respond more favorably to patients who express some. Let her know that you understand the frustrating, externally imposed constraints under which she is laboring. You know how hard it is to be a good doctor these days, and you're thankful she's there for you despite everything. Even if you have to reach a bit to express such sentiments, your doctor will appreciate it—and may become more solicitous toward you and your medical needs.

Strategy 2—Respect the office rules, even the absurd ones Try to play by the rules the doctor has established for his practice, even if those rules appear arbitrary and restrictive. Do your best to cooperate with the office staff, as surly as they may be, and minimize interruptions and special requests. If you do have to make a special request, be polite to the office gatekeepers even to the point of physical pain, and try to make sure you let the doctor's staff know how appreciative you are for their assistance (even if you think they've been downright mean to you).

Strategy 3—Become engaged in your own good health Especially in the era of covert rationing, few things frustrate doctors more than patients who, they feel, completely neglect their own health, then expect them to pull out all the stops when they get into medical difficulties.

Look, this isn't fair. Try to look at it not from the standpoint of what's right, but instead from the standpoint of the modern doctor. Consider two patients who need special permission for some medical service from a recalcitrant HMO, one an obese smoker who has made no visible effort to take care of himself; the other a diabetic who has carefully tried to follow her difficult diet and drug regimens. For which of these patients is a doctor more likely to risk his viability-determining cost profile? Perhaps neither, of course, but he's more likely to jeopardize his professional security to fight for a patient who is fighting at his side for the same thing.

So look at it this way. Here's yet another reason to take good care of yourself (aside from the much better reason that it might help you avoid the healthcare system in the first place). Your doctor is likelier to fight for you if you are fully engaged in maintaining your own health.

Strategy 4—Optimize the time you spend with your doctor For your own benefit you should try to optimize the 7.5 minutes the doctor is going to spend with you. Plan a visit with your doctor the same way you'd plan an important business meeting. Set specific goals for the visit and write down a list of items you'd like to cover. You might even send your doctor an e-mail (if he's not a Luddite) before the appointment to let him know what your goals are. Bring all pertinent information your doctor might need to know, such as a list of all the medications you're taking. Take notes during the visit, writing down the important points your doctor makes with you. Repeat back to your doctor what you think you heard him say. Consider taking an extra pair of ears with you to the visit. A sympathetic spouse or a good friend can later confirm and reinforce the messages your doctor has given you. Finally, after the visit go over your list once again and make sure your issues were each addressed. If not, you ought to consider e-mailing your doctor within a day or so (while your visit is still fresh in his mind), and ask for clarification of the outstanding issues.

Strategy 5—Trust but verify Even the best doctors forget and omit things. So always do your own independent study after you see your doctor, just to make sure the information and explanations you've gotten are proper and complete. When you do find inconsistencies—and you will—it's fine to call your doctor's attention to them on the next visit, but try to do this in a non-confrontational way (remember, you're nurturing a relationship, not playing gotcha). Just say that you've found a somewhat different view on one of the matters you discussed on the last visit, and you'd appreciate a chance to explore the topic further with him. Reasonable doctors will suppress their natural defensiveness at such a thing, and will engage in a genuine conversation on the matter. Most doctors are used to this sort of thing now that we are more than a decade into the Internet era, and don't take such challenges personally anymore. If nothing else, your request will remind him of your sophistication regarding your medical condition—you're listening to what he says, but you're also checking things out for yourself.

With the right doctor, the right nurturing, and the right strategies, it is unlikely your doctor will attempt to withhold potentially important medical information from you. Not only will you be a more informed patient and a better partner with your doctor in managing your healthcare but also you will be immunizing yourself against covert rationing. If every patient did these things, widespread covert rationing would not be possible.

Be willing to pay for empowerment

Commerce is a wonderful thing. If some people have a strong desire to acquire an item, and some other people have a strong desire to provide that item, the transaction is going to occur eventually. This is why Prohibition did not work, why marijuana is California's biggest cash crop, and why there will always be pictures of naked women on the Internet.

And it is why, if patients are willing to pay to control their own healthcare, entrepreneurs will trip over themselves to provide the products and services that enable them to do so.

Patients are vulnerable in a healthcare system that will do almost anything to avoid having to spend money on them. Placing all their trust in such a system is dangerous to their health and survival. People who understand that will be willing to invest some of their own funds to safeguard their medical welfare. The demand for products and services that provide these safeguards will grow in direct proportion to the public's awareness of just how vulnerable they are.

This awareness is increasing daily. We are just seeing the beginnings of the self-empowerment industry, and most of it is still below the radar. Before we look at what some doctors are doing and what entrepreneurs can do to create tools for patient empowerment, I want to point out two rules about self-empowerment that will become increasingly important over the next few years. We will need to remember these rules when Wonkonians and Gekkonians notice what is going on and stop at nothing to put an end to it.

The first rule of empowerment: Only you can pay for your own empowerment In our entitlement society, whenever anything "good" shows up that is in any way related to healthcare, people expect it to be provided for "free." This will no doubt be true for products and services that advance patient empowerment. No sooner will such things appear than people will start calling for it to be "covered." We cannot allow this to happen. When the central authorities agree to pay for empowerment services and technologies, they will control them. And when they control the means to empowerment, they will destroy their usefulness. They will have to—because patient empowerment wrecks covert rationing.

The most obvious example of this is physician services. Doctors are designated by tradition, ethics, and law to be the patient's advocate. In other words, they are the original empowerment tool for patients. But not only have the central authorities who pay for healthcare strangled the advocacy role of physicians, they have actually converted doctors from a tool for patient empowerment into a tool for covert rationing.

If we allow the new empowerment tools to be co-opted by the government or third-party payers, the same thing will happen. How they will co-opt the new empowerment tools is predictable. When Wonkonians and Gekkonians notice the movement toward patient empowerment, they will initially try to stifle it altogether. Once these efforts prove ineffective, they will change tactics. "You are right," they will say, "these methods for improving patient empowerment are vitally important. They're so important, we've decided, that it would be unfair of us not to provide them, so as to guarantee equal access to everyone." If this happens, patient empowerment will go the way of the doctor–patient relationship. Individuals must be responsible for their own empowerment.

The second rule of empowerment: Self-empowerment is not a sin You will be told that by using the tools of self-empowerment, by going outside the designated and approved pathways for your own healthcare, you are contributing to societal discord; that you are an elitist, helping to create a two-tiered healthcare system; that you are broadening the gulf between the haves and the have-nots, between the privileged and the underclass; that you are joining with the cigar-smoking, brandy-quaffing, expense-account-spending, numb-hearted oppressors of the masses; that your kind will be the subject of news articles in the *New York Times* and exposés on *60 Minutes*; that—there is no way around it—you are evil.

Do not listen to these aspersions. They are not genuine; they are desperate attempts to bring you back into compliance with covert rationing (and, on another level, with the central authority). Remember: You are spending your own money to protect yourself and your loved ones from people who are trying to kill you (or who are at least willing to let you die).

And remember something else: While the primary reason you're empowering yourself is (and should be) self-preservation, by doing so you are also taking up a higher cause. You are joining an army that is fighting with the only weapon at its disposal against an enemy that is choking the life out of patients, the public, and the principle of individual autonomy. By fighting for your own self-empowerment you are not leaving others behind, you are leading them to safety.

What health professionals should do

Of the many negative ramifications to Quadrant III healthcare, only one directly affects all patients and all doctors all the time: the loss of the traditional doctor–patient relationship.

When we get sick, every aspect of the healthcare system we rely upon to restore our health is concerned mainly with not having to spend too much money on us. A concern about spending is to be expected—and it is necessary. We want regulators to be concerned about maximizing the benefits of healthcare for society. We want HMOs to be concerned about maximizing benefits for their subscribers. We want everybody to be concerned about spending our limited resources wisely.

But what we don't want is for our doctors—as they sit at our bedside and make decisions about our health—to be primarily concerned about the needs of society or about their continued ability to earn a living if they spend too much. We want them to be primarily concerned about *our* needs. Just like the citizen accused of a felony, we need that highly trained professional who takes up our cause and jealously protects our rights and welfare in the face of all opposition. For, as long as our doctors fail to assume their traditional roles as our personal advocates, we will be at the mercy of a healthcare system geared toward saving or making money. Thus, the deterioration of the doctor–patient relationship puts us in immediate peril.

The destruction of the doctor–patient relationship weighs on physicians more than on patients. While loss of this relationship may affect both doctors and patients all the time, few people are patients all the time, while doctors are always doctors. Doctors feel the loss every day of their lives. It is particularly frustrating to doctors that they have been coerced into becoming the engine of destruction of this relationship. Many of them understand, deep down and better than their patients, that without the classic doctor–patient relationship, their worth as professionals is fatally devalued; their profession is, in fact, ended.

Physician heal thyself

Is there anything doctors can do to heal themselves, other than leave practice and become florists, deep-sea fishermen, or authors? There is. They can find a way to create a demand for a restored doctor–patient relationship and then provide the means for achieving it.

This is already happening in one form, though it is generally not described in those terms, and its practitioners do not yet think of what they are doing in that way. Here and there, across the country, a new type of medical practice arrangement is appearing that is founded on restoring the classic doctor–patient relationship. This new style of practice arrangement is called "boutique" or "concierge" or "retainer" medicine. There are many flavors of retainer practices, but they all involve patients paying doctors directly for their services.

That's it. Patients pay the doctors directly.

It's simple, but the change in medical dynamics is revolutionary. The doctors in retainer practices don't work any more for HMOs, or for insurance companies, or for the government—and none of those entities any longer determine their viability as practitioners. Instead, it is the patient who is the customer, who must be kept satisfied, and who will determine the doctor's professional viability. The doctor is not only free once again to act solely as the patient's advisor and advocate, he is obligated to act in this way.

There are still only a handful of retainer practices in the U.S., but the number of doctors showing interest in this form of practice is growing rapidly.

Problems with the current retainer model

There are at least two major problems with the current retainer model of medical practice.

The ideal retainer practice would collect money only from patients and not from Medicare or insurance companies. Less pure financial arrangements are unfortunately common among current retainer practitioners; and less purely restore the physician–patient compact. Doctors in mixed retainer practices are still beholden to the third-party payer, and how purely they're able to advocate for their patients is an open question.

The more important problem is that retainer practitioners are wide open to the charge of elitism. Most current retainer practitioners limit the number of patients they care for to several hundred (instead of the typical several thousand). Patients enrolled in the practice pay an annual retainer fee that is often quite stiff; in return they get personalized, twenty-four hour access to the doctor by cell phone and e-mail, guaranteed same day or next day appointments, detailed and leisurely medical examinations, personalized education and risk modification plans, personalized coordination of all medical care, and in some cases house calls.

It is a shame that these new-style physicians and their sophisticated marketers insist on adopting (and emphasizing) these elitist practices (as desirable as they may sound). Even the names by which these practitioners originally referred to themselves ("boutique," "concierge") smack of ostentatious, country club exclusivity.* Retainer practices have opened themselves up to, and even invited, the charge of elitism. It is hard to argue that the charge is unjustified.

In fact the main benefit patients get from a retainer practitioner is the one thing our Quadrant III health-care system insists they not have—an advocate who guards against their becoming victims of covert rationing.

* The largest and best known retainer practitioner organization calls itself MDVIP. And the name more recently adopted by many of these practitioners, "retainer," is only marginally less elitist.

The elitist aspect of retainer practice is not essential; it is merely how most of these doctors have chosen to establish their businesses to date. There is nothing inherent in the retainer practitioner model that requires that they limit themselves to only the rich. A high-volume, lower-unit-cost, retainer-style relationship (that is, one in which patients pay their doctors) is entirely plausible. America used to have one; it was once the traditional model for the doctor-patient relationship.

But because retainer practitioners have not chosen to design their practices that way to this point, their enemies have a powerful weapon to wield against them.

The opposition

While retainer practitioners themselves don't seem to understand the significance of what they are doing—they seem to regard the elitist aspects of their practices as the major innovation, almost never mentioning restoring the broken doctor–patient relationship and providing advocacy for their patients—their opposition gets it quite clearly. And they are apoplectic.

You can, by now, predict the response. Medical ethicists and many others decry the elitism, claiming it undermines the ethical obligations of the medical profession. They bemoan the fact that doctors practicing this way are caring for only several hundred patients, when they could be managing (and *managing* is the correct word) thousands. They complain that this style of practice creates a two-tiered healthcare system.

There is certainly truth to these complaints, which boil down to the argument of fairness. And it is not fair for only some Americans to have access to a restored doctor–patient relationship.

But it's a start. If it turns out that providing some individuals an opportunity to function under a traditional doctor–patient relationship is such a useful thing as to rise to the level of unfairness, then perhaps instead of taking it away from everybody, we ought to make it possible for everybody to have it. I have already argued that this kind of fairness is entirely possible. (One way of paying for such a broadly restored doctor–patient relationship is discussed in detail in Chapter 8.)

Wonkonians, Gekkonians, and various activist groups have wasted no time in initiating efforts to have Congress declare retainer practices illegal. Opponents of retainer practices are taking every opportunity to label the physicians who operate them as greedy, lazy, and unethical and the patients who associate with them as elitists. Some activist groups are even attempting to have retainer practices legally designated as insurance companies, arguing that retainer physicians, like insurance companies, are taking money today for services that may be needed in the future. (The lawyers framing this argument are apparently not making the same case for their own retainer-dependent profession.) Because state statutes require insurance companies to be capitalized for millions of dollars, if retainer practices are declared to be a form of insurance, they will have to close down immediately.

This sort of all-out response against what is really just a fledgling idea (one that ought still to be below the radar) tells us that the real problem here is more than one of elitism. (Would that the responsible authorities treat with as much alacrity the *real* inequities coursing through our healthcare system.) This kind of take-no-prisoners response can only be a testimony to just how dangerous Wonkonians and Gekkonians consider the threat of a restored doctor–patient relationship to be. And it gives us an idea of just what we are up against in the effort to encourage patient empowerment.

The arguments being used today against retainer practices could be applied to *any* experimental step toward restoring the doctor–patient relationship, not just to retainer practices. As the benefits of any such effort will not be available to every person from the very first day, they can all immediately be condemned as unfair and thus deserving of quick termination.

Some free advice to retainer practitioners

Note to retainer practitioners: The opposition is coming after you with an ethical argument—that you're creating a great unfairness within the healthcare system that must be stopped—and they're coming hard. You haven't been effective in countering this ethical argument with one of your own. You haven't even tried.

You're too busy touting the niceties of your service—the leisurely office visits and round-the-clock access, you know, the elitist stuff—and you're missing the main point. You are in a race, and while you are kneeling at the starting line tying your shoe, your opponent has already made the first turn. You need to articulate a clear message that makes a strong ethical argument for retainer practices, one that is easy to grasp and is intuitively appealing, and you need to do it fast. If you don't, you'll be back working for The Man before you know it.

The message might look something like this: *In retainer practices, insurance companies and the government can no longer dictate physicians' behavior and force them to ration healthcare covertly, at the bedside.*

Instead, the patient is the physician's only customer. Retainer physicians can truly place their patients' needs first, protect their interests, and make sure that they get the care they need and deserve within an increasingly hostile healthcare system.

You aren't taking fairness out of the system—you are putting it back in. You are restoring a measure of fairness to patients who have been callously abandoned by an inhospitable healthcare system. And while it is true that not every patient today has the opportunity to work with a retainer physician, you are working hard to see that some day every patient will. Now *that* would be fair.*

In the meantime, those who want to put a stop to retainer practices would take this option away and leave *all* patients at the mercies of an uncaring healthcare system, forsaken and without hope. (Presumably, these same individuals also would have objected to freeing *any* slaves before the Thirteenth Amendment, because to do so would have allowed a manifestly unfair two-tier class structure to exist for African-Americans.)

Unless you can articulate why retainer practices are an important step in *restoring* some fairness to the healthcare system and paint those who would take it away as trying to deny patients a fair chance against powerful forces, I am afraid you are lost.

* I am giving you the benefit of the doubt here. In reality, I see little evidence that you are working at all to devise a high-volume, low-cost business model that offers a restored doctor–patient relationship to any patient who wants it. You are, in fact, behaving like elitists; and if you keep behaving this way you will not only ruin your own practices but you will also ruin any chance that some future physician-led movement can re-establish a traditional doctor–patient business model.

A fallback position for medical professionals

I hope doctors won't need a fallback position, because a fallback position from retainer practices—which already require doctors to take the risk of abandoning traditional practice models—would be a desperate one indeed. But here one is: A cadre of doctors from around the country can quit the practice of medicine altogether to establish a brand new profession. Call it personal healthcare advocate.

Personal healthcare advocates

Personal healthcare advocates (PHAs) would fill the advocacy vacuum that now exists in the healthcare system. Individuals could retain their own personal advocates—professionals who work for them and them alone and who place their interests above all others on matters related to their healthcare—just as they might retain an attorney on legal matters.* Patients have as much right to a strong advocate as do accused felons, and PHAs would model themselves not after the medical profession but after the legal profession.

PHAs would not practice medicine. Instead, they would practice medical advocacy, doing whatever is necessary to guard the rights and welfare of their clients in all their interactions with a hostile healthcare system.

A mission statement for PHAs

A PHA mission statement might read something like this: As PHAs, we will perform the same service within the healthcare system that attorneys perform within the legal system. We will become our clients' advocates and advisors, assuring that a dedicated and knowledgeable professional is representing them, protecting them, and advancing their rights and welfare within the healthcare system. Our relationships with our clients will be built on trust; we will hold their confidences in private; we will assiduously avoid conflicts of interest; and we will work directly for them and for no one else.

This mission statement establishes that PHAs serve in an advisory and advocacy role aimed solely at protecting the rights and welfare of their clients. It establishes that PHAs will model themselves after lawyers rather than doctors ("client" is used instead of "patient," both to reinforce the "attorney–client" paradigm and to emphasize that PHAs do not practice medicine). It establishes a fiduciary relationship between the PHA and the client, ensuring that the PHA will always act with the client's interests in mind.

Why PHAs?

If doctors opt to become PHAs, the opponents of retainer practice will have won, and it will finally be illegal for doctors to work directly for their patients. Doctors who insist on providing advocacy services for patients—the kind that an intact doctor–patient relationship provides—will have no choice but to abandon the practice of medicine altogether, thereby shedding the guidelines, regulations, laws, and constraints with which doctors will have been burdened.

Will doctors actually do this? Some will. Doctors like me—the older kind, the kind who once were able to practice medicine relatively unencumbered by MBAs, intimidating federal regulators, and high school graduates reading from lists of covered services—are ready to leave the practice of medicine in droves. There are lots of reasons for this, including all the ones you've heard—the drop in income, the mounting paperwork, the oppressive regulations, and the loss of control over their practices. They're all good reasons, too. The main reason doctors are frustrated, though, is that they can no longer practice medicine the way they know they should. They cannot be their patient's advisors and advocates. This is why so many doctors are talking seriously about leaving medical practice.

Some doctors will be attracted to such a thing as the PHA profession. As PHAs, doctors will be able to concentrate on the one thing doctors ought to be concentrating on but cannot—advocacy. Many doctors will find this prospect attractive, even at a substantially lower income, especially if they are considering leaving medicine.

Again, the opposition

The healthcare system is geared up to covertly ration healthcare; covert rationing requires destruction of the doctor–patient relationship; and PHAs are a sneaky way of reestablishing that relationship outside the present system. There is only one way for the healthcare system to respond. The usual suspects—the insurance industry, the government, activist groups striving for a centralized healthcare system, and, this time, organized medicine—will immediately recognize the threat posed by PHAs and will try to stifle this new profession.

They will try to declare PHA activities illegal, to block PHAs from access to their clients' medical records, and to block them from maintaining a bedside presence. PHAs will be threatened with liability suits. Opponents will assert that PHAs are practicing medicine after all, and therefore their activities must fall under the same constraints as those of doctors. If any of these attempts take root, the PHA movement will die on the vine.*

* I am not implying that physicians are the only people who can be PHAs. Experienced nurse practitioners could be very effective as PHAs, maybe even better PHAs than physicians. But I am trying to find something useful and fulfilling for disaffected doctors to do if they can't be retainer practitioners anymore.

The outcome will depend on whether patients finally understand the reality of the situation. It will be much harder to publicly attack PHAs than it is to attack retainer practices. It will be, much more blatantly, a naked assault on a patient's right to hire a private, personal consultant on healthcare matters. The whole point of creating this new profession, of course, is to move the doctor–patient relationship—rather, the PHA–client relationship—to a new realm where the relationship can flourish again. When Wonkonians and Gekkonians argue that such a thing is bad, they will finally be tipping their hand, revealing their true agenda.

When patients understand the stakes and become outraged at a crass attempt to eliminate their rights as consumers and patients, all those powerful forces will be vanquished. An aroused public is invincible.

What biomedical entrepreneurs should do

The classic Quadrant IV healthcare system was a boon to the biomedical industry; as long as its products promised some measurable (or perceived) benefit to patients, the Tooth Fairy would pay for them. This "if you build it, they will come" paradigm led to explosive growth within the biomedical industry in the decades following World War II and to remarkable progress in our understanding and management of a host of diseases. Unfortunately, it also led to one of the most convoluted business models that capitalism has ever produced.

A complicated business model

The biomedical industry* is unlike any other. To successfully sell a medical product in the American healthcare system, a business must: (a) invent, develop and build the product; (b) convince the FDA, often with evidence from randomized clinical trials (at a cost of $10–50 million and several years effort), that the product is safe and effective; (c) once FDA approval is gained, convince insurance carriers and Medicare that they ought to pay for it; and finally, (d) convince doctors to prescribe it.

* "Biomedical industry" is a term of convenience. It is my way of lumping pharmaceutical companies, medical device companies, biotech companies, and other enterprises that make sophisticated medical products, under one name. I do recognize that there are some important differences in the business models and practices among these entities; but with occasional exceptions, the comments that follow generally apply to all of them.

Each of these steps is costly and complicated. Both the business risk and overhead expense of such a business model are massive; these costs guarantee that most products this industry sells, even if the unit cost of manufacturing an item is small, will be very expensive.

Nobody would design a business model like this on purpose. It evolved. But a few score of large biomedical companies have adapted to it, and over the decades successful companies have developed all the processes and subsystems necessary to function within this complex model. Companies that have learned to operate under this model are not anxious to change it, because it creates a huge barrier to entry for new competitors.

Threats to the biomedical industry

There are two major threats to the biomedical industry as it now exists. The first is that in a Quadrant III healthcare system, the built-in complexity of their business model, combined with their dependence on hostile third-party payers, makes biomedical companies vulnerable targets for covert rationing.* The second is that these businesses usually have little or no contact with those who benefit from their products, the patients. Their chief potential allies, therefore, are largely indifferent to them.

Biomedical companies often have trouble articulating who their customers are. This is because they have many customers—the FDA, Medicare, other federal agencies, insurance companies, HMOs, professional organizations and societies, and, especially, doctors. But patients have little to do with the decision to purchase the products of these companies. While these companies loftily proclaim that patients are their primary reason for existence, in general patients are no more the customers of the biomedical industry than poodles are of the companies that make doggie sweaters.

The distance between the industry and the patients who benefit from their products is not an accident. Biomedical companies have found it in their best interests to avoid a close relationship with patients. Keeping patients at a distance has been an essential part of their business, because doctors (their chief customers) have traditionally wanted to control any communication with patients. (In insisting that everyone else keep their hands off *their* patients, doctors invoke the sanctity of the doctor–patient relationship.) The companies' arm's-length relationship with their end-users has led to public indifference and sometimes suspicion or anger.

This leaves the biomedical industry vulnerable to demonization. Drug companies especially, but increasingly others as well, are no

* In addition to being direct targets for covert rationing, they are, flagrantly, indirect targets. This is because they are dependent on physicians to prescribe their products—and physicians have been co-opted by the Wonkonians and Gekkonians who determine their viability as practitioners. A big part of covert rationing is to see that doctors do *not* mention to their patients the latest, most expensive medical options, even those that are highly effective.

longer spoken of as good corporate citizens or as institutions whose dedicated efforts cure disease and alleviate suffering. Instead, they are painted as evil and corrupt, as willing to satisfy their greed through graft, double-dealing, animal abuse, and even manslaughter.

Wonkonians and Gekkonians want to demonize the biomedical industry. One of the key reasons for our exploding healthcare costs, they insist, is "too much expensive technology." Blaming the technology itself—which the public finds useful and wants more of—for the healthcare crisis is a tough sell; but accusing the capitalists who supply this technology of waste, fraud, corruption, price-gouging, etc.—well, that's an argument with legs. Wonkonians demonize the biomedical industry and the press abets them. This strategy has traction with the public, placing many Americans squarely in the Wonkonians' camp. Wonkonians would fix the problem with new laws and regulations to bring the out-of-control biomedical industry to heel.

Most executives in targeted companies wonder why they, who consider themselves in the business of helping mankind, are under attack. But covert rationing *requires* the biomedical industry to be brought under control. Today's biomedical industry is not compatible with covert rationing, and it has to go.*

Painting the industry as greedy and untrustworthy is a necessary strategy for Wonkonians and is a good strategy for Gekkonians, too. It creates the political mandate needed to regulate and prosecute the biomedical industry into submission.

Why the biomedical industry needs the support of patients

In the battle over its future, the biomedical industry has few allies. Many of its customers—especially the federal government and HMOs—are customers only reluctantly and resentfully and are among its demonizers. The industry's other main customers, the doctors, are engaged in a battle for survival themselves and are not likely to be effective or focused allies.

The industry's only natural allies in this fight are those who directly benefit from its products and who have good cause to defend it from destruction—the

* I am not suggesting that biomedical companies are as pure as snow. They are not. Some have engaged in sleazy practices, especially in how they go about endearing themselves to their physician customers. And without the scrutiny of the regulators and the press, their transgressions might be worse. I am asserting that painting this industry as evil has become automatic and that the reason for this is covert rationing. I offer no proof here, but you can observe what's happening in the wild to confirm this for yourself. If you are a member of the general public, you may ignore this assertion and go on believing what you like, as it's not your problem. If you are a member of the biomedical industry, however, you ignore this warning at your peril.

patients. Patients would be powerful allies if they rose up in the industry's defense. But the public in general and patients in particular do
not usually have warm feelings for the industry and are all too happy
to line up with its persecutors.

For the most part, the biomedical industry just doesn't get it yet.
They don't realize that they are in a battle for survival, one that will
determine whether they are to continue as innovators or instead as
assembly lines churning out government-approved quotas of government-approved widgets and pills. While the industry continues playing under the old rules, keeping patients at arm's length, Wonkonians
and Gekkonians and their allies are filling the public's head with hor-
ror stories, trying to work the public into a frenzied cry for those in the
greedy and callous biomedical industry to be tossed to the lions.

Unless the biomedical industry wakes up and figures out how to get
the public on its side, it faces ruin.

How can the biomedical industry recruit patients to its cause?

A multi-million dollar public relations campaign is not the way for the
biomedical industry to get patients on its side. The public is already
convinced that biomedical companies routinely engage in price goug-
ing, in withholding vital information to keep their unsafe products
on the market, in lying about the supposed benefits of their products,
and in bribing doctors. The public is being fed this story every day in
a hundred ways by prestigious newspapers, medical journals, politicians, medical experts, cable news channels, and talk show hosts. (By
their actions companies often enough provide plenty of fodder for this
story.) Against this unrelenting attack, even the slickest advertising
campaign won't work. Battling the press in the press isn't a winning
strategy.

A better way to win patients over would be to give them something
they want and cannot easily get. That something is empowerment.

Empowering patients

Biomedical companies that want to assure their survival as independent and self-directed enterprises should partner with patients whose
goal is to become self-empowered. Businesses that learn how to enable

patient empowerment will be immunizing themselves against subjuga-
tion by Wonkonians. Empowered patients will not stand by and watch
the destruction of the entities that make their empowerment possible.

Companies in the biomedical industry will find this hard to do.
They don't sell products directly to patients or know how to interact
with patients. They don't know what patients want. They are geared up
for the much more complicated task of selling things to the healthcare
system. They are intimidated by actual patients.

Even the remote contacts they do sometimes have with patients,
such as producing educational materials or running TV commercials,
are viewed as controversial or inappropriate (because doctors reserve
the authority to determine what patients ought to know). Avoiding
direct contact with patients is embedded in their corporate cultures,
and many companies will find the idea of starting a patient empowerment business counter to their values.

Companies that want to remain successful over the long term have
to find ways to work around this barrier. The demand for empowerment tools among the public is a massive business opportunity. Setting
that aside, unless these companies develop a patient empowerment
business model, they risk extinction.

Biomedical companies should not abandon their current businesses
to concentrate on patient empowerment. But they should engage in
patient empowerment so they can *continue* their core businesses. This
might require establishing spin-off enterprises that can develop and
market patient empowerment tools without contaminating the core
business. But they should take this effort seriously, as if some day
the patient empowerment side of the business might be their chief
endeavor. Because some day it might.

What will patient empowerment look like?

Nobody knows what patient empowerment will actually look like,
because it hasn't been invented yet. Like most entries into new markets,
this one will probably begin with tentative and primitive forays into
the landscape, seeing what patients will respond to and not respond
to. When they recognize the possibilities, patients will begin asking
for specific products, services, and features; that is, the customers will
begin to better define the market. And, seeing the growing demand,

more and more entrepreneurs will jump into the fray, testing an array of ideas. Sooner or later, there may come a killer app, a VisiCalc* of patient empowerment, that forever changes expectations and makes the empowered patient as common as the personal computer. If we reach this stage, covert rationing will be doomed.

We already know some of the things patients want. More than increased longevity, they want to remain healthy and independent into their old age. They want to avoid disability and institutionalization. The sandwich generation wants the tools to keep their aging parents out of institutions, without neglecting their own young families. Patients with chronic illnesses that need a lot of management—diabetes, heart failure, and difficult-to-control hypertension immediately come to mind—want the tools to do most of that management themselves. And those at high risk for treatable cardiovascular emergencies—heart attack and stroke—want to prevent these emergencies and, if they cannot be prevented, to immediately detect and treat them whenever and wherever they occur. These are among the things that many people will pay for themselves.†

A lot of tools can be brought to bear to begin meeting these needs, including a multitude of technologies, sophisticated communication systems, and data management and decision support systems, all aimed at providing remote monitoring, self-monitoring, effective diagnostics, and novel therapies and services. Rather than trying to create a list of products and services that could advance patient empowerment, thereby revealing my limited powers of imagination, I offer instead a vignette to illustrate a few possibilities.

* VisiCalc, for those of you under baby boomer age, was the first commercially successful electronic spreadsheet. The appearance of VisiCalc, probably more than any other single event, created the tipping point for personal computers, taking them beyond the realm of hobbyists and converting them into a practical, if not indispensable, tool.

† Individuals will pay out of pocket for desired healthcare services that insurance does not provide. Americans pay over $10 billion a year for alternative medicine. They pay for baldness remedies and for cosmetic surgery. They pay for their own total body scans. And LASIK surgery for nearsightedness has become a booming self-pay business (the best thing that ever happened to the LASIK industry was when Medicare refused to cover it). If people perceive a desired health benefit they will pay for it themselves.

Sam becomes empowered through technology

For his fifty-fifth birthday, Sam's wife Mary gives him an E-Doc Health Console (informally called ED), along with a paid subscription to a fully integrated Charlotte Medical Institute (CMI) Health Suite.

"Charlotte Medical Institute?" asks Sam, who had been hoping for a new riding mower. "Isn't that in North Carolina? Isn't this still Wyoming?"

"Not to worry," replies Mary. "*Medical Consumer OnLine* still ranks the CMI Health Suite as the best personal health manager around—fifth year in a row. CMI was started by all those disgruntled doctors from Duke and UNC, who got tired of being bossed around by HMOs and government bureaucrats, and they're supposed to be the best docs around. Besides, that Dr. Fyfe down at General, the one Sophie's brother says is the best internist in Cheyenne? Well, she's a CMI-certified doctor, and part of the CMI Network. So now you have an automatic in with her. See, with CMI Health Suite, *anybody* can have a CMI doctor."

Sam understands why his wife gave him the CMI Health Suite instead of a Cub Cadet. His older brother died three months ago of congestive heart failure due to a cardiomyopathy. Naturally, Sam and his remaining brother, Charlie, had gone for gene scans themselves and learned that they, too, had genetic predispositions to cardiomyopathy. Their gene scans also confirmed what they already knew from their family history—they had a high risk of developing early coronary artery disease. Forty-eight-year-old Charlie was a fatalist and resolved to eat, drink, and be merry. But Sam's ambition was to become an old man, so he consulted his physician.

"You can't change your genes, Sam," old Doc Martin had said, laughing at his own pun. "Eat right and get some exercise, and with luck, you'll be okay."

When Sam later related this exchange to Mary, she had replied, "So much for old Doc Martin," and turned to the Internet seeking better advice. Soon, she had settled on Sam's birthday present.

Sam opens the box containing his ED console. It is the size of a portable DVD player, with a small LCD screen, some buttons, a few connectors, and a finger-sized hole. When he plugs in the power cord, ED wakes up and tells him what to do next. Obediently, Sam attaches ED to his PC with a USB cable and identifies himself with a retinal scan; he's in business.

On his PC monitor, up pops a welcoming screen, "ED Proudly Presents the CMI Health Suite. Press Enter to start the CMI Health Scout." Sam presses Enter. Once Sam gives it the appropriate permissions, the CMI Health Scout (the computer interface of the CMI Health Suite) greets him for the first time. Health

Scout, a pleasant voice explains to Sam, scours data sources on the Internet, compiling information from Sam's electronic medical record, from his genetic profile, from relevant clinical trials, and from professional guidelines, as well as from data gathered periodically about Sam himself by his ED console. It feeds this information to algorithms that monitor his health status, detect problems, and predict problems. Health Scout then presents that processed information to Sam, along with any relevant recommendations about his health status, whenever appropriate and in a user-friendly format. This information is updated continuously and can be viewed by Sam whenever he wishes. All this information compiled by Health Scout is accessible only by Sam himself and by individuals he designates.

The CMI version of Health Scout gives Sam access to health maintenance and treatment algorithms developed by and for the doctors of the Charlotte Medical Institute. Health professionals associated with CMI—primarily, Dr. Fyfe, his local CMI-certified primary care doctor—monitor his medical status right along with him and make recommendations, respond to alerts, give him advice, and answer his questions.

Sam's CMI Health Suite also gives him access to the entire CMI network of physicians—doctors around the world certified to meet the high standards of CMI, who work in a virtual group practice and who are adept at managing the treatment algorithms developed by CMI. This means that when Sam and Mary travel, as they often do, he will always have access to a CMI-certified doctor, just about anywhere. But more important, it means that here at home, Sam has an internist who always meets a high standard of care and who participates enthusiastically in his personal health maintenance efforts through the CMI Health Suite.

No sooner does Sam activate his ED console than his new internist, Dr. Fyfe, sends him an automated welcome message. Her message also instructs him to record some baseline tests.

Following the video instructions on his monitor, Sam puts on an elastic contrivance that resembles a halter top and has a cable that plugs into ED; he places his index finger in the mysterious hole in the console. The Health Scout says, "Sam, this won't hurt a bit," and Sam feels a slight prick. He sits quietly for three minutes, as instructed, then places a small tube in his mouth and blows hard for fifteen seconds.

In less than a minute, the Health Scout has a report ready for him. He sees that his new ED contraption has just performed a large battery of tests, including an electrocardiogram, a portable echocardiogram, some blood tests, lung capacity tests, and a screening test that checks his breath for chemical signs of various nasty medical conditions. (It also measures his blood alcohol level in case he is thinking about driving.) Health Scout announces it is ready to tell him about the test results and also to summarize the health-related information it has compiled about him. Health Scout offers to tutor him, at his convenience, on some things it thinks he ought to know about heart disease. But right now his wife is waiting with a birthday cake. Before he lets Health Scout tell him he needs to change his diet, he goes off to enjoy some.

He returns to his computer a while later and reviews a summary of his medical report. His blood pressure and cholesterol are a bit high—Health Scout seems especially concerned about something called oxidized LDL cholesterol—but everything else is apparently okay. Sam notices that Dr. Fyfe has already left a message for him. She wants to see him in a few days and has made arrangements for him to stop for an MRI scan on the way to her office.

Sam hits it off with Dr. Fyfe. She knows a lot about him before he walks into her office, so they spend most of their time together talking about his medical status. She describes how she wants to manage his blood pressure and his other risk factors for coronary artery disease—Sam expected that—but then she tells him she is concerned that he might develop heart failure. It seems that Sam's MRI shows subtle but unmistakable evidence of early cardiomyopathy—the same condition that killed his older brother.

The CMI doctors have done a lot of work on arresting the progression of cardiomyopathy, and Dr. Fyfe has access to some promising investigational protocols through CMI. She briefly describes the one she thinks is most suitable for Sam; she advises him to study it in detail with Health Scout and to get back to her when he's ready.

She also urges Sam to consider an implantable heart failure device. Several companies make them, she says, and they all interact well with his ED console. "They're actually marketed mainly for patients with advanced heart failure," she tells Sam, "but they have some important things to offer you, as well."

Sam does his research with Health Scout and elects to enroll in the experimental CMI cardiac protection protocol that Dr. Fyfe recommended.

He also elects to receive the implantable heart failure device Dr. Fyfe had discussed with him. The device, called the MyoTak, is expensive, and as he does not yet meet the strict criteria for the Universal Health Plan to fund it, he'll have to pay for it himself. The MyoTak company has a monthly leasing plan for patients in his situation—those who would benefit from the device but who are not covered for it. Sam finds the leasing arrangement reasonable, considering all the MyoTak will do for him. A few days later Dr. Fyfe implants the MyoTak herself, during a twenty minute office procedure.

Sam's new MyoTak is a small, implantable computer. It is billed as a lifetime device, as it is powered by a rechargeable battery (recharged twice a year, overnight, while he is sleeping) and it can be reprogrammed whenever necessary by wirelessly uploading new firmware to it.

Sam's device can automatically defibrillate his heart if he should ever suffer a cardiac arrest. He is glad for this feature, because this is what killed his brother. His MyoTak can also pace his heart simultaneously from several different locations (a feature called multifocal pacing) to recoordinate the action of his heart muscle. Cardiomyopathy, Sam has learned, often causes the heart muscle to work in a discoordinated fashion. This discoordination can accelerate the development of heart failure. Sam does not need multi-focal pacing at the moment, but he realizes he is likely to need it in the future.

The main reason Sam has elected to get a MyoTak is to help him manage the progression of his heart problem, so he can stay healthy as long as possible. His MyoTak uses an array of physiologic sensors to continuously monitor his cardiovascular status. The device transmits data wirelessly to the Internet, where Sam can monitor it on Health Scout. He can also elect to make this information available to healthcare professionals, and he has done so in the case of Dr. Fyfe. In addition, Sam wears a special wristwatch that also communicates with his MyoTak. It can show basic cardiovascular information such as his heart rate and blood pressure; more important, if MyoTak detects a possible cardiac emergency—such as a heart attack—it triggers an alarm in his watch.

A year after Sam gets his MyoTak, Health Scout alerts him that his exercise capacity has significantly decreased, and that his weight has increased by five percent. (Sam's scale is also Internet-enabled.) Because MyoTak has revealed that Sam's lung fluid index (the amount of extra fluid in his lung tissue, an indicator of how well the heart is working) is normal, Health Scout tells Sam that he is just getting fat and out of shape; he is not in heart failure—yet. Online, Dr. Fyfe confirms this information. Sam's obvious lack of exercise and weight gain, she says, combined with his family history and genetic profile, now place him—according to Health Scout—at a thirty-eight percent risk of having a myocardial infarction before age sixty-two. A change in lifestyle, she tells him, can reduce that risk to less than ten percent.

Sam responds to this information favorably; and over the next year his exercise capacity, weight, and cholesterol levels improve significantly. Dr. Fyfe and Health Scout both tell him what a fine specimen he has become, and Sam's insurance company seconds that opinion by reducing the premiums he pays for his Option A coverage by fifteen percent.

When Sam turns fifty-eight, MyoTak detects a new problem with his blood pressure—he has developed a nearly daily rise in systolic blood pressure, to about 170, between nine and eleven in the morning. Health Scout alerts both Sam and Dr. Fyfe, who adds a short-acting beta blocker in the morning to Sam's blood pressure regimen. Sam's blood pressure control becomes excellent once again.

A year later, Sam's MyoTak detects the beginnings of discoordinated cardiac muscle contraction. MyoTak automatically begins multifocal pacing to prevent further deterioration of his heart muscle. Sam takes note of this on Health Scout and discusses it with Dr. Fyfe, but feels entirely well.

In the meantime, Sam's brother Charlie has not fared as well. He has had two large myocardial infarctions and has developed significant heart failure. After three hospital admissions over a six-month period, Charlie finally allows Sam to get involved with his healthcare.

Sam makes Charlie say goodbye to his old-fashioned doctor, and gets him plugged in to the latest version of ED and the CMI Health Suite. Within a few days of seeing his CMI-certified cardiologist, Charlie has his own MyoTak device implanted.

Charlie feels quite a bit better almost instantly with multifocal pacing, and a month later he is rescued from sudden cardiac death by MyoTak's automatic defibrillator. While Charlie is glad his MyoTak prevented his sudden death, he is even more impressed when he turns out not to need any more hospitalizations for over a year. Charlie's new CMI cardiologist communicates with him frequently over the phone and online, making adjustments in his treatment regimen and relying heavily on the data provided through MyoTak and Charlie's ED console.

Unfortunately, Charlie's new-found medical stability does not last forever. Fifteen months after enrolling with the CMI Health Suite, Charlie is back in the hospital with severe heart failure—and this time Charlie is *really* sick. Is it finally time for an artificial heart?

Charlie's doctor consults with his colleagues in Charlotte. In an online conference they review all of Charlie's data, including his most recent MRI scan. "Let's try some left ventricular reengineering." They all agree.

Charlie is taken to the nearest CMI Medical Robotic Facility in Denver. There, in a state-of-the-art MRI operating room, Charlie undergoes a minimally invasive procedure called ventricular retromodeling. A cardiac surgeon in Charlotte operates a robotic surgical device in Denver, performing a combination of micro-resection surgery, to provide Charlie with a more normally shaped left ventricle, and targeted stem-cell myogenesis, to strengthen the remaining heart muscle.

Charlie feels much better almost immediately. He knows that sooner or later he will need an artificial heart but is determined to put that day off for as long as possible. He thanks Health Scout, his CMI doctors, and his brother Sam every day for helping him do just that.

As for Sam, at sixty-two he is still nearly the picture of health. Dr. Fyfe has refined his treatments several times over the years, based on data provided by Sam's implanted and external sensors and on treatment algorithms that CMI has continually improved upon (thanks to the huge database of clinical information available to them through the Health Scout system). Sam has had nothing but green lights from Health Scout for years.

But now Dr. Fyfe has a new recommendation for him. A new company has developed an add-on to his MyoTak implantable device, and he should consider receiving it. This tiny device, about the size and shape of a dime, can be inserted under the skin of his forearm, where it communicates wirelessly with MyoTak. If MyoTak should detect the onset of either an acute myocardial infarction or stroke, then during the critical minutes when MyoTak is alerting Sam (and calling 911), the dime-size device will pump a drug into his bloodstream to help dissolve the clot that is causing the emergency. The sad fact is, according to both Dr. Fyfe and Health Scout, Sam remains relatively likely to experience a heart attack or stroke over the long term.

Sam thinks about it for a couple hundred nanoseconds. "Sign me up," he says. After all, not only has his CMI-enabled Health Scout kept Sam healthy, but also the E-Doc portion of his stock portfolio has helped to keep him wealthy.

This vignette describes a modular, expandable, subscription- and lease-based health maintenance service in which patients are the primary customer. Companies can make money selling implantable and external hardware, software upgrades, various creative user interfaces, subscription services, and single-use replaceables (such as the finger-stick units for blood chemistries). Physicians and other healthcare providers can use the infrastructure maintained by the fictitious E-Doc company to support a variety of integrated services for patients, under a retainer model, as exemplified by the fictitious Charlotte Medical Institute. This infrastructure, in fact, creates a brand new, dynamic and robust healthcare marketplace, in which an unlimited number of companies and organizations can compete to deliver to patients whatever products and services they may want or need.

The technology for most of what I have described already exists. All it needs is to be refined, integrated, implemented, and delivered.

Companies that choose to do this—or something similar—will end up empowering both the patients and the doctors. They will catalyze a renewed doctor–patient relationship—one based on *mutual* strength and respect. This can only change the direction of the healthcare system and of our American culture for the better. The companies that provide the products and services that enable a restored doctor–patient relationship will establish themselves as indispensable to both parties.

A healthcare reformation

None of this will be easy. Powerful forces will align to stop the creation of a patient-empowering healthcare marketplace. All the necessary players—patients, doctors, and entrepreneurs—will need to persist in their efforts despite increasingly strident, desperate, and threatening attempts by Wonkonians and Gekkonians (but especially Wonkonians) to stop them and to denounce them as elitist, criminal, and immoral. The covert rationing establishment is at least as entrenched (and corrupt) as the early sixteenth-century Church; the notion of patients becoming self-empowered is at least as frightening as the notion of the teeming masses communicating directly with God; physicians answering only to their patients is at least as threatening as renegade priests answering to parishioners; and empowering technologies are at least as heretical as printing the Bible in the vernacular. The coming fight will resemble nothing, in terms of its intensity and potential for acrimony (and worse), so much as the Reformation.

Most of us will enter the fray not to become reformers but rather to protect ourselves, our families, our professional legitimacy, and our businesses from a broken healthcare system—that is, for ostensibly selfish reasons. To survive the attacks that will come our way, we need to remind ourselves of the higher cause we are serving.

Is what we're doing unfair? It is not. It would be difficult to imagine a healthcare system more unfair and inequitable than the one we have now, in which money is being taken from the paychecks of workers to pay for the healthcare of others, when they themselves have no health insurance; in which deceptions, half-truths, outright lies, and coercion are routinely employed by the central authorities entrusted with managing the healthcare system; in which the interests of doctors have been systematically divorced from the interests of their individual patients; and in which patients are left to fend for themselves, without their rightful advocates, at a time when they are least capable of doing so, within a confusing and dangerous healthcare system. What we are doing—learning to protect our own rights and welfare, in the process exposing the truth of covert rationing, and establishing the systems and methods for others to follow—is restoring, not destroying, equity.

Is what we're doing immoral? It is not. By insisting on our right to self-determination, we are reestablishing a foundational American principle that has eroded in recent years in part because of covert rationing. By taking the steps necessary to empower ourselves and to enable that same empowerment for others, we are asserting our right to self-determination in matters related to our own personal needs. It is an American birthright. Others are trying to take it away. We are stopping them.

If we allow this attack on our ideals to go unanswered or if we fight back and lose, we will pay a much higher price than a bad healthcare system. This is why we owe it to ourselves and to future generations of Americans to take up the cause.

We need to recognize covert rationing for what it is. We need to shine a bright light into the dark corners where it lurks. We need to point to it, call it by its name, illuminate its methods and reveal its secret language. We need to show what it is afraid of—truth, equity, and the intrinsic worth of the individual.

The shrillness of the cries and the brazenness of the protests against our efforts at self-empowerment should be recognized for what they are—signs of just how far we've already fallen away from those founding ideals and of how close the idea of individual empowerment strikes at the heart of the enemy. If anything, these protests should steel our resolve. We are fighting for our own rights and welfare, but we are also fighting a battle to restore every American's right to self-determination. It won't be easy. But we are not sinners; we are holy warriors.

"Here I stand; I can do no other."*

*   After Martin Luther purportedly made this reply to Emperor Charles V's demands that he recant (Diet of Worms, 1521), the emperor pronounced him a heretic—a status with lethal prospects. Having stood, Luther immediately went south.

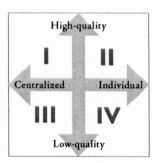

Afterword

I STUMBLED UPON DR. FOGOROS'S website late one night, long past my bedtime. I was bleary and exhausted, but I couldn't pull myself away from my laptop. I was fascinated by his theory that our disordered healthcare system would give birth to a new type of doctor—one who would give up regular practice to doggedly advocate for patients facing serious illnesses. I wasn't just interested—I was shocked. Dr. Fogoros was describing a practice model I thought I had invented; he was describing my fledgling practice. I had mixed emotions as I explored page after page: His ideas challenged my originality, but they also endorsed my credibility and validated my passion.

In *Fixing American Healthcare*, Dr. Fogoros accurately describes the desperate state of out healthcare system—a system that frustrates both doctors and patients and has turned us against each other. As he describes, I have rushed through thirty patients in a day, unable to give adequate time to any of them. I have received reports from insurance companies comparing my spending to those of my peers and argued angrily with HMO medical directors about declined medical procedures. I even understand the fear of government regulatory attack, as I was a resident at Thomas Jefferson University during Medicare's aggressive and unfair audit.

I entered medicine idealistic and hopeful, but I soon saw that things weren't as I had anticipated. I knew something wasn't right. My patients were overwhelmed, frustrated, and easily angered. My colleagues complained about their demanding, needy, and ungrateful patients. Society seemed to imply that doctors had become greedy and lazy. No one was happy. The doctor–patient relationship was heading for divorce court, and patients seemed to be getting lost in all the bickering. I gave the best care that I could, first in a small, rural practice and then in a suburban family medicine residency program; and I suppressed years of nagging doubts. Ultimately, two compelling events disrupted my inertia: My oldest daughter developed significant health problems and my closest childhood friend got breast cancer.

I suddenly found myself on the other side of the healthcare fence, and the view from there was disturbing. Wearing the hats of doctor, mother, and friend, I helped my loved ones navigate the medical maze. I noticed missed diagnoses; perfunctory doctors; conflicting medical advice; and powerful, yet unacknowledged, emotions. Despite the intensity inherent in advocating for my daughter and my friend, I found that I loved the process. I was energized by poring over medical literature and gratified by offering middle-of-the night support. I had an epiphany about the experience of illness and tried to translate that into better care for my own patients. I get it now, I told myself; and yet, to my dismay, I was unable to provide the kind of care to my own patients that I wanted for my loved ones. I couldn't give intense, holistic, patient-centered care in the fifteen-minute office visit demanded by the system in which I practiced.

So I did the unthinkable. I left my job as an attending physician at a teaching hospital and christened myself a Private Medical Care Advisor.

This road, from "regular" doctor to the amorphous and slippery place that I now find myself has been challenging. Malpractice insurers, ignoring my pristine record and declining to offer explanation, initially rejected my request for coverage. Some patients, even those with adequate financial resources, can't get past the idea that I don't take insurance. Some doctors are disdainful, as though I have somehow sold out or broken ranks. Even some of my close physician friends have a measured—and slightly suspicious— tone as they ask me about my new practice. I feel a little like an Amish woman who has begun wearing brightly colored clothing. I haven't been shunned yet, but they are keeping an eye on me.

It is difficult to be a pioneer, and I do have moments of doubt. But my perspective has been permanently altered, and there is no going back. Dr. Fogoros's book has renewed my determination to find a new, mutually satisfying way to practice my craft. Patients must reclaim their healthcare, and doctors need to help them find their power. We must get over our need to control the healthcare encounter and be willing to roll up our sleeves and get dirty. We need to wade into people's fears, doubts, and uncertainties and assure them that we will help them the best that we can. However if we doctors are going to expose the imperfections of our potions and our procedures, then patients, insurers, and government regulators need to cut us some slack. It is unhelpful and unfair to insist on the whole truth, then to crucify us when that truth turns out to be other than desired.

We must embrace, along with patient empowerment, a holistic view of health—one that not only strives for magic cures but also recognizes the crucial role of emotional contentedness, spiritual connectedness, and self-awareness. To do this, doctors must have not only the motivation but also the time. No matter how pure the intentions, fifteen minutes is not enough time to delve into the realms of illness where the sickest patients dwell.

I realize that I cannot change the system; I can only change myself. But I believe that by offering patients a taste of a holistic doctor–patient relationship, uncomplicated by conflicting loyalties, I can begin to change their expectations. Once they feel nurtured, powerful, and in control of their health and their healthcare, they will not want to go back to the darker days. These empowered patients will initially be frightening to doctors' egos, but it is only the transition that will be hard. Clearly, most doctors want their patients to get well; and I believe they will quickly realize the benefits of working with educated, motivated and empowered people.

Imagine if one day a group of physicians-in-training learns not how to improve a patient's compliance but how to enhance her empowerment. What an exciting and healthy time that will be. We physicians are not Gods, we are guides. We cannot guarantee cure but we can provide the comfort of compassionate partnership. And, most important, we can walk beside our patients when they are ill, sharing our wisdom, our humanity, and ourselves.

DELIA CHIARAMONTE, MD

President, Insight Medical Consultants, LLC

www.insightmedicalconsultants.com

July 2007

Index

NOTE: An italicized page numbers indicates that you will find a figure on that page. A lowercase n following a page number indicates that the information will be found in the note on that page.

About the author

Richard N. Fogoros, MD, is a former professor of medicine. He spent over twenty years as a practitioner of internal medicine, cardiology, and cardiac electrophysiology and as a clinical researcher, author, and teacher. At various times he was also a healthcare entrepreneur, an amateur medical ethicist, and, as infrequently as possible, a patient. In 2000 he left both the practice of medicine and academics and devoted his time to writing and consulting.

As DrRich, he writes a patient-oriented website on heart disease (http://heartdisease.about.com), in accordance with one of the major implications of the GUTH—that it is hard to practice covert health-care rationing against the interests of enlightened patients.

Dr. Fogoros's consulting work has centered on helping biotech companies devise long-term product development, regulatory, and overall business strategies based on a practical understanding of the current behavior and the likely future behavior of the American healthcare system. The GUTH has been instrumental in communicating such understanding to corporate America and this book brings that same understanding to anyone who takes the time to read and understand it.

You can read more from Dr. Fogoros at his site on the Grand Unification Theory of Healthcare (http://GUTHealthcare.com), and his Covert Rationing Blog (http://covertrationingblog.com).

For additional copies ...

If you would like additional copies of *Fixing American Healthcare* for your family, friends, and colleagues, or to purchase in bulk for your organization, please write to sales@publishorperishdbs.com to inquire about prices and shipping charges.